R. M. ADIB

Reliability Evaluation of Engineering Systems:

Concepts and Techniques

Roy Billinton *PhD, DSc, FEIC, FRSC, FIEEE, PE*

C. J. MacKenzie Professor of Electrical Engineering
University of Saskatchewan

and **Ronald N Allan** *PhD, FSRS, MIEEE, MIEE, CEng*

Senior Lecturer in Electrical Power Systems
University of Manchester Institute of Science and Technology

Pitman Advanced Publishing Program

BOSTON · LONDON · MELBOURNE

PITMAN PUBLISHING LIMITED
128 Long Acre, London WC2E 9AN

PITMAN PUBLISHING Inc.
1020 Plain Street, Marshfield, Massachusetts 02050

Associated Companies
Pitman Publishing Pty Ltd, Melbourne
Pitman Publishing New Zealand Ltd, Wellington
Copp Clark Pitman, Toronto

First published in Great Britain 1983
Reprinted 1985 (twice)

Published in the United States of America by Plenum Press

British Library Cataloguing in Publication Data

Billinton, R.
  Reliability evaluation of engineering systems
  1. Reliability (Engineering)
  I. Title II. Allan, R. N.
  620′.0045   VS173

  ISBN 0-273-08484-4

Printed at The Bath Press, Avon

Contents

Preface

This book has evolved from our deep interest and involvement in the development and application of reliability evaluation techniques. Its scope is not limited to any one engineering discipline as the concepts and basic techniques for reliability evaluation have no disciplinary boundaries and are applicable in most, if not all, engineering applications.

We firmly believe that reliability evaluation is an important and integral feature of the planning, design and operation of all engineering systems; from the smallest and most simple to the largest and most complex. Also, we believe that all engineers involved with such systems should be aware of, and appreciate, not only the benefits which can accrue from reliability assessment, but also how such assessments can be made.

Our primary objective has been to compile a book which provides practising engineers and engineering graduates who have little or no background in probability theory or statistics, with the concepts and basic techniques for evaluating the reliability of engineering systems. It is hoped that the material presented will enable them to reach quickly a level of self-confidence which will permit them to assimilate, understand and appreciate the more detailed applications and additional material which is available in the journals and publications associated with their own discipline.

We have attempted to structure the book in such a way that only one new concept or technique is introduced and applied at a time. We have also made frequent use of numerical examples to consolidate the concepts and techniques. We believe that this structure will permit the reader to become confident with the application and understanding of reliability evaluation and enable the book to be used either as a self-tutorial text or as the text for a formally taught reliability evaluation course at under-graduate and postgraduate level.

It would not have been possible for us to have written this book without our involvement and close association with many individuals and organizations: the students who have been on our respective (post) graduate research programmes, our colleagues on IEEE, CEA and IEE committees and at our respective universities, and the engineers in the various industries with which we have been involved.

Several typists have helped in the preparation of the manuscripts and we would like to express our appreciation to them as a group. Finally, but by no means least, we would like to thank our respective wives, Joyce and Diane, for their perseverance and constant encouragement and for their assistance in reading and checking the manuscript.

August 1982   Roy Billinton
                                                     Ron Allan

1 Introduction

In our modern society, professional engineers are responsible for the planning, design, manufacture and operation of products and systems ranging from the simple product to the complex system. The failure of these can often cause effects which range from inconvenience and irritation to a severe impact on society and on its environment. Users expect that the products and systems they purchase should be reliable and safe. A question which arises is '*how reliable or how safe will the system be during its future operating life?*' This question can be answered, in part, by the use of quantitative reliability evaluation. In consequence a considerable awareness has developed in the application of such techniques in the design and operation of simple and complex systems.

Reliability assessment as such is not new; engineers have always strived to operate systems that are relatively free from failures. In the past, however, this reliability generally has been achieved from the subjective and qualitative experience of design and operating engineers. This method of assessing the reliability of a system is often referred to by the sceptics of modern reliability evaluation techniques as engineering judgement. It is a fallacy, however, to suggest that engineering judgement is displaced by quantitative reliability evaluation since as much, if not more, engineering judgement is required in its use. In addition to providing a set of numerical indices, reliability evaluation can be used to indicate how a system may fail, the consequences of failures and also to provide information to enable engineers and managers to relate the quality of their system to economics and capital investment. In so doing it can lead to better and more economic designs, and a much improved knowledge of the operation and behaviour of a system.

The development of reliability evaluation techniques was associated with the aerospace industry and military applications. Initial developments were followed rapidly by applications in the nuclear industry, which is continuously under pressure to ensure safe and reliable nuclear reactors, the electricity supply industry, which is expected to supply energy on demand without local failures or large scale blackouts, and continuous process plants such as steel plants and chemical plants which can suffer large scale losses and idling if system failures occur. All of these examples relate to either large scale systems or systems in which failure can result in severe social consequences. Modern reliability evaluation techniques are also used in a much wider range of applications including domestic appliances, automobiles and other products which individually have little socio-economic effect when they fail. It is evident that all engineers should have some awareness of the basic concepts associated with the application of reliability evaluation techniques.

Once it has been decided that quantitative reliability evaluation is needed it becomes necessary to decide on the method to use and the indices required. In essence, all techniques are concerned with future behaviour of a component or system. This future behaviour time may vary between a matter of seconds, such as in the case of the operational phase of a ground to air missile, and several decades, such as in the case of electrical generating units. In all cases the problem cannot be defined as deterministic but as stochastic in nature, i.e., it varies randomly with time. Complete assessment of a stochastic process can only be achieved using probability techniques. However, the reader should note that probability theory alone cannot predict either the reliability or the safety of a system. The assessment requires a thorough understanding of the system, its design, the way it operates, the way it fails, its environment and the stresses to which it is subjected. It is in this aspect of reliability evaluation that engineering judgement is paramount and no amount of probability theory can circumvent it. Probability theory is only a tool available to the engineer in order to transform his knowledge of the system into a prediction of its likely future behaviour.

There are many variations on the definition of reliability but a widely accepted form [1] is as follows: *Reliability is the probability of a device performing its purpose adequately for the period of time intended under the operating conditions encountered.*

This definition breaks down into four basic parts: probability— adequate performance—time—operating conditions.

The first part, probability, provides the numerical input for the assessment of reliability and also the first index of system adequacy. In many instances it is the most significant index but there are many more parameters calculated and used, the most appropriate being dependent on the system and its requirements. These parameters are generally all termed reliability indices and in consequence, the term reliability is frequently used as a generic term describing all these indices rather than being solely associated with the term probability. Typical examples of additional indices are:

—the expected number of failures that will occur in a specified period of time;

—the average time between failures;

—the average outage duration or down-time of a device;

—the expected loss in revenue due to failure;

—the expected loss of output due to failure.

The appropriate reliability index or indices are determined using prob-ability theory. A single all-purpose reliability formula or technique does not exist. The approach used and the resulting formula, if it exists, depends upon the problem and the assumptions which can be made. Many assumptions must be made in all practical applications of probabil-ity and statistical theory. The validity of the reliability analysis of a system is directly related to the validity of the model used to represent the system. Actual failure distributions seldom completely fit the analytical descriptions used in the analysis and care must be taken to ensure that significant errors are not introduced through oversimplification of a problem.

The other three parts, adequate performance, time and operating conditions are all engineering parameters and probability theory is of no assistance for this part of the assessment. Often, only the engineer responsible for a particular system can satisfactorily supply information relating to these. The 'time intended' may be continuous or very sporadic and the 'operating conditions' may be perfectly uniform or extremely variable, as in the propulsion phases associated with space rockets and in the take-off, cruising and landing of commercial flights. Products and systems operating outdoors have a very variable operating environment. Component failure rates are usually closely related to the operating conditions and stress level of the environment in which they function and great care is required to ensure that all phases of operation are accounted for and modelled satisfactorily.

The criterion of 'adequate performance' is an engineering and mana-gerial problem. Failure of a system may be a catastrophe or a complete failure to operate, or it may be caused by a violation of the required system function; for example, the power output of a mechanical pump may fall below a minimum requirement although the pump may still be operating. An assessment of adequate performance is a matter of en-gineering appraisal and appreciation. It requires a detailed investigation of the modes of failure for each component and the system. It is impossible to specify an adequate reliability level, as this will obviously vary with the system and associated consequences of failure. In many practical cases, the important factor is perhaps not the actual or absolute level of reliability (though clearly this cannot be ignored, particularly in the case of safety-orientated systems in which minimum levels of reliabil-ity are paramount) but the incremental reliability cost or relative im-provement in reliability per dollar invested. In such cases, the question posed is: 'Where should the next dollar be invested in the system to achieve the maximum reliability benefit?' These are extremely difficult questions to answer but it should be realized that they cannot be answered at all if consistent quantitative reliability indices for all points within the system are not evaluated.

It is important to recognize that the reliability assessment of a product or system must be performed during and as an integral part of the design process. It is not practical to attempt to consider or add reliability at a later date and to attempt to do so could prove unrewarding and involve considerable and unnecessary cost even if it is physically possible. It follows that a product or system has an inherent reliability created during design. This can only be transformed into the manufactured product or system by a high standard of quality control. Poor quality control can seriously degrade the inherent reliability although perfect quality control will not increase the reliability above that which has been in-built at the design stage. It is evident that reliability and quality control are very much related. Even after manufacture, the inherent reliability can be easily degraded due to poor operation, misuse or abuse, and poor quality maintenance procedures. Reliability and its attainment should be in the minds of all engineers responsible for a product or system from the inception stage right through to obsolescence.

This book is not intended to be a rigorous mathematical discourse on reliability evaluation nor is it intended to cover all aspects of reliability evaluation in a detailed mathematical manner. It is intended to provide the practising engineer and engineering student, who have little or no background in probability theory, statistics or reliability evaluation, with the basic concepts of reliability evaluation and to illustrate sufficient theoretical techniques and applications to permit them to apply quantitative reliability analysis in their own work. An attempt has been made to structure the book so that it can be used as a self-teaching text as well as being suitable for formal lecturing purposes.

In conclusion it is important to appreciate that the most important requirement of any reliability study is a complete understanding of the engineering implications of the system, the criteria for success and the possible modes of failure. Without this complete understanding, quantitative analysis is simply an exercise in mathematical manipulation which can give results that are quite incorrect and misleading. Reliability evaluation using probability methods provides a quantitative prediction of the system performance and, perhaps even more important, a way of consistently evaluating the respective and relative reliability levels of alternative proposals. Reliability engineering is both a measure and a discipline.

2 Basic probability theory

2.1 Probability concepts

The word 'probability' is used frequently in a loose sense implying that a certain event has a good chance of occurring. In this sense it is a qualitative or subjective measure. It is important to realize that it has a strict technical meaning and is a scientific 'measure of chance', i.e., it defines quantitatively the likelihood of an event or events. Mathematically it is a numerical index that can vary between zero which defines an absolute impossibility to unity which defines an absolute certainty. This scale of probability is illustrated in Figure 2.1. A philosopher might argue that the two ends of the scale do not exist. An engineer might disagree from a pragmatic viewpoint. For example, the probability that a man will live for ever is zero, and the probability that one day he will die is unity.

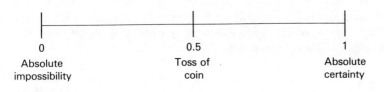

| 0 | 0.5 | 1 |
| Absolute impossibility | Toss of coin | Absolute certainty |

Fig. 2.1 Probability scale

From the definition of probability it is reasonable to assume that very few events are associated with the extreme values of the probability scale; most will have probability indices between these values. For such events it follows that each will have at least two possible outcomes, one of which can be considered as the favourable outcome or success and the other as the unfavourable outcome or failure. For an event that has more than two possible outcomes, it is often possible to group together those outcomes which can be called favourable or successes and those which can be called unfavourable or failures. Grouping outcomes in this way and therefore creating subsets of outcomes from the complete set of possible outcomes,

5

enables the probability of success and failure to be deduced as follows:

$$P(\text{success}) = \frac{\text{number of successes}}{\text{number of possible outcomes}} \left.\vphantom{\frac{a}{b}}\right\}$$

$$P(\text{failure}) = \frac{\text{number of failures}}{\text{number of possible outcomes}}$$

(2.1)

Therefore if $s = $ number of ways success can occur and

$f = $ number of ways failure can occur:

$$P(\text{success}) = p = \frac{s}{s+f}$$

$$P(\text{failure}) = q = \frac{f}{s+f}$$

and $p+q=1$

Example 2.1

Consider a coin and the probability of getting a head or a tail in a single toss. In this example $s = f = 1$. Therefore the probability of getting a head or a tail in a single throw is 1/2.

Example 2.2

Consider a die and the probability of getting a 4 from a single throw. If a 4 is called success, then $s = 1$ and $f = 5$ since there are five ways of not getting a 4. Therefore the probability of getting a 4 is 1/6 and the probability of not getting a 4 is 5/6.

Example 2.3

Consider 2 dice and the probability of getting a total of 9 spots in a single throw of both dice. In this case, the successful outcomes are:

$(3+6), (4+5), (5+4)$ and $(6+3) = 4$ ways $= s$

The failed outcomes are:

$(1+1), (1+2), (1+3), (1+4), (1+5), (1+6)$

$(2+1), (2+2), (2+3), (2+4), (2+5), (2+6)$

$(3+1), (3+2), (3+3), (3+4), (3+5)$

$(4+1), (4+2), (4+3), (4+4), \qquad (4+6)$

$(5+1), (5+2), (5+3), \qquad (5+5), (5+6)$

$(6+1), (6+2), \qquad (6+4), (6+5), (6+6) = 32$ ways $= f$

Therefore the probability of getting a total of 9 spots in a single throw of two dice $= 4/36 = 1/9$ and similarly the probability of not getting a total of 9 spots is $32/36 = 8/9$.

2.2 Permutations and combinations

2.2.1 General concepts

In the previous examples, the probabilities of success and failure were evaluated by enumerating all the physical states or outcomes of the system or event, combining those classed as success and those classed as failure and finally, by applying the concept of Equation 2.1, evaluating the probability of each. If the system or the number of possible outcomes is large, this method can be cumbersome and tedious, and consequently subject to error. However, the state enumeration method is an important and useful technique and will be discussed in more detail later. Rather than using this method, the evaluation of probabilities using the concept of Equation 2.1 can often be more easily handled in some problems by using the concept of permutations and combinations. These are concerned with the number of ways that items can be arranged or combined together; permutations relate to the order of the arrangement whereas combinations do not.

2.2.2 Permutations

The number of permutations of n different items is the number of different ways these items can be arranged. If all the items are used in the arrangement, the number of permutations is designated as $_nP_n$. If only some are used, say r where $r < n$, the number of permutations is designated as $_nP_r$.

Example 2.4

Consider the number of permutations of 3 different books A, B, C taken three at a time. Using the state enumeration method these arrangements are:

ABC, ACB, BAC, BCA, CAB, CBA, i.e. a total of 6 possibilities.

Therefore $_3P_3 = 6$

Alternatively, this value can be obtained by considering the number of ways each actual position can be filled.
Position 1—as all books are available there are 3 choices for this position.
Position 2—as one book has been used to fill position 1, there are only 2 choices for this position.

Position 3—as two books have now been used, there is only 1 choice for the last position.

Consequently $_3P_3 = 3 \times 2 \times 1 = 3! = 6$ choices as before.

This example demonstrates that the number of permutations of n items taken n at a time is $n!$ In general the number of permutations of n items taken r at a time is:

$$_nP_r = \frac{n!}{(n-r)!} \tag{2.2}$$

which reduces to $n!$ when $r = n$ since $0! = 1$.

Example 2.5

Evaluate how many ways three books can be selected from seven books and placed on a shelf.

$$_7P_3 = \frac{7!}{(7-3)!} = 7 \times 6 \times 5 = 210 \text{ ways}$$

This can be explained since there are 7 ways of filling the first position, 6 ways of filling the second and 5 ways of filling the third, giving a total of 210 ways. It follows that the probability of using any one arrangement is 1/210.

In many examples and problems involving permutations, Equation 2.2 is applicable and thus eliminates the need for enumerating all the states involved in the problem. However, its applicability is not universal and care must be exercised in its use. In general, it is applicable when all of the three following rules are satisfied;

(a)   all items are different,

(b)   no restrictions are imposed on the positioning of an item, and

(c)   no item can be used more than once.

To illustrate these rules, consider the next two examples:

Example 2.6

How many three digit numbers can be formed from the numbers 0, 1, 2, 3, 4, 5, 6, 7, 8, 9 if zero can not be used to fill the first place and if (a) each number can be repeated, (b) each number can be used once only?

(a)   First digit—Since zero cannot be used for the first digit, there are 9 ways.

Second and third digit—Since all numbers can be repeated, there are 10 ways for each of these digits.

Therefore the total number of different sequences is $9 \times 10 \times 10 = 900$

(b)   First digit—As before, there are 9 ways.

Second digit—Although one number has been used to fill the first place, there are still 9 ways since the zero can now be used.

Third digit—As two numbers have now been used, there are 8 ways. The total number of different sequences is $9 \times 9 \times 8 = 648$.

Example 2.7

How many different patterns can be made in a row of 12 balls using 3 blue balls, 2 red balls and 7 green balls?

If all the balls were of different colours, then the number of patterns would be $= 12! = 479001600$. In this example, many patterns would be identical as only 3 colours are available and not 12.

Since r items can be arranged in $r!$ different ways, it follows that there are exactly 3! identical arrangements of blue balls, 2! identical arrangements of red balls and 7! identical arrangements of green balls. Therefore the number of different patterns using the numbers and colours available is:

$$\frac{12!}{3! \, 2! \, 7!} = 7920$$

and the probability of obtaining any one pattern is $1/7920$.

This example can be expressed more formally since the number of permutations of n items taken all at a time when the n items consist of r_1 alike, r_2 alike $\ldots r_k$ alike such that $r_1 + r_2 + \ldots + r_k = n$ is:

$$\text{permutations} = \frac{n!}{r_1! \, r_2! \ldots r_k!} \tag{2.3}$$

2.2.3 Combinations

The number of combinations of n different items is the number of different selections of r items, each without regard to the order or arrangement of the items in the group. It is this disregard for order which distinguishes combinations from permutations. Therefore, for given values of n and r, the number of combinations must be less than or equal to the number of permutations. The number of combinations of r items from n items is designated as $_nC_r$.

Since it is only the disregard of order that affects the number of combinations, the latter can be evaluated from the number of permutations. If it is again noted that r items can be arranged in $r!$ different ways, it follows that the number of permutations is $r!$ times greater than the equivalent number of combinations, i.e.,

$$_nC_r = \frac{_nP_r}{r!} = \frac{n!}{r! \, (n-r)!} = \frac{n(n-1) \ldots (n-r+1)}{r!} \tag{2.4}$$

Example 2.8

Consider again Example 2.5 which was concerned with selecting 3 books out of 7. It was found that there were 210 ways in which the books could be selected and arranged on the shelf. Many of these arrangements involve the same set of three books. If only the number of sets of books which can be selected and not the order in which they are selected is required, the 210 ways must be reduced by the number of ways in which 3 books can be arranged, i.e., reduced by 3! ($= 6$). Therefore, the number of combinations of 3 books out of 7 is $210/6 = 35$. This value can of course be evaluated directly from Equation 2.4 without first deducing the number of permutations. Also, it follows that the probability of selecting any one set of 3 books is 1/35.

In practice it may be desired to evaluate the number of possible combinations of a group of items that involve subsets of these items with certain restrictions, or conditions, imposed on the use of these subsets. To illustrate this consider the following example.

Example 2.9

From 6 men and 5 women, how many committees of 6 members can be formed when each committee must contain at least 3 women?

The condition that at least 3 women must be present on each committee is satisfied in three ways, when
(a)   there are 3 women and 3 men, or
(b)   there are 4 women and 2 men, or
(c)   there are 5 women and 1 man.

This example is not concerned with the order, only the total composition of the committees. Therefore using the principle of Equation 2.4
(a)   can be selected in $_5C_3 \times _6C_3$ ways
(b)   can be selected in $_5C_4 \times _6C_2$ ways
(c)   can be selected in $_5C_5 \times _6C_1$ ways
giving the total number of committees as

$$(_5C_3 \times _6C_3) + (_5C_4 \times _6C_2) + (_5C_5 \times _6C_1) = 281$$

This number of possible committees can be compared with 462 committees when no conditions are imposed on the composition of each committee.

In this example, the number of committees that can be formed from a given number of men and a given number of women in case (a) involving 3 men and 3 women, was obtained from the product of the number of combinations of each subset or group; $_5C_3 \times _6C_3$. This product is applicable when it is noted that each possible combination of one subset can be combined with each possible combination of the other subset to produce a unique combination of committee members. Similarly for (b) and (c).

2.2.4   Comparison of permutations and combinations

In Section 2.2.3 it was stated that the number of combinations of any given problem is less than or equal to the number of permutations of the same problem. This can be seen from a comparison of the two concepts and from the numerical examples considered in the previous sections.

To illustrate the relative changes in the number of combinations and permutations with the values of n and r, consider the following example:

Example 2.10

Deduce the number of permutations and the number of combinations that can be obtained from:
(a)   4 items taken $r(=1, 2, 3, 4)$ at a time, and
(b)   7 items taken $r(=1, 2, \ldots, 7)$ at a time.

Using Equations 2.2 and 2.4, these results are shown in Table 2.1.

Table 2.1   Number of permutations and combinations

n	4		7	
r	Permutations	Combinations	Permutations	Combinations
1	4	4	7	7
2	12	6	42	21
3	24	4	210	35
4	24	1	840	35
5			2520	21
6			5040	7
7			5040	1

These results illustrate that, when choosing 1 at a time, the number of permutations and combinations are identical but as the value of r increases, the number of permutations increases very sharply and continuously whereas the number of combinations first increases to a maximum and then decreases to unity.

2.2.5   Application in probability evaluation

In practical reliability applications, the concept of combinations is usually, but not universally, of more use and importance than permutations, since it is generally necessary to know which events, when combined together, lead to system failure, and of less concern to know in which order they occur. There are exceptions to this and examples will be discussed later in the text.

This section describes the application of combinations to simple probability problems. In the previous examples it was relatively easy to evaluate the probability of an event because all outcomes were equally likely, e.g., the probabilities of obtaining a head or a tail in a toss of a coin are both equal to 1/2; they are equally likely outcomes.

Example 2.11

Four balls are drawn at random from a box containing 20 balls of which 10 are white and 10 are black. What is the probability of getting four balls (a) all black, (b) of the same colour, and (c) all black if each ball is replaced before drawing the next one?

(a) The number of ways of drawing 4 balls from 20 balls is $_{20}C_4 = 4845$, the number of ways of drawing 4 black balls from 10 white and 10 black is $_{10}C_4 = 210$,

therefore, the probability of getting 4 black balls $= 210/4845 = 0.043344$.

(b) The number of ways of drawing 4 white balls or 4 black balls from the 20 balls is $(_{10}C_4 + _{10}C_4) = 2 \times _{10}C_4 = 420$,

therefore, the probability of getting 4 balls of the same colour $= 420/4845 = 0.086687$.

(c) If each ball is replaced before the next one is drawn then the total number of ways of drawing 4 balls is 20^4 since at each draw there are 20 balls to choose from. Similarly the total number of ways of drawing 4 black balls is 10^4,

therefore the probability of getting 4 black balls $= 10^4/20^4 = 0.0625$.

In case (c), another method of evaluation can be used. At each draw, there are 20 balls; 10 white and 10 black. Therefore, if drawing a black ball is considered as success and drawing a white ball is considered as failure, the concept of Equation 2.1 can be applied to give the probability of drawing a black ball at each draw as $10/(10+10) = \frac{1}{2}$. The probability of drawing 4 black balls in 4 draws which, because the balls are replaced after each draw, are 'independent', becomes $\frac{1}{2} \times \frac{1}{2} \times \frac{1}{2} \times \frac{1}{2} = (\frac{1}{2})^4 = 0.0625$, as before.

The concept of 'independent' events will be discussed in Section 2.5 but the example of case (c) demonstrates an important aspect concerning the application of probability methods which occurs frequently in system reliability evaluation. This is that there are frequently a number of different ways in which the same problem can be solved and no one way is automatically the best. This point will be demonstrated several times in the following chapters on evaluation techniques in which various methods are used to solve the same problem.

In the previous examples, each outcome was equally probable. In real engineering reliability problems, this is very rarely the case and the events causing system failure can have very marked differences in individual values of probability. The concepts and principles remain the same. To illustrate this, reconsider Example 2.11 as follows.

Example 2.12

Reconsider Example 2.11 but with 4 white balls and 16 black balls.

(a) The number of ways of drawing 4 balls from 20 is still 4845, the number of ways of drawing 4 black balls is now $_{16}C_4 = 1820$, therefore, probability of getting 4 black balls $= 1820/4845 = 0.375645$.

(b) The number of ways of drawing 4 white balls or 4 black balls is $(_4C_4 + _{16}C_4) = 1821$,

therefore, the probability of getting 4 balls of the same colour $= 1821/4845 = 0.375851$.

(c) If each ball is replaced before the next is drawn, probability of getting 4 black balls $= 16^4/20^4 = 0.4096$.

Comparing the results for (a) and (b), it is evident, as expected, that the contribution made to the overall probability by considering the drawing of 4 white balls is very small. This is dependent on the probability of drawing a white ball (1/5 on the first draw) being much smaller than that of drawing a black ball (4/5 on the first draw). If drawing the four white balls had been ignored, the inaccuracy would be only about 0.05%. This aspect is frequently used in system reliability evaluation where events of known very low probability compared with others are often ignored.

Although considerable stress has been placed in this section on evaluating combinations and permutations, it should be noted that not all problems require these methods. The first few examples in this chapter were solved without utilising them. The main benefit of using combinations and permutations is in relieving the tediousness of, for example, state enumeration methods. This can be shown by reconsidering Example 2.3 in which the total number of outcomes were deduced by state enumeration. It would have been considerably simpler if the total number of outcomes had been deduced from principles of combinations, since it is known that each face on one die can be combined with each face of the other die to give a unique combination, i.e., there are altogether 6×6 ($= 36$) combinations or outcomes ($= s + f$). The total number of successes (or failures) would still have to be enumerated as described previously.

2.3 Practical engineering concepts

In the previous sections and examples, it was possible to determine the probability of an outcome from a simple knowledge of the geometry or design of the object (the shape of the coin or die), or of the mathematical specification of the problem (the number of books which can be selected). This permits a precise value of probability to be defined and evaluated without any further experimentation.

In most engineering applications, deduction of success and failure probabilities cannot be found from a simple knowledge of geometry, design or mathematical specification. In these cases it is necessary to obtain experimental evidence to determine the probabilities. In some cases, e.g., small items such as electronic components, this information is obtained from repeated testing of a large number of such components under the conditions they are likely to encounter in normal operation. With large and expensive devices such as power stations, telecommunication systems, chemical engineering plants and so on, it is not possible or practical to test such items to destruction. In these cases alternative methods, generally applied in combination, are used. These are;

(a)   the device or system is subdivided into one or more hierarchical levels such that probability data for the lowest hierarchical level is more easily obtained. The failure probability of the complete device or system is then deduced using system reliability evaluation techniques,

(b)   the required data is not established from special testing procedures but from actual operating experience.

It is preferable and in many cases absolutely essential to establish a feedback system from the user to the designer or manufacturer so that a continuous assessment concerning the reliability of the components, device or system can be obtained in order that future improvements can be made. One of the most developed feedback systems occurs in the aircraft industry, particularly in relation to aeroengines; all aeroengine manufacturers monitor continuously the performance and behaviour of each engine in service.

In order to apply the concepts discussed in this chapter and previously to these types of engineering problems, it is necessary to establish a link between the purely mathematical concept of probability and the empirical concept of evidence of behaviour regularity in repeated or continuous experiments. This link is established through the relative frequency interpretation of probability. Using data collected from experimental methods, both pre-operational and operational, then:

$$P(\text{of a particular event occurring}) = \lim_{n \to \infty} \left(\frac{f}{n} \right) \qquad (2.5)$$

where n = number of times an experiment is repeated

f = number of occurrences of a particular outcome

Equation 2.5 is similar to Equation 2.1 and is a measure of the relative frequency of the outcome compared with the experiment. It is evident that the true probability is measured only after an infinite number of trials. Consequently the sample size must be very large before a realistic and reasonably accurate value of probability is achieved.

The correspondence between statistical and empirical probability also exists for all cases in which the event probabilities are known from the geometry of the system. This frequency or empirical approach is very useful in the analysis of physical systems which possess statistical regularity such as certain types of equipment failures, equipment life expectancies, defects in manufactured products and so on. If there is no evidence of statistical regularity, then probability theory may not be applicable.

One example of particular importance, in all branches of engineering, is finding the probability of a particular piece of equipment being on outage or failed. If the equipment has passed through its initial commissioning period (sometimes known as debugging or burn-in) and has not entered the fatigue or wear-out period, it can be considered to exist in what is generally known as its useful life period (to be discussed in more detail in Chapter 6). In this period, equipment failures occur at random and therefore with statistical regularity. The best estimate of the probability of finding the piece of equipment on outage or failed at some future time is generally known as its unavailability:

$$\text{unavailability} = \frac{\text{time on outage or failed}}{\text{time on outage} + \text{operating time}} \tag{2.6}$$

2.4 Venn diagrams

In reliability evaluation problems it is necessary to combine probabilities associated with individual events to give the probability of overall system behaviour. There are a certain number of probability rules which permit this to be done. The ones which are significant in system reliability evaluation are defined and discussed in Section 2.5. They can be expressed mathematically in terms of set theory concepts and it is neither possible to describe them without recourse to some aspects of set theory nor is it valid to do so since this would impede a reader from extending his knowledge on this subject. However, it is not the intention of this book to be a rigorous text on either these probability rules or on set theory, there are many texts available for further reading [2–8].

The rules that will be discussed are not always easily understood without the benefit of some pictorial representation of the concept. In set theory applications this is normally done by the use of Venn diagrams. Before describing the rules and using Venn diagrams to represent them pictorially, the basic concepts of Venn diagrams are described.

A Venn diagram is normally drawn as a rectangle which represents the total probability space S, as shown in Figure 2.2. The area S encloses or represents the entire space being considered. There may be two or more events within this space for which the probabilities must be combined.

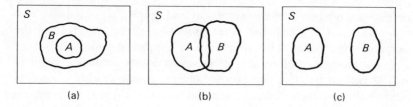

Fig. 2.2 Venn diagrams

This consideration may be restricted to two events A and B. If event A is totally enclosed by event B (Figure 2.2a), then event A is a subset of event B. This is one particular association between A and B and a more general relationship is that A and B partly overlap (Figure 2.2b) or do not overlap at all (Figure 2.2c).

2.5 Rules for combining probabilities

2.5.1 Rule 1—Independent events

Two events are said to be independent if the occurrence of one event does not affect the probability of occurrence of the other event.

Example 2.13

Throwing a die and tossing a coin are independent events since which face of the die is uppermost does not affect the outcome of tossing a coin.

Events are often assumed to be independent in practice even when it is not strictly correct to do so. This normally occurs when the information or available data is insufficient to establish the degree of dependence. If the degree of dependence is known or can be estimated however, it must be included in the evaluation exercise. The assumption of event independence may lead to an optimistic assessment of system reliability.

2.5.2 Rule 2—Mutually exclusive events

Two events are said to be mutually exclusive (or disjoint) if they cannot happen at the same time.

This is represented by the Venn diagram shown in Figure 2.2c where the two events A and B do not overlap. When event A has occurred, event B cannot occur. In the Venn diagram of Figure 2.2c, other events besides A and B are possible because the space occupied by events A and B does not occupy the whole space S.

Example 2.14

When throwing a single die, the events *1 spot, 2 spots, 3 spots, 4 spots, 5 spots, 6 spots* are all mutually exclusive because two or more cannot occur simultaneously. Similarly success and failure of a device are mutually exclusive events since they cannot occur simultaneously.

2.5.3 Rule 3—Complementary events

Two outcomes of an event are said to be complementary if, when one outcome does not occur, the other must.

This is represented by the Venn diagram shown in Figure 2.3. It follows

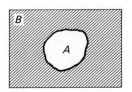

Fig. 2.3 Complementary events

from this Venn diagram and also the principle established by the equations in Section 2.1 that, if the two outcomes A and B have probabilities $P(A)$ and $P(B)$, then:

$$P(A) + P(B) = 1 \quad \text{or} \quad P(B) = P(\bar{A}) \tag{2.7}$$

where $P(\bar{A})$ is the probability of A NOT occurring.

Example 2.15

When tossing a coin, the outcomes *head* and *tail* are complementary since:

$$P(head) + P(tail) = 1 \quad \text{or} \quad P(head) = P(\overline{tail})$$

Similarly if a device can either be in a success state or in its failed state, these success and failed states are complementary.

From this it is evident that complementary events are also mutually exclusive but that the converse is not necessarily true, i.e., two mutually exclusive events are not necessarily complementary.

2.5.4 Rule 4—Conditional events

Conditional events are events which occur conditionally on the occurrence of another event or events.

Consider two events A and B and also consider the probability of event A occurring under the condition that event B has occurred. This is described mathematically as $P(A \mid B)$ in which the vertical bar is interpreted as GIVEN and the complete probability expression is interpreted as the 'conditional probability of A occurring GIVEN that B has occurred'.

This value of probability can be deduced from an analysis of the Venn

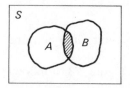

Fig. 2.4 Intersection

diagram shown in Figure 2.4 since

$$P(A \mid B) = \frac{\text{number of ways A and B can occur}}{\text{number of ways B can occur}}$$

This is an application of Equation 2.5 since the total 'number of times an experiment is repeated' is equivalent to B, some of which will lead to the occurrence of A and B together, this being the 'particular outcome' of interest.

The number of ways A and B can occur is the hatched area shown in Figure 2.4 and is represented mathematically as $(A \cap B)$, the probability of which can be deduced by again applying Equation 2.5 as

$$P(A \cap B) = \frac{(A \cap B)}{S}$$

similarly $\quad P(B) = \dfrac{B}{S}$

therefore $P(A \mid B) = \dfrac{S \cdot P(A \cap B)}{S \cdot P(B)}$

$$= \frac{P(A \cap B)}{P(B)} \tag{2.8}$$

similarly $\quad P(B \mid A) = \dfrac{P(A \cap B)}{P(A)}$

The application of this equation and its derivatives is given in conjunction with the subsequent rules.

2.5.5 Rule 5—Simultaneous occurrence of events

The simultaneous occurrence of two events A and B is the occurrence of BOTH A AND B.

In terms of a Venn diagram, this occurrence is the hatched area shown in Figure 2.4 and considered in connection with Rule 4 and conditional probability. Mathematically it is known as the intersection of the two events and is represented as:

$$(A \cap B), \quad (A \text{ AND } B) \quad \text{or} \quad (AB)$$

In this rule there are two cases to consider, the first is when the two events are independent and the second is when they are dependent.

(a) Events are independent

If two events are independent, then the probability of occurrence of each event is not influenced by the probability of occurrence of the other. In this case

$$P(A \mid B) = P(A) \quad \text{and} \quad P(B \mid A) = P(B)$$

Therefore from Equation 2.8, the probability that they both occur is:

$$P(A \cap B) = P(A) \cdot P(B) \tag{2.9}$$

This equation expresses formally the principle used in previous sections of this chapter for evaluating combined probabilities. If there are n independent events, the principle can be extended to give:

$$P(A_1 \cap A_2 \cap \ldots \cap A_i \cap \ldots \cap A_n) = \prod_{i=1}^{n} P(A_i) \tag{2.10}$$

Example 2.16

An engineer selects two components A and B. The probability that component A is good is 0.9 and the probability that component B is good is 0.95. Therefore the probability of both components being good is:

$$P(A \text{ good} \cap B \text{ good}) = P(A \text{ good}) \cdot P(B \text{ good})$$
$$= 0.9 \times 0.95 = 0.855$$

(b) Events are dependent

If two events are not independent, then the probability of occurrence of one event is influenced by the probability of occurrence of the other. In this case Equation 2.8 can still be used but not simplified as in the case of independence. Thus:

$$P(A \cap B) = P(B \mid A) \cdot P(A)$$
$$= P(A \mid B) \cdot P(B) \tag{2.11}$$

Example 2.17

One card is drawn from a standard pack of 52 playing cards. Let A be the event that it is a red card and B be the event that it is a court or face card.

What is the probability that both A and B occur.

$P(A) = 26/52$

Given that A has occurred, the sample space for B is 26 states of which 6 states are those of a court or face card.

Therefore $P(B \mid A) = 6/26$

and $\quad P(A \cap B) = 6/26 \times 26/52 = 6/52$

Alternatively

$P(B) = 12/52$

Given that B has occurred, the sample space for A is 12 states of which 6 states are those of a red card,

Therefore $P(A \mid B) = 6/12$

and $\quad P(A \cap B) = 6/12 \times 12/52 = 6/52$ (as before)

In this example the solution could have been simplified since the essence of the question was to evaluate the probability of selecting a red court or face card. It is readily known that there are 6 such cards in the pack, thus required probability $= 6/52$. However, the principle shown here is of fundamental importance and will be used frequently in the following chapters.

2.5.6 Rule 6—Occurrence of at least one of two events

The occurrence of at least one of two events A and B is the occurrence of A OR B OR BOTH.

In terms of a Venn diagram, this occurrence is the hatched area shown in Figure 2.5. Mathematically it is known as the union of the two events

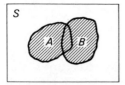

Fig. 2.5 Union

and is expressed as:

$(A \cup B),$ $\quad$ (A OR B) $\quad$ or $\quad (A + B)$

In this rule there are three cases to consider; the events are independent but not mutually exclusive, the events are independent and mutually exclusive and, finally, the events are not independent.

(a) *Events are independent but not mutually exclusive*

There are two ways in which the appropriate equation can be deduced; using an analytical method and using the Venn diagram. Consider first the analytical technique.

$$P(A \cup B) = P(A \text{ OR } B \text{ OR BOTH } A \text{ AND } B)$$
$$= 1 - P(\text{NOT } A \text{ AND NOT } B)$$
$$= 1 - P(\bar{A} \cap \bar{B})$$
$$= 1 - P(\bar{A}) \cdot P(\bar{B}) \qquad \text{from Equation 2.9}$$
$$= 1 - (1 - P(A)) \cdot (1 - P(B)) \qquad \text{from Equation 2.7}$$
$$= P(A) + P(B) - P(A) \cdot P(B) \qquad (2.12)$$

Consider now the use of the Venn diagram.

$$P(A \cup B) = \text{the hatched area shown in Figure 2.5}$$
$$= P(A) + P(B) - P(A \cap B) \qquad (2.13)$$

The probability value $P(A \cap B)$ must be subtracted in this equation since this value represents the intersection of A and B and would otherwise be included twice in the sum $P(A) + P(B)$. Therefore from Equation 2.9:

$$P(A \cup B) = P(A) + P(B) - P(A) \cdot P(B) \qquad \text{(as before)}$$

Example 2.18

Reconsider Example 2.16: The probability that component A or component B or both is good:

$$P(A \text{ good} \cup B \text{ good}) = P(A \text{ good}) + P(B \text{ good})$$
$$- P(A \text{ good}) \cdot P(B \text{ good})$$
$$= 0.9 + 0.95 - 0.9 \times 0.95$$
$$= 0.995$$

(b) *Events are independent and mutually exclusive*

In the case of events A and B being mutually exclusive, then the probability of their simultaneous occurrence $P(A) \cdot P(B)$ must be zero by definition. Therefore from Equation 2.12

$$P(A \cup B) = P(A) + P(B) \qquad (2.14)$$

This can also be derived from a Venn diagram representation. In this case the Venn diagram is the one shown in Figure 2.2c in which event A and event B do not overlap. It follows that the intersection of the two events is zero and

$$P(A \cup B) = P(A) + P(B)$$

If there are n independent and mutually exclusive events

$$P(A_1 \cup A_2 \cup \ldots \cup A_i \cup \ldots \cup A_n) = \sum_{i=1}^{n} P(A_i) \tag{2.15}$$

Example 2.19

Reconsider Example 2.3 which evaluated the probability of getting a total of 9 spots in a single throw of 2 dice. In this example the 4 different ways of getting a total of 9 are mutually exclusive since if one way occurred, all other ways could not. Since each way has a probability of occurrence of 1/36, then the probability of getting a total of 9 spots in a single throw is:

$$P(9) = 1/36 + 1/36 + 1/36 + 1/36 = 4/36 \quad \text{or} \quad 1/9$$

(c) *Events are not independent*

If the two events A and B are not independent then from Equations 2.11 and 2.13

$$P(A \cup B) = P(A) + P(B) - P(A \cap B)$$
$$= P(A) + P(B) - P(B \mid A) \cdot P(A)$$
$$= P(A) + P(B) - P(A \mid B) \cdot P(B) \tag{2.16}$$

Example 2.20

Reconsider Example 2.17 and evaluate the probability that the drawn card is red, court or face card, or both.

As before $P(A) = 26/52$, $\qquad P(B) = 12/52$

$\qquad\qquad P(A \mid B) = 6/12$, $\qquad P(B \mid A) = 6/26$

therefore $\quad P(A \cup B) = (26/52 + 12/52) - (6/26 \cdot 26/52) = 32/52$

or $\qquad P(A \cup B) = (26/52 + 12/52) - (6/12 \cdot 12/52) = 32/52$

2.5.7 Rule 7—Application of conditional probability

The concept of conditional probability was introduced in Rule 4 when it was considered that an event A was dependent on another event B. This principle can be extended to consider the occurrence of an event A which is dependent upon a number of mutually exclusive events B_i.

From Equation 2.8

$$P(A \cap B) = P(A \mid B) \cdot P(B) \tag{2.17}$$

Using Equation 2.17, the following set of equations can be deduced for each B_i:

$$P(A \cap B_1) = P(A \mid B_1) \cdot P(B_1)$$
$$P(A \cap B_2) = P(A \mid B_2) \cdot P(B_2)$$
$$\vdots$$
$$P(A \cap B_i) = P(A \mid B_i) \cdot P(B_i)$$
$$\vdots$$
$$P(A \cap B_n) = P(A \mid B_n) \cdot P(B_n)$$

or, when combined:

$$\sum_{i=1}^{n} P(A \cap B_i) = \sum_{i=1}^{n} P(A \mid B_i) \cdot P(B_i) \tag{2.18}$$

If Equation 2.18 is summed over the exhaustive list of events B_i then,

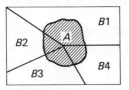

Fig. 2.6 Conditional probability

as illustrated by the consideration of four such events in Figure 2.6:

$$\sum_{i=1}^{n} P(A \cap B_i) = P(A)$$

which reduces Equation 2.18 to the following conditional probability equation

$$P(A) = \sum_{i=1}^{n} P(A \mid B_i) \cdot P(B_i) \tag{2.19}$$

This equation has many uses in reliability evaluation some of which are considered in following chapters. The use of this equation is best considered by way of example:

Example 2.21

A certain item is manufactured at two plants. Plant 1 makes 70% of the requirement and plant 2 makes 30%. From plant 1, 90% meet a particular standard and from plant 2 only 80%. Evaluate, (a) out of every 100 items purchased by a customer, how many will be up to standard and,

(b) given that an item is standard, what is the probability that it was made in plant 2?

(a) Using the concept of Equation 2.17, consider A as the event that the item is up to standard, B_1 as the event that the item is made in plant 1 and B_2 as the event that the item is made in plant 2.

Therefore, $P(A\,|\,B_1) = 0.9$, $P(A\,|\,B_2) = 0.8$, $P(B_1) = 0.7$, $P(B_2) = 0.3$

$$P(A) = 0.9 \times 0.7 + 0.8 \times 0.3$$
$$= 0.63 + 0.24 = 0.87$$

and out of every 100 items purchased by the customer

$$100 \times 0.87 = 87$$

will be standard.

(b) The probability that the item comes from plant 2 given that it was standard, is $P(B_2\,|\,A)$. This is a direct application of Equation 2.17 (or alternatively the application of Equation 2.18 for one value of i only, in this case when $i = 2$).

From part (a), the probability that the component is standard AND comes from plant 2, $P(A \cap B_2) = 0.24$ and the probability that it is standard, $P(A) = 0.87$. Therefore

$$P(B_2\,|\,A) = \frac{P(A \cap B_2)}{P(A)}$$
$$= 0.24/0.87 = 0.276$$

If the occurrence of an event A is dependent upon only two mutually exclusive events for component B, i.e., success and failure, which can be designated as B_s and B_f respectively then Equation 2.19 becomes

$$P(A) = P(A\,|\,B_s) \cdot P(B_s) + P(A\,|\,B_f) \cdot P(B_f) \tag{2.20}$$

In reliability evaluation, the object of the analysis is usually to estimate the probability of system failure (or success). Thus Equation 2.20 can be written:

$P(\text{system failure}) = P(\text{system failure } \textit{given } B \text{ is good}) \cdot P(B_s)$

$\qquad\qquad + P(\text{system failure } \textit{given } B \text{ is bad}) \cdot P(B_f) \tag{2.21a}$

The complementary situation is also true if event A is described as system success:

$P(\text{system success}) = P(\text{system success } \textit{given } B \text{ is good}) \cdot P(B_s)$

$\qquad\qquad + P(\text{system success } \textit{given } B \text{ is bad}) \cdot P(B_f) \tag{2.21b}$

Equation 2.21 is versatile and has many useful applications in reliability evaluation.

Example 2.22

Consider a system containing two components A and B and assume that the system fails only if both A and B fail. Deduce the probability of system failure if Q_A and Q_B are the probabilities of failure of the respective components.

From Equation 2.21a

$$P(\text{system failure}) = P(\text{system failure} \mid B \text{ good}) \cdot (1 - Q_B)$$
$$+ P(\text{system failure} \mid B \text{ bad}) \cdot Q_B$$
$$= 0 \cdot (1 - Q_B) + Q_A \cdot Q_B$$
$$= Q_A \cdot Q_B$$

In this derivation, the system cannot fail if B is assumed to be good and can only fail due to failure of A if B is assumed to be bad. The same result could have been obtained from Equation 2.9 since

$$P(\text{system failure}) = P(A \text{ fails}) \cdot P(B \text{ fails})$$
$$= Q_A \cdot Q_B$$

The derivation using the conditional probability approach may appear cumbersome in this particular case. It can, however prove to be invaluable in more complex situations. This example also illustrates a point made earlier that, for any given problem, there may frequently be more than one way to solve it.

The reader should verify the above result by considering A good and A bad and also deduce the complementary result for system success.

2.6 Probability distributions

2.6.1 Random variables

In the preceding sections, the concepts have mainly been described and the problems solved using a knowledge of the design, geometry or specification of the events, experiments or systems. In practice this knowledge is not readily available, and a series of experiments must be performed or a data collection scheme instituted to deduce sufficient knowledge about the system's behaviour for the application of probability theory to reliability evaluation. This empirical determination of data is unlikely to lead to a single, precisely known value of probability and frequency of occurrence of an event, or a single outcome from a series of events. Instead it is most likely that a whole range of values or outcomes will emerge.

In order that probability theory can be applied to the occurrence of these values or events, it is essential that they occur by chance, i.e., randomly in time, or space, or both. The parameter of the event being measured (e.g. failure rate of a component, length of repair time, value of a resistor, mechanical strength of a component) is therefore a variable that randomly varies in time and/or space. It may be defined as a discrete or continuous random variable.

A discrete random variable is one that can have only a discrete number of states or countable number of values. For example, the toss of a coin is a discrete variable since there are only two discrete states that can occur, head and tail. Similarly a throw of a die is a discrete variable as only six discrete states are possible.

A continuous random variable is one that can have an infinite number of values. This does not mean that the range must extend from $-\infty$ to $+\infty$, only that there are an infinite number of possibilities of the value. For example, if an electric current can have any value between 5 A and 10 A but no others, it is a continuous random variable.

2.6.2   Density and distribution functions

Data that is collected empirically, either by special experimentation or from the use of a data collection scheme, must be analysed and assessed for it to be of value in evaluation exercises. This can be done by using probability density functions and (cumulative) probability distribution functions. These functions and their application are considered in detail in Chapters 3, 6 and 7; however, at this stage it is useful to introduce their basic properties and principles. In order to do this consider the following numerical example.

Example 2.23

A machine cuts extruded copper into lengths of approximately 6 m. Using random sampling, a quality control engineer measures 20 of these cut lengths as 5.97, 5.97, 5.98, 5.98, 5.98, 5.99, 5.99, 5.99, 5.99, 5.99, 6.00, 6.00, 6.00, 6.00, 6.00, 6.01, 6.01, 6.02, 6.02, 6.02.

These results may be plotted as a frequency distribution as shown in Figure 2.7a, which pictorially represents the frequency of occurrence of each specific length of copper. An alternative method of plotting this data is to group together sets of data of approximately equal value. This is convenient if the amount of data is very large since it reduces the amount to be manipulated and produces a pictorial representation that is easier to interpret. Although this is not necessary with the data of Example 2.23, these data could be reconsidered and grouped into the sets 5.965–5.985, 5.985–6.005, 6.005–6.025. This new frequency distribution is shown in

Figure 2.7b. In this case the impulses of Figure 2.7a become bars; the resultant graph is called a (frequency) histogram.

At this point probability has not been considered but this can be deduced from the data and the two frequency distributions using the concept of relative frequency of probability described by Equation 2.5.

In Example 2.23, the 'number of experiments' is 20. If the frequency of occurrence of each length or of each group of lengths is divided by 20, the quotient gives the probability of occurrence of each length or group of lengths. In Figures 2.7a and 2.7b, the ordinate axis has been scaled in terms of these probabilities. When scaled in this way, the resultant graphs

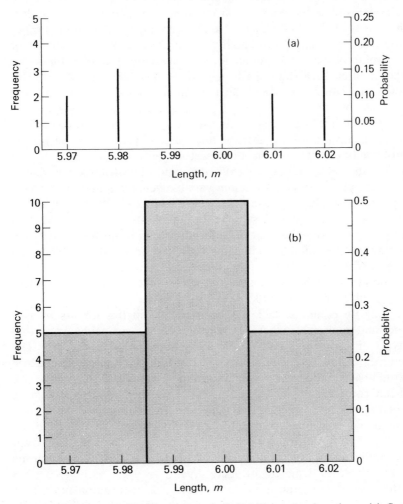

Fig. 2.7 Frequency distributions and probability mass functions. (a) Separate data. (b) Grouped data

are known as probability mass functions though frequently they are loosely referred to as probability density functions. Since all possible outcomes of the sample space being considered have been included in Figure 2.7, it follows that the summation of the probabilities must equal unity, i.e.,

$$\sum_{i=1}^{n} P(x_i) = 1 \tag{2.22}$$

where x_i represents outcome i or, in the case of Example 2.23, represents length i.

A further method of presenting the same set of data is to use the (cumulative) probability distribution function. This is obtained by ordering the values of the random variable in ascending (or descending) order and, by starting with the probability of occurrence of the smallest (or largest) value, sequentially summate, i.e., cumulate, the probabilities of occurrence of each value until all such values have been cumulated. This is shown in Figure 2.8a and 2.8b for the individual sets of data and grouped sets of data respectively of Example 2.23.

Since all possible outcomes of the sample space have been considered in this summation, it follows that the final value of probability reached by the probability distribution function must be unity.

The advantage to be gained from this type of distribution is that it indicates the probability of a random variable being less than or equal to some predefined value. For example, from Figure 2.8a, the probability of a length of copper being less than or equal to 5.99 m is 0.5. This probability value could have been deduced directly from the defined data by summating the number of lengths less than or equal to 5.99 m and dividing this number by the total number of lengths. The probability distribution function has important uses in reliability evaluation and these are discussed later in the book.

The data of Example 2.23 has been treated in this discussion as a discrete random variable whereas the reader could reasonably expect that this type of problem would be a continuous random variable. The discreteness of this problem occurred because of the limited sample size and would have tended to a continuous random variable if the sample size had been considerably increased. In this case the discontinuous steps exhibited in Figure 2.8 diminish and the distribution will tend to a continuous curve. Consequently, for a continuous random variable the probability distribution function is a continuous curve starting from zero and becoming asymptotic to unity, or reaching unity, depending upon the random variable as depicted in Figure 2.9a.

In the case of a discrete random variable, the distribution function is obtained by summating, i.e. numerically integrating, the mass (density) function. Similarly a probability density function $f(x)$ can be deduced (see

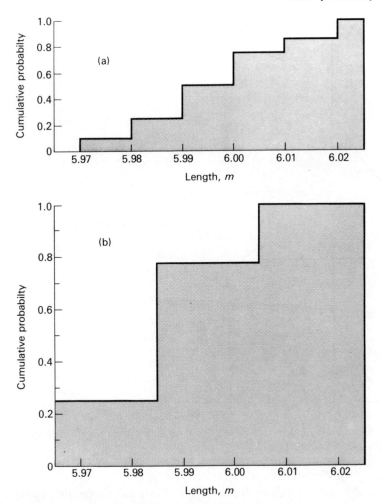

Fig. 2.8 Probability distribution functions. (a) Separate data. (b) Grouped data

Figure 2.9b) by differentiating the probability distribution function $F(x)$ of a continuous random variable, i.e.,

$$f(x) = \frac{\mathrm{d}F(x)}{\mathrm{d}x} \tag{2.23}$$

or

$$F(x_1) = \int_{-\infty}^{x_1} f(x)\,\mathrm{d}x \tag{2.24}$$

Equation 2.24 is equivalent to the summation performed for a discrete

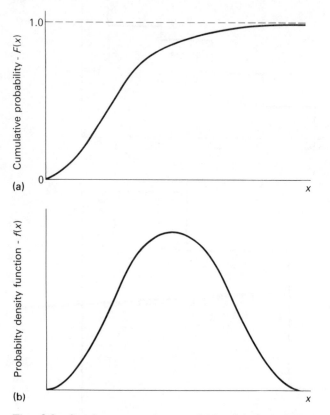

Fig. 2.9 Continuous random variable. (a) Probability distribution function. (b) Probability density function

random variable and gives the probability of the random variable being less than or equal to the predefined value x_1.

The limits of Equation 2.24 can be changed to two intermediate values of the density function, say a and b, so that the resultant integration gives the probability of the random variable being between or equal to these two new limits, i.e.

$$P(a \leqslant x \leqslant b) = \int_a^b f(x)\, \mathrm{d}x \tag{2.25}$$

One interesting feature that can be deduced from Equation 2.25 is that the probability of occurrence of any given value of x is zero, i.e.

$$P(x = a) = \int_a^a f(x)\, \mathrm{d}x = 0$$

This result can be explained in terms of the following analogy. Consider an express train travelling at 160 km/h. Although travelling at a considerable speed, the train moves zero distance at any given point in time but moves an increasing distance as the time interval being considered increases. Similarly, a random variable has zero probability of occurrence at any given value of the variable but has an increasing probability of occurrence as the variable interval being considered increases.

This section is not meant to be an exhaustive or mathematical discussion of distribution functions, and for a more detailed discussion the reader should refer to more specialized texts [2–8]. However, the material presented should be sufficient to understand and implement many reliability evaluation techniques. In practice it is often found that random variables follow one of a number of standard distributions. Typical standard discrete distributions are the binomial and Poisson distributions, and typical standard continuous distributions are the normal (Gaussian), lognormal, exponential, Weibull, gamma and Rayleigh distributions. These together with their special characteristics and useful applications are discussed in Chapters 3, 6 and 7.

2.6.3 Mathematical expectation

In practice it is useful to describe the random behaviour of a system or a set of data by one or more parameters rather than as a distribution. This is particularly true in the case of system reliability evaluation. This parametric description can be achieved using numbers known mathematically as the moments of a distribution.

The most important of these moments is the expected value, which is also referred to as the average (mean) value or population mean. Mathematically it is the first moment of the distribution.

Most people are familiar with the idea of calculating the average value of a set of data simply by summating the values of each item of the data and dividing by the number of items. Using the data of Example 2.23, the average length of copper is

$$\frac{1}{20}(5.97 + 5.97 + 5.98 + 5.98 + 5.98 + 5.99 + 5.99 + 5.99 + 5.99 +$$
$$5.99 + 6.00 + 6.00 + 6.00 + 6.00 + 6.00 + 6.01 + 6.01 + 6.02 +$$
$$6.02 + 6.02) = 5.9955$$

The same result is obtained if each possible length is weighted by its relative frequency of occurrence (Equation 2.5), i.e., the average length is

$$5.97 \times \frac{2}{20} + 5.98 \times \frac{3}{20} + 5.99 \times \frac{5}{20} + 6.00 \times \frac{5}{20}$$

$$+ 6.01 \times \frac{2}{20} + 6.02 \times \frac{3}{20} = 5.9955$$

Because the relative frequency of occurrence is the probability of occurrence, this leads to the following definition of expected value $E(x)$ of a discrete random variable x having n outcomes x_i each with a probability of occurrence p_i

$$E(x) = \sum_{i=1}^{n} x_i p_i \qquad (2.26)$$

where $\sum_{i=1}^{n} p_i = 1$.

In the case of a continuous random variable, Equation 2.26 can be modified from a summation to an integration to give:

$$E(x) = \int_{-\infty}^{\infty} xf(x)\,dx \qquad (2.27)$$

where $\int_{-\infty}^{\infty} f(x)\,dx = 1$.

Example 2.24

A die is tossed many times. What is the expected number of dots on the upper face.

$$E(\text{number of dots}) = \left(1 \times \frac{1}{6}\right) + \left(2 \times \frac{1}{6}\right) + \left(3 \times \frac{1}{6}\right) + \left(4 \times \frac{1}{6}\right) + \left(5 \times \frac{1}{6}\right)$$

$$+ \left(6 \times \frac{1}{6}\right)$$

$$= 3.5$$

This simple example produces a result with great practical implications. The expected number of dots is found to be 3.5, a result which is physically impossible to obtain in a single throw of the die. Mathematical expectation and the expected value is therefore not something that is 'expected' in the ordinary sense but is only the long term average as the number of trials is increased to infinity. This implies that it is not the most frequently occurring value or the most probable; in fact, as in this example, it may be physically impossible.

Example 2.25

The probability that a 30 year old man will survive a fixed time period is 0.995. An insurance company offers him a $2000 insurance policy for this period for a premium of $20. What is the company's expected gain?

Gain = +$20.00 if man lives

= −$1980.00 if man dies

Probability that he lives = 0.995

Probability that he dies = 0.005

1.000

expected gain = (+20) × 0.995 + (−1980) × 0.005

= $10

This expected gain must be positive and greater than some minimum value for the company to make a profit.

2.6.4   Variance and standard deviation

Although the expected value is probably the most important distribution parameter in reliability evaluation, the underlying shape of the distribution is lost when only this parameter is deduced. The amount of 'spread', or more correctly dispersion, of a distribution is measured by the second central moment of the distribution which is known as the variance $V(x)$.

In general the kth central moment of a distribution is defined as

$$M_k = E[x − E(x)]^k$$

Therefore $V(x) = E[x − E(x)]^2$ (2.28)

$$= E[x^2 − 2xE(x) + E^2(x)]$$

$$= E(x^2) − E(2xE(x)) + E[E^2(x)]$$

$$= E(x^2) − 2E(x)E(x) + E^2(x)$$

$$= E(x^2) − E^2(x) \qquad (2.29)$$

This derivation requires some knowledge of the properties of expected values (refer to texts [2,4]).

Equations 2.28 and 2.29 lead to two possible methods for evaluating the variance since, from these equations and the concept of expected values given by Equation 2.27

$$V(x) = \sum_{i=1}^{n} (x_i − E(x))^2 P_i \qquad (2.30)$$

or

$$V(x) = \sum_{i=1}^{n} (x_i^2 P_i) − E^2(x) \qquad (2.31)$$

The same principle applies in the case of continuous random variables with the requirement that in Equations 2.30 and 2.31, the summations are replaced by integrations to follow the principle of Equation 2.27.

In practice, the value of variance is not frequently used but instead its positive square root known as standard deviation and denoted as σ is more commonly quoted, i.e.:

$$\sigma = +\sqrt{V(x)} \tag{2.32}$$

Example 2.26

Evaluate the variance and standard deviation of the lengths of copper measured in Example 2.23.

In this example, the variable x is the length of copper. Therefore, from Equation 2.31

$$V(x) = 5.97^2 \times \frac{2}{20} + 5.98^2 \times \frac{3}{20} + 5.99^2 \times \frac{5}{20} + 6.00^2 \times \frac{5}{20} + 6.01^2 \times \frac{2}{20}$$

$$+ 6.02^2 \times \frac{3}{20} - 5.9955^2$$

$$= 2.248 \times 10^{-4}$$

and $\sigma(x) = 1.499 \times 10^{-2}$ m

The same result would be obtained using Equation 2.30 and it is suggested that the reader should verify this using the same data.

This result indicates that, as expected, the value of variance and standard deviation is small if the spread or dispersion of values is small. This can lead to difficulties, as the evaluation of $V(x)$ is obtained in such cases by subtracting two large, nearly equal numbers. Consequently, care and precision are required when evaluating variance and standard deviation.

2.7 Conclusions

In this chapter some of the fundamental concepts and principles of probability theory required in reliability evaluation have been introduced and discussed. No attempt has been made to incorporate rigorous mathematical descriptions and derivations; for this the reader is referred to more specialized texts [2–8].

The basic principles and concepts have been described predominantly with the use of simple numerical examples. They will be enhanced through frequent use in later chapters and their real significance to practical problems should become evident.

Problems

1) The probability that a man will be alive in 10 years is 0.8 and the probability that his wife will be alive in 10 years is 0.9. Find the probability that in 10 years:
   (i)   Both will be alive;
   (ii) Only the man will be alive;
   (iii) Only the wife will be alive;
   (iv) At least one will be alive.

2 The probability of Inspector #1 on a production line finding a defective item is 0.8 and of Inspector #2, down the line, 0.7. What is the probability of a defective item getting through?

3 Three urns contain, respectively, 1 white and 2 black balls, 2 white and 1 black balls, 2 white and 2 black balls. A blindfold man transfers one ball from the first urn into the second, then one ball from the second urn into the third. A ball is drawn from the third urn. What is the probability of its being white?

4) A worker operates three machines. The probability that for the duration of an hour a machine does not require the attention of the worker is 0.9 for the first machine, 0.8 for the second and 0.85 for the third. What is the probability that in any one hour none of the machines require his attention? What is the probability that at least one of the machines does not require any attention during any one hour?

5) Two dice are tossed together. Let A be the event that the sum of the faces are odd, B the event that at least one is a one. What is the probability that:
   (a)   Both A and B occur;
   (b)   Either A or B or both occur;
   (c)   A and not B occurs;
   (d)   B and not A occurs?

6 A box contains a normal coin and a two headed coin. A coin is selected at random and tossed. If heads appear, the other coin is tested, if tails appear, the same coin is tossed.
   (a)   Find the probability that heads appear on the second toss.
   (b)   If heads appeared on the second toss, find the probability that it also appeared on the first toss.

7 A shopper buys two cartons of a dozen eggs each. His habit is to inspect 3 eggs picked at random from each carton and to reject the carton if he finds one or more cracked eggs. If the first carton contains two cracked eggs and the second, one cracked egg, find the probability that:
   (a)   Carton 1 is rejected and carton 2 is accepted.
   (b)   Both cartons are accepted.
   (c)   Neither carton is accepted.

8 A piece of equipment contains six identical items and it is known that three of them are defective. The items are tested one after the other until the three defective items are found.
   (a)   What is the probability that the testing process is stopped on the (i) third test (ii) fourth test.
   (b)   If the process is stopped on the fourth test, what is the probability that the first item is not defective.

3 Application of the binomial distribution

3.1 Binomial distribution concepts

Some of the general concepts and properties of distributions were introduced in Chapter 2. A number of standard distributions such as binomial, Poisson, normal, lognormal, exponential, gamma, Weibull, Rayleigh were also mentioned. Most of these distributions and their application in reliability evaluation are discussed in Chapter 6. However, it is useful to single out the binomial distribution at this stage.

Essentially the binomial distribution can be directly associated with the type of combinational problems considered in Chapter 2. Many of these problems can be evaluated more readily from a knowledge of the binomial distribution and the solution to more complicated reliability problems becomes possible. First it is necessary to establish the link between the combinational type of problem presented in Chapter 2 and the binomial distribution.

Consider again the single toss of a coin. It is known that the outcome can be a head (H) or a tail (T) each having a probability of occurrence of 1/2. All possible outcomes and their probability of occurrence could have been expressed as

$$P(H) + P(T) = [P(H) + P(T)]^1 \tag{3.1}$$

Now consider when the coin is tossed twice. The possible outcomes are (HH), (HT), (TH) or (TT). If only the combination of the outcomes is of interest, and not the order, these may be expressed as (HH), 2(HT), (TT), with probabilities of occurrence of 1/4, 1/2, 1/4, respectively. The same result is obtained by expressing the outcomes and their probability of occurrence as

$$P(H) \cdot P(H) + 2P(H) \cdot P(T) + P(T) \cdot P(T) = P^2(H) + 2P(H) \cdot P(T) + P^2(T)$$
$$= [P(H) + P(T)]^2 \tag{3.2}$$

Finally consider the case when the coin is tossed three times. If the order is again considered to be unimportant then, as previously, the outcomes and their probability of occurrence may be expressed as

$$P^3(H) + 3P^2(H) \cdot P(T) + 3P(H) \cdot P^2(T) + P^3(T) = [P(H) + P(T)]^3 \tag{3.3}$$

The left hand side of Equations 3.1 to 3.3 indicate all the possible outcomes of the experiment, the number of ways (combinations) that each outcome can occur and the probability of occurrence of each way. For example, $3P^2(H) \cdot P(T)$ in Equation 3.3 indicates that one outcome is 2 heads and 1 tail (given by appropriate power index), that there are 3 ways in which this outcome can occur (given by the pre-multiplier) and that the probability of occurrence of each of these ways is $P^2(H) \cdot P(T)$ or that the probability of getting 2 heads and 1 tail is $3P^2(H) \cdot P(T)$.

The right hand side of Equations 3.1 to 3.3 is the conventional binomial expression of order 1 (Equation 3.1), order 2 (Equation 3.2) and order 3 (Equation 3.3), in which the order, or exponent, of the binomial expression represents the number of times the experiment is performed.

From this simple example of tossing a coin, it should be evident that the binomial distribution represents all possible outcomes, and their probability of occurrence, of an experiment, or event, which can be represented by the binomial expression $(p+q)^n$. It is also evident that it is directly associated or linked with the type of problems discussed in Chapter 2 that were concerned with combinations. In the previous discussion, the basic concept of the binomial distribution by an example involving the outcome *head* and the outcome *tail* due to the toss of a coin has been described. If the outcome *head* is defined as success and the outcome *tail* is defined as failure, the previous discussion becomes more general and the concepts described can be related to reliability concepts in which p now represents the probability of success and q $(=1-p)$ represents the probability of failure.

3.2 Properties of the binomial distribution

3.2.1 General characteristics

From the previous section, the binomial distribution can be represented by the general expression:

$$(p+q)^n \tag{3.4}$$

For this expression to be applicable, four specific conditions are required. These are:
(a) there must be a fixed number of trials, i.e., n is known,
(b) each trial must result in either a success or a failure, i.e., only two outcomes are possible and $p+q=1$,
(c) all trials must have identical probabilities of success and therefore of failure, i.e., the values of p and q remain constant, and
(d) all trials must be independent (this property follows from (c) since the probability of success in trial i must be constant and not affected by the outcome of trials $1, 2, \ldots, (i-1)$).

In order to apply the binomial distribution and to evaluate the outcomes and their probability of occurrence of a given experiment or set of trials, the expression $(p+q)^n$ must be expanded into the form of Equations 3.1 to 3.3, and

$$(p+q)^n = p^n + np^{n-1} q + \frac{n(n-1)}{2!} p^{n-2} q^2 + \ldots$$

$$+ \frac{n(n-1)\ldots(n-r+1)}{r!} p^{n-r} q^r + \ldots + q^n \quad (3.5)$$

If Equation 3.5 is compared with Equation 2.4, it is seen that the coefficient of the $(r+1)$th term in the binomial expansion represents the number of ways, i.e., combinations, in which exactly r failures and therefore $(n-r)$ successes can occur in n trials and is equal to $_nC_r$. Therefore each coefficient in Equation 3.5 can be directly evaluated from the definition of $_nC_r$ as discussed in Section 2.2.3 and the probability of exactly r successes or $(n-r)$ failures in n trials can be evaluated from

$$\begin{aligned} P_r &= \frac{n!}{r!(n-r)!} p^r q^{n-r} \\ &= {}_nC_r p^r q^{n-r} \\ &= {}_nC_r p^r (1-p)^{n-r} \end{aligned} \quad (3.6)$$

Substituting Equation 3.6 into Equation 3.5 gives

$$(p+q)^n = \sum_{r=0}^{n} {}_nC_r p^r q^{n-r} = 1 \quad (3.7)$$

Consider the application of the binomial distribution to the following examples.

Example 3.1

A coin is tossed 5 times. Evaluate the probability of each possible outcome and draw the probability mass (density) function and the probability distribution function.

In this example $n=5$, $p=q=1/2$. Using the binomial expansion given by Equations 3.5 to 3.7, the outcomes, the probability of exactly r heads or $(n-r)$ tails and the cumulative probability are shown in Table 3.1. In this table the probability of exactly r heads has been defined as 'individual' probability in order to differentiate it clearly from the 'cumulative' probability. This term will also be used consistently throughout the book.

In Table 3.1, the values of individual probability have been summated and a value of unity obtained. This summation is a worthwhile exercise particularly if the cumulated values are not evaluated since, if the summation is not equal to unity either an arithmetic error has been made

Table 3.1   Results for Example 3.1

Number of heads	tails	Individual probability expression	value	Cumulative probability
0	5	$_5C_0(1/2)^0(1/2)^5$	1/32	1/32
1	4	$_5C_1(1/2)^1(1/2)^4$	5/32	6/32
2	3	$_5C_2(1/2)^2(1/2)^3$	10/32	16/32
3	2	$_5C_3(1/2)^3(1/2)^2$	10/32	26/32
4	1	$_5C_4(1/2)^4(1/2)^1$	5/32	31/32
5	0	$_5C_5(1/2)^5(1/2)^0$	1/32	32/32
			$\Sigma = 1$	

or one, or more, system states have not been considered. This is quite possible in the analysis of a complicated system or problem. The results of Table 3.1 are plotted as a probability mass (density) function and probability distribution functions in Figures 3.1a and 3.1b. In this example Figure 3.1a is symmetrical. This only occurs when $p = q = 1/2$ since in this case the success and failure events can be interchanged without any

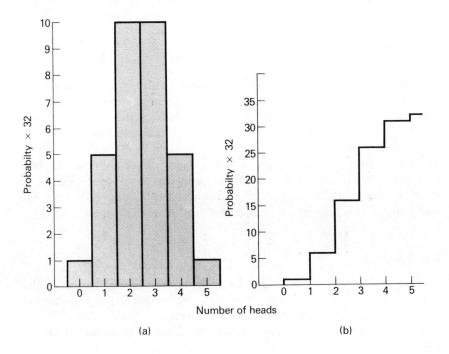

(a)   (b)

Fig. 3.1 Results for Example 3.1. (a) Probability density (mass) function. (b) Probability distribution function

alteration in the numerical value of any of the individual outcomes. This is not the case in the next example when $p \neq q$.

Example 3.2

Consider the case in which the probability of success in a single trial is 1/4 and four trials are to be made. Evaluate the individual and cumulative probabilities of success in this case and draw the two respective probability functions.

In this example $n = 4$, $p = 1/4$, $q = 3/4$, the results are shown in Table 3.2 and the probability functions in Figure 3.2.

Table 3.2   Results for Example 3.2

Number of successes	failures	Individual probability	Cumulative probability
0	4	$(3/4)^4 = 81/256$	81/256
1	3	$4(1/4)(3/4)^3 = 108/256$	189/256
2	2	$6(1/4)^2(3/4)^2 = 54/256$	243/256
3	1	$4(1/4)^3(3/4) = 12/256$	255/256
4	0	$(1/4)^4 = 1/256$	256/256
		$\Sigma = 1$	

In the preceding problems and discussion, only two outcomes were possible for each trial. This is one of the essential conditions for the binomial distribution to be applicable, i.e., condition (b). However, there are many problems which can be solved using the binomial distribution where more than two outcomes are possible from each trial. One simple example is the throwing of a die in which six outcomes are possible. This type of problem can be solved if the outcomes can be grouped together to form two separate complementary events, classed for example as success and failure. This principle was discussed and used in Chapter 2.

Example 3.3

A die is thrown 6 times. Evaluate the probability of getting 2 spots on the upper face 0, 1, 2, ..., 6 times and draw the probability mass (density) function and the probability distribution function.

On each throw, the probability of getting 2 spots on the upper face is 1/6 and the probability of not getting 2 spots is 5/6. If these two events are defined as success and failure respectively, then, although there are six possible outcomes on each throw, the problem has been constrained to have two outcomes and the binomial distribution becomes applicable.

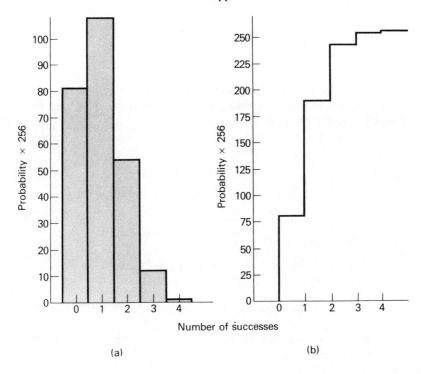

Number of successes

(a)　　　　　　　　　　　　　　(b)

Fig. 3.2 Results for Example 3.2. (a) Probability density (mass) function. (b) Probability distribution function

Consequently $n = 6$, $p = 1/6$ and $q = 5/6$. The probability results are shown in Table 3.3.

Table 3.3　Results for Example 3.3

Number of successes	Individual probability	Cumulative probability
0	$(5/6)^6 = 15625/46656$	15625/46656
1	$6(1/6)\,(5/6)^5 = 18750/46656$	34375/46656
2	$15(1/6)^2(5/6)^4 = 9375/46656$	43750/46656
3	$20(1/6)^3(5/6)^3 = 2500/46656$	46250/46656
4	$15(1/6)^4(5/6)^2 = 375/46656$	46625/46656
5	$6(1/6)^5(5/6) = 30/46656$	46655/46656
6	$(1/6)^6 = 1/46656$	46656/46656
	$\Sigma = 1$	

3.2.2　Binomial coefficients

One essential aspect of the binomial distribution is to evaluate $_nC_r$ or the number of combinations of exactly r successes in n trials. This can become quite tedious as it involves factorials which, even when n is relatively small, can mean a considerable number of individual multiplications. Various alternatives are available for the evaluation of these binomial coefficients:

(a) When n is small, direct hand evaluation of $_nC_r$ is practical.
(b) Also, when n is relatively small, the coefficients can be found from Pascal's triangle as follows:

$$
\begin{array}{ccccccccc}
 & & & & 1 & & & & \\
 & & & 1 & & 1 & & & \\
 & & 1 & & 2 & & 1 & & \\
 & 1 & & 3 & & 3 & & 1 & \\
1 & & 4 & & 6 & & 4 & & 1 \\
\end{array}
$$

for $(p+q)^1 = 1p + 1q$

$(p+q)^2 = 1p^2 + 2pq + 1q^2$

$(p+q)^3 = 1p^3 + 3p^2q + 3pq^2 + 1q^3$

etc.

$$
\begin{array}{ccccccccccccc}
 & & & 1 & & 5 & & 10 & & 10 & & 5 & & 1 \\
 & & 1 & & 6 & & 15 & & 20 & & 15 & & 6 & & 1 \\
 & 1 & & 7 & & 21 & & 35 & & 35 & & 21 & & 7 & & 1
\end{array}
$$

etc.

(c) For large factorials, the coefficients can be approximated using Stirling's formula

$$n! \simeq e^{-n}n^n\sqrt{2\pi n}$$

(d) Using special binomial distribution tables [9–11] which give binomial probabilities for a range of data.
(e) Many, but not all, electronic calculators now have pre-programmed functions for evaluating factorials. This enables the value of $_nC_r$ to be evaluated easily for any size of n within the capacity of the calculator.

3.2.3 Expected value and standard deviation

As discussed in Section 2.6, two of the most important parameters of a distribution are the expected, or mean value, and the standard deviation. The binomial distribution is a discrete random variable and therefore the expected value and standard deviation can be evaluated using Equations 2.26 and 2.29.

First consider the expected value; from Equation 2.26

$$E(X) = \sum_{x=0}^{n} x \cdot {}_nC_x p^x q^{n-x}$$

$$= \sum_{x=0}^{n} x \cdot \frac{n!}{x!\,(n-x)!}\, p^x q^{n-x}$$

As the contribution to this summation made by $x = 0$ is zero then

$$E(X) = \sum_{x=1}^{n} \frac{n!}{(x-1)!\,(n-x)!}\, p^x q^{n-x}$$

$$= \sum_{x=1}^{n} \frac{n(n-1)!}{(x-1)!\,(n-x)!}\, p \cdot p^{x-1} q^{n-x}$$

$$= np \sum_{x=1}^{n} \frac{(n-1)!}{(x-1)!\,(n-x)!}\, p^{x-1} q^{n-x}$$

Letting $n - 1 = m$ and $x - 1 = y$, then:

$$E(X) = np \sum_{y=0}^{m} \frac{m!}{y!\,(m-y)!}\, p^y q^{m-y}$$

But

$\displaystyle\sum_{y=0}^{m} \frac{m!}{y!\,(m-y)!}\, p^y q^{m-y}$ is the complete binomial expansion of $(p+q)^m$ and therefore is equal to unity.

Therefore $E(X) = np$ (3.8)

Therefore, for a binomial distribution, the expected number of successes is equal to the number of trials multiplied by the probability of success or conversely, the expected number of failures is equal to the number of trials multiplied by the probability of failure.

Now consider evaluation of the standard deviation. From Equation 2.29

$$V(X) = E(X^2) - E^2(X)$$

and $E(X^2) = \displaystyle\sum_{x=0}^{n} x^2 \cdot {}_nC_x p^x q^{n-x}$

$$= \sum_{x=0}^{n} x(x-1) \cdot {}_nC_x p^x q^{n-x} + \sum_{x=0}^{n} x \cdot {}_nC_x p^x q^{n-x}$$

$$= \sum_{x=0}^{n} x(x-1) \cdot {}_nC_x p^x q^{n-x} + np$$

since the second summation is the expected value of $(p+q)^n$. Also, using the same logic as that used to deduce $E(X)$

$$E(X^2) = np + \sum_{x=2}^{n} \frac{n(n-1)(n-2)!}{(x-2)!\,(n-x)!}\, p^2 p^{x-2} q^{n-x}$$

$$= np + p^2 n(n-1) \sum_{x=2}^{n} \frac{(n-2)!}{(x-2)!\,(n-x)!}\, p^{x-2} q^{n-x}$$

$$= np + p^2 n(n-1) \cdot 1$$

$$= n^2 p^2 + np - np^2$$

and $V(X) = (n^2p^2 + np - np^2) - (np)^2$

$$= np(1 - p)$$

$$= npq \tag{3.9}$$

and $\sigma = \sqrt{npq}$ (3.10)

From Equations 3.9 and 3.10 it is seen that, although the expected value of success is different to the expected value of failure if $p \neq q$, the variance and standard deviation of success and failure are identical for all values of p and q.

Example 3.4

A product is claimed to be 90% free of defects. What is the expected value and standard deviation of the number of defects in a sample of 4?

In this example $n = 4$, $p(\text{defect}) = 0.1$, $q(\text{no defect}) = 0.9$.

From Equation 3.8

$$E(\text{defects}) = 4 \times 0.1 = 0.4$$

From Equation 3.10

$$\sigma(\text{defects}) = \sqrt{4 \times 0.1 \times 0.9} = 0.6$$

The same result can be achieved in a more tedious way by the direct application of Equations 2.26 and 2.31, as shown in Table 3.4.

Table 3.4 Results for Example 3.4

Defects	Individual probability	$E(X)$	$E(X^2)$
0	0.6561	—	—
1	0.2916	0.2916	0.2916
2	0.0486	0.0972	0.1944
3	0.0036	0.0108	0.0324
4	0.0001	0.0004	0.0016
	1.0000	0.4000	0.5200

therefore $E(\text{defects}) = 0.4$

$\sigma(\text{defects}) = \sqrt{0.52 - 0.4^2} = 0.6$

3.3 Engineering applications

3.3.1 Restricting the assessment

The preceding sections were concerned with the concept, properties and probability functions of the binomial distribution. Consequently, all possible outcomes were enumerated and the probability of occurrence of each was evaluated. In practice it may not be necessary to go in to so much detail as only a restricted number of outcomes and their probabilities may be required. This depends upon the requirements of the problem, and these should be assessed carefully before any attempt to apply probability concepts is made. An important aspect in the application of probability methods to any engineering problem is to ensure that they do not dominate it and preclude engineering judgement and understanding of the real problem. Consider, for example, the following problem:

Example 3.5

It is known that, in a certain manufacturing process, one percent of the products are defective. If the average customer purchases 50 of these products selected at random, what is the probability that he receives two or less defective products?

In this example only a restricted number of possibilities need be considered. These are the probability that the customer receives 2, 1 or zero defective products. The principle of the binomial distribution can still be used but only three values of probability need be evaluated. In this example, $n = 50$, $p = 0.01$, $q = 0.99$ and $r = 0, 1, 2$ giving

$$P(2 \text{ defective}) = {}_{50}C_2(0.01)^2(0.99)^{48}$$
$$P(1 \text{ defective}) = {}_{50}C_1(0.01)^1(0.99)^{49}$$
$$P(0 \text{ defective}) = {}_{50}C_0(0.01)^0(0.99)^{50}$$

therefore $P(2 \text{ or less defective}) = {}_{50}C_2(0.01)^2(0.99)^{48} + {}_{50}C_1(0.01)(0.99)^{49}$
$$+ {}_{50}C_0(0.99)^{50}$$
$$= 0.0756 + 0.3056 + 0.6050$$
$$= 0.9862$$

3.3.2 Implication of economics

This book is essentially concerned with reliability models and evaluation techniques and not with management judgement or economic operation and manufacture of components, devices and systems. It is important to realize that reliability and its evaluation cannot be divorced from economic and management decisions, and reference is made to their interrelation at various points in this book. At this stage it is sufficient to stress that reliability and economics are integrated subjects at the management level and the interrelation should be recognized by all engineers involved in reliability assessment and evaluation even if this involvement is only at a very basic level. This important concept of reliability economics can be illustrated by reconsidering Example 3.5.

Example 3.6

The manufacturing company referred to in Example 3.5 has a policy of replacing, free-of-charge, all defective products that are purchased. If the product manufacturing cost is $10 per unit and each product is sold for $15, how much profit is made?

From the data of Example 3.5

$$E(\text{defect}) = 0.01 \text{ for each product } (n = 1)$$

Therefore $1 + 0.01(= 1.01)$ products are supplied for each product purchased and

$$\text{Manufacturing cost} = \$10 \times 1.01 = \$10.10 \text{ per product}$$
$$\text{Income} = \$15 \text{ per product}$$
$$\text{therefore, profit} = \$15 - 10.10 = \$4.90 \text{ per product}$$

If none of the products is defective then the profit increases to $5.00. It is theoretically impossible to improve the reliability to 100% and achieve the $5 profit margin. However, scope does exist for improving the quality of the product, the manufacturing process and the manufacturing quality control. Such improvements may, or may not, increase the profit although they are likely to improve customer goodwill. This interrelation is usually complex and cannot be discussed at length in this book. However, consider one particular improvement the company could make which increases the unit manufacturing cost to $10.05 and decreases the expected number of defects to 0.1%. In this case the profit becomes

$$\text{profit} = \$15 - 10.06 = \$4.94$$

which is an increase of $0.04 without increasing the selling price or changing company replacement policy. This is a simple example but illustrates the need to consider a variety of alternatives, the reliability of each alternative and the economic impact of each alternative. The management of the company can then make an objective assessment of the alternatives based on economic and profitability considerations.

3.3.3 Effect of redundancy

In the above discussion, the need for sensitivity analysis was stated, i.e., different alternatives should be considered and the impact of each assessed. In the case of Example 3.6 it was suggested that these analyses should be associated with the effect of improving the quality or reliability of the product. Instead of increasing the reliability of the components, the overall reliability of a system can generally be improved by increasing the amount of redundancy in the system. This point is discussed in more detail in subsequent chapters. The basic principle and the need for sensitivity analysis is illustrated by means of the following examples which make use of the binomial distribution.

Example 3.7

Consider a system consisting of 4 components. These components could be water pumps in a mechanical engineering problem, supporting structures in a civil engineering problem, generating station transformers in a power system problem, microprocessors in a control system problem or heat exchangers in a chemical engineering problem. Therefore, although the problem is described in general terms, it can represent a wide variety of engineering applications. In this example consider the components to be identical with a success probability of 0.9 and therefore a failure probability of 0.1.

The states in which the components can exist and the number of combinations in each state can be expressed as

$$S^4 + 4S^3F + 6S^2F^2 + 4SF^3 + F^4$$

in which S = success, F = failure, power index = number of components in the success or failure state and premultiplier = number of combinations of the state. The sum of the binomial coefficients is 16. This is the total number of states, i.e., $2^4 = 16$.

This expression is equivalent to the binomial expansion $(S + F)^4$ and the binomial distribution can be applied to this type of problem provided that all components are identical. If the components are not identical, the state expression shown above is still applicable but the probability of residing in, for example, each of the four S^3F states will be different. Alternative methods are required for evaluating systems with non-identical components and these techniques are discussed in Sections 3.3.7 and 3.3.8. In the present example, all components are identical and a direct application of the binomial distribution can be made to give the results shown in Table 3.5.

Table 3.5   Results for Example 3.7

System state	Individual probability
all components working	0.9^4 $= 0.6561$
1 component failed	$4 \times 0.9^3 \times 0.1 = 0.2916$
2 components failed	$6 \times 0.9^2 \times 0.1^2 = 0.0486$
3 components failed	$4 \times 0.9 \times 0.1^3 = 0.0036$
all components failed	0.1^4 $= 0.0001$
	1.0000

At this point it is not possible to say how good the system is in performing its intended function without knowing the system requirements of the four components, i.e., in addition to a knowledge of the state probabilities as shown in Table 3.5, it is also necessary to have a criterion for system success or failure. Knowledge of this criterion is vitally important in all system reliability evaluation techniques. In its assessment, a sound and thorough engineering appreciation of the requirements and behaviour of the system is required. This assessment must be left to the system planner, designer or operator. Assume that the following four criteria for success are to be examined:

(a)   all components are required for success,
(b)   3 components are required for success,
(c)   2 components are required for success, and
(d)   1 component is required for success.

The same criteria can be expressed in terms of failure as;

(a)   failure of one or more components causes system failure,
(b)   failure of two or more components causes system failure,
(c)   failure of three or more components causes system failure, and
(d)   failure of four components causes system failure.

A system obeying criterion (a) is known as a non-redundant system, a system obeying criterion (d) is known as a fully redundant system and systems obeying criteria (b) and (c) are known as partially-redundant, majority vote or m-out-of-n systems. These types of systems are discussed in more detail in Chapters 4 and 7.

When the criterion for success or for failure is known, the values of state probabilities shown in Table 3.5 can be combined as appropriate to give the success probability or reliability R of the system and the failure probability Q of the system. For example, using criterion (b)

$$R = 0.6561 + 0.2916 = 0.9477$$
$$Q = 0.0486 + 0.0036 + 0.0001 = 0.0523 = 1 - R$$

Using a similar method for combining the success and failure probabilities for conditions (a), (c) and (d) gives the reliability and unreliability results shown in Table 3.6, columns 6, 7. In practice it is advisable to perform sensitivity studies to see the effect of increasing, for instance, the amount of redundancy and to relate this effect to system economics. Two possible sensitivity studies in this problem are to study the effect of changing the number of available components and to change the number of components required for system success. Using the previous technique, the results for up to 6 components available are also shown in Table 3.6.

Several interesting and important reliability features can be deduced

Table 3.6   Sensitivity studies for Example 3.7

| Number of components required for system success | Number of components available | | | | | | | | | | |
| | 6 | | 5 | | 4 | | 3 | | 2 | | 1 | |
	R	Q	R	Q	R	Q	R	Q	R	Q	R	Q
6	0.531441	0.468559	—	—	—	—	—	—	—	—	—	—
5	0.885735	0.114265	0.59049	0.40951	—	—	—	—	—	—	—	—
4	0.984150	0.015850	0.91854	0.08146	0.6561	0.3439	—	—	—	—	—	—
3	0.998730	0.001270	0.99144	0.00856	0.9477	0.0523	0.729	0.271	—	—	—	—
2	0.999945	0.000055	0.99954	0.00046	0.9963	0.0037	0.972	0.028	0.81	0.19	—	—
1	0.999999	0.000001	0.99999	0.00001	0.9999	0.0001	0.999	0.001	0.99	0.01	0.9	0.1

from the results shown in Table 3.6. These are discussed in more depth in subsequent chapters but are nevertheless worth while identifying and recognizing at this stage. The most important features are:

(a)   for systems with no redundancy, the reliability of the system decreases as the number of components increases, compare the results for one component required in a one component system, two components in a two component system, and so on,

(b)   for systems containing total redundancy, the reliability of the system increases as the number of components increases, compare the results for a one out of one component system, one out of two, one out of three, and so on.

The results shown in Table 3.6 were evaluated using a success/failure criterion based on the number of components. In many applications this criterion is the most appropriate one to use. Examples of this are mechanical structures, aircraft flight control circuits, safety or hazard monitors and detectors, and so on. However, in some engineering problems that involve 'flow' a different criterion may be more appropriate. Examples of 'flow' occur in electrical power systems, chemical process plants, cooling water circulators, manufacturing industries, and so on. In these cases, a criterion based, not on numbers of components, but on percentage throughput, flow or output is usually more desirable.

Example 3.8

Reconsider Example 3.7 with 4 components available but introduce the additional aspect of component rating expressed as a percentage of the required system output. Assume (a) the components are connected in parallel and that the operation or inoperation of any pump does not affect that of the others, (b) system success is defined as a minimum percentage of maximum system output so that an output less than this minimum output is defined as a system failure.

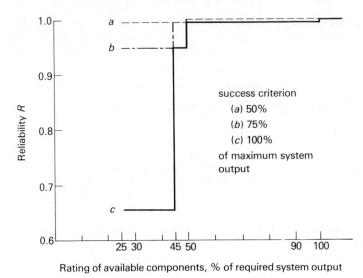

Rating of available components, % of required system output

Fig. 3.3   Results for Example 3.8

Using the results shown in Table 3.5, the system reliability for a range of component ratings and system success criteria are shown in Table 3.7 and Figure 3.3.

The results in Table 3.7 and Figure 3.3 show an over-simplification of many flow type problems since flows less than a certain value are classed as failures whereas in practice these may contribute to system effectiveness albeit at a less desirable level. This problem area is discussed in the next section. However, the results are applicable to some engineering applications, such as safety situations, in which flows greater than a

Table 3.7   Results for Example 3.8

Component rating, % of required system output	Success criterion, % of maximum system output					
	100		75		50	
	Components required	R	Components required	R	Components required	R
100	1	0.9999	1	0.9999	1	0.9999
90	2	0.9963	1	0.9999	1	0.9999
50	2	0.9963	2	0.9963	1	0.9999
45	3	0.9477	2	0.9963	2	0.9963
30	4	0.6561	3	0.9477	2	0.9963
25	4	0.6561	3	0.9477	2	0.9963

certain level create a safe situation and flows less than this create an unsafe situation.

In these cases and in the general application of reliability techniques, the results demonstrate the need for a clear and sound engineering appreciation of system requirements and economics. For instance, if a reliability of 0.9963 is considered acceptable and the components available are those shown in column 1 of Table 3.7, there is no need to choose a rating greater than 50% if the success criterion is 100% or a rating greater than 25% if the success criterion is 50%. This selection process can have a major impact on system economics and can only be quantified using reliability evaluation techniques. The above conclusions concerning rating are applicable only if the component failure probability remains constant as the throughput varies. If they are not applicable the evaluation becomes more complicated and the binomial distribution becomes inappropriate although the general concepts and need for quantification remains valid.

3.3.4 Effect of partial output (derated) states

In Section 3.3.3 it was assumed that the system states could be combined to form a 2-state system in which one group of states could be classed as success and the other as failure. This method neglected the fact that, in practice, some of the system states may not fall into either of these groups, for example, a process plant may be running at full capacity with no failures, zero capacity because of total failure or at some intermediary capacity because of partial system failure or the failure of some of its production plant. In such cases the latter output capacity cannot be deemed to be either success or failure, it is a partial output, or derated state, of the system and should be analysed as such.

This type of problem can be solved by deducing a 'capacity outage (available) probability table' using the binomial distribution if all components are identical and relating each state of this table with the system requirement using the concept of mathematical expectation. To illustrate the formation of capacity outage probability tables and their use in reliability evaluation, consider the following example:

Example 3.9

A small generating plant is to be designed to satisfy a constant 10 MW load. Four alternatives are being considered:
(a) 1×10 MW unit
(b) 2×10 MW units
(c) 3×5 MW units
(d) $4 \times 3\frac{1}{3}$ MW units

Although this is a specific engineering problem, the concepts can be applied equally well to similar problem, i.e., the 10 MW load is equivalent to the desired full output of a process plant or the water flow demand on a particular cooling system. The units considered are equivalent to the plant output capacities or the water pump ratings. The concepts of the problem do not change, only the unitary system will be different.

In this example the first alternative has zero redundancy whereas the other three alternatives have a one unit reserve above the demand level of 10 MW.

Assume that the probability of a unit failing is the same for all units and equal to 0.02. In most engineering applications this is known as the unavailability of the unit although in generating plant studies it is more generally known as the forced outage rate. The availability is therefore 0.98.

The capacity outage probability tables for each of the four alternatives are constructed as shown in Table 3.8.

Table 3.8 Capacity outage probability tables

Units out	Capacity, MW Out	Available	Individual probability
(a) 1×10 MW unit			
0	0	10	0.98
1	10	0	0.02
			1.00
(b) 2×10 MW units			
0	0	20	$0.98^2 = 0.9604$
1	10	10	$2 \times 0.98 \times 0.02 = 0.0392$
2	20	0	$0.02^2 = 0.0004$
			1.0000
(c) 3×5 MW units			
0	0	15	0.941192
1	5	10	0.057624
2	10	5	0.001176
3	15	0	0.000008
			1.000000
(d) $4 \times 3\frac{1}{3}$ MW units			
0	0	$13\frac{1}{3}$	0.92236816
1	$3\frac{1}{3}$	10	0.07529536
2	$6\frac{2}{3}$	$6\frac{2}{3}$	0.00230496
3	10	$3\frac{1}{3}$	0.00003136
4	$13\frac{1}{3}$	0	0.00000016
			1.00000000

The capacity outage probability tables shown in Table 3.8 are similar in concept to Table 3.5. They provide an indication of probable capacity deficiencies for each alternative but do not indicate the relative reliability merits. To achieve this it is necessary to relate these tables to the requirement of the system. In this example the requirement is to satisfy a demand of 10 MW. The relative reliability merit of each alternative can be evaluated by considering each state in the capacity outage probability table, deducing how much of the load is not satisfied (load loss) and calculating the expected load loss using the concept of mathematical expectation by weighting the load loss in each state by its probability of occurrence. This evaluation is shown in Table 3.9 for all four alternatives.

Table 3.9 Expected load losses

Capacity out MW	Probability	Load loss MW	Expected load loss MW
(a) 1 × 10 MW unit			
0	0.98	0	—
10	0.02	10	0.2
			0.2 MW
(b) 2 × 10 MW units			
0	0.9604	0	—
10	0.0392	0	—
20	0.0004	10	0.004
			0.004 MW
(c) 3 × 5 MW units			
0	0.941192	0	—
5	0.057624	0	—
10	0.001176	5	0.00588
15	0.000008	10	0.00008
			0.00596 MW
(d) 4 × 3$\frac{1}{3}$ MW units			
0	0.92236816	0	—
3$\frac{1}{3}$	0.07529536	0	—
6$\frac{2}{3}$	0.00230496	3$\frac{1}{3}$	0.00768320
10	0.00003136	6$\frac{2}{3}$	0.00020907
13$\frac{1}{3}$	0.00000016	10	0.00000160
			0.00789387 MW

At this point a comparison can now be made between the relative merits of each alternative. On the basis of expected load loss only, alternative (b), i.e., 2×10 MW units, is the most reliable. However, this does neglect the economics of the system and, as stated previously, the concept of economics must be included in the overall reliability assessment. In general, the plant costs would be made up of the annual charges plus the operating and maintenance costs. Assume for the purpose of this example that these are proportional to the total installed capacity taking 10 MW to represent 1 per unit cost. The investment cost for each alternative on this basis is shown in Table 3.10.

Table 3.10　Investment costs of plant

System	Expected load loss MW	Investment cost p.u.
1×10 MW	0.2	1.0
2×10 MW	0.004	2.0
3×5 MW	0.00596	1.5
$4 \times 3\frac{1}{3}$ MW	0.00789387	1.33

A comparison of the relative reliability merits becomes more difficult using the results shown in Table 3.10 since, in this example, as the reliability increases, the investment cost also increases. Therefore, in deciding the most appropriate system, a balance between cost and reliability must be achieved taking into account the operational requirements of the system and benefits accruing from increasing system reliability.

The reliability index of expected load loss indicates the amount of load which cannot be supplied but gives no indication of the expected number of hours for which load loss may occur. This can be achieved by evaluating the expected load curtailment index. If it is assumed that the plant defined in Example 3.9 is to be used continuously, i.e., for 8760 hr/yr, then the expected load curtailment can be evaluated by weighting this number of hours by the probability of loss of load. For the present example, these results are shown in Table 3.11.

Table 3.11　Expected load curtailment

System	Probability of loss of load	Expected load curtailment, hr/yr
1×10 MW	0.02	175.2
2×10 MW	0.0004	3.504
3×5 MW	0.001184	10.37814
$4 \times 3\frac{1}{3}$ MW	0.00233648	20.46756

Both of these indices, expected load loss and expected load curtailment, have merits and demerits. The first index provides the expected loss of load with no indication of time, and the second indicates the expected number of hours of load loss with no indication of the magnitude of lost load. The choice of index depends on the type of process the plant is to supply.

3.3.5   Effect of unavailability

In the numerical example used to illustrate the construction and use of capacity outage probability tables, the value of unavailability or forced outage rate was assumed to be 0.02 or 2%. This parameter is of fundamental importance in reliability evaluation and it is useful to indicate the effect that changes in it can have on the reliability of a system.

Reconsider Example 3.9 but now consider the effect on the system reliability for unit unavailabilities of 2%, 4% and 6%. The values of expected load loss for each of the systems and for each value of unit unavailability are shown in Table 3.12.

Table 3.12   Effect of unavailability

System	1×10 MW	2×10 MW	3×5 MW	$4 \times 3\frac{1}{3}$ MW
Unavailability, %	Expected load loss, MW			
2	0.2	0.004	0.00596	0.00789387
4	0.4	0.016	0.02368	0.03112407
6	0.6	0.036	0.05292	0.06909417

These results indicate that the expected load loss, and in fact any reliability index, is very sensitive to an increase in the value of unavailability. Two points can be concluded from this sensitivity study. The first is the need to observe the long term reliability behaviour of the plant and its components. The second is that considerable improvements can be achieved in system reliability by careful design, manufacture, quality control and maintenance of the system plant and components to ensure an initial and continuing high inherent reliability.

3.3.6   Effect of one unit in reserve

One criterion which is often postulated for reserve determination in generating capacity planning and other applications is the installation of one unit in excess of the maximum system load requirement. This criterion can be easily examined in terms of a probabilistic risk. In order to illustrate this comparison, the system risk expressed as the probability of outage in excess of 1 unit has been evaluated for a system having 2–10 identical units. The results obtained for units having an unavailability of 2% are shown in Table 3.13. Also shown in Table 3.13 are the values of relative risk which were obtained assuming the 2 unit risk level to be 1

Table 3.13   System risk with one unit in reserve

Number of units	Probability of outage in excess of 1 unit	Relative risk
2	0.000400	1.00
3	0.001184	2.96
4	0.002336	5.85
5	0.003842	9.60
6	0.005687	14.22
7	0.007857	19.64
8	0.010337	25.84
9	0.013115	32.79
10	0.016178	40.44

per unit. These values are shown in Figure 3.4 for 2–10 identical units having unavailabilities of 2%, 4%, 6%, 8% and 10%.

It is evident that a criterion based on a one unit reserve does not result in a constant risk as the number of units and the unavailability of units increase. This conclusion can also be derived from the results shown in Table 3.6 which showed the results obtained for Example 3.7.

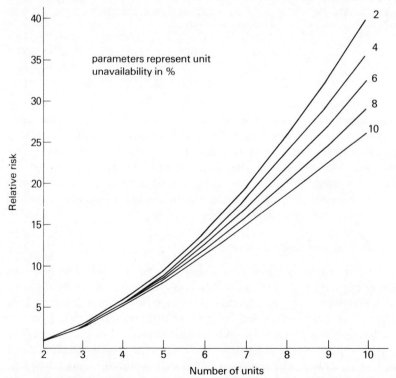

Fig. 3.4   Relative risk using a one unit reserve criterion. Parameters represent unit availability in per cent

The conclusions derived from Table 3.13 only apply to systems containing identical units. Frequently as systems develop, the latest additions tend to increase in size. If this is the case, then the error indicated in Table 3.13 decreases; the amount by which the error decreases depends on the relative size between existing unit sizes and that of the additions. However, the general conclusion remains valid and a criterion based on a one unit reserve is not a sound risk criterion.

3.3.7 Non-identical capacities

It is a prerequisite for the applicability of the binomial distribution that each trial should have the same significance or impact on the system being considered.

If this significance is the number of units or plant in and out of service then the binomial distribution is applicable irrespective of the capacity or size of each unit providing the unavailability of each is identical. If on the other hand a capacity outage probability table is to be deduced for a system containing units of non-identical capacities it is evident that the state caused by the outage of one unit is different to that caused by the outage of another unit. In this case the binomial distribution cannot be applied in its direct sense, although the principle behind it and the concept of combinations can be used to deduce the appropriate capacity outage probability table.

To illustrate this application consider the following example.

Example 3.10

A pumping station has 2×20 t/hr units and 1×30 t/hr unit. Each unit has an unavailability of 0.1. Calculate the capacity outage probability table for this plant and compare this with the unit outage probability table.

(a) *Unit outage probability table*

This data can be evaluated directly using the binomial distribution (Table 3.14).

Table 3.14 Unit outage probability

Units out of service	Individual probability
0	$0.9^3 = 0.729$
1	$3 \times 0.9^2 \times 0.1 = 0.243$
2	$3 \times 0.9 \times 0.1^2 = 0.027$
3	$0.1^3 = 0.001$
	$\overline{1.000}$

(b) *Capacity outage probability table*

In this example not all units are identical and therefore the binomial distribution cannot be used directly. However, a procedure which may be used is the following. First, combine together all identical units using the binomial distribution. Second, combine together, one at a time, these groups of tables by identifying all possible system states and evaluating the probability of each state using Rule 5a of Section 2.5. The use of this rule is applicable since all the system events are independent and mutually exclusive. Application of this technique to Example 3.10 gives the solution shown in Table 3.15.

Table 3.15 Capacity outage probability

Capacity outage table for 2×20 t/hr units		Capacity outage table for 1×30 t/hr unit	
Capacity out of service, t/hr	Individual probability	Capacity out of service, t/hr	Individual probability
0	$0.9^2 = 0.81$	0	0.9
20	$2 \times 0.9 \times 0.1 = 0.18$	30	0.1
40	$0.1^2 = 0.01$		1.0
	1.00		

In this example there are two groups and these can be combined as in Table 3.16.

Table 3.16 Combined capacity outage

Capacity out of service, t/hr	Individual probability
0	$0.81 \times 0.9 = 0.729$
20	$0.18 \times 0.9 = 0.162$
30	$0.81 \times 0.1 = 0.081$
40	$0.01 \times 0.9 = 0.009$
50	$0.18 \times 0.1 = 0.018$
60	—
70	$0.01 \times 0.1 = 0.001$
	1.000

If the unit outage and capacity outage tables are compared, it is seen that the only identical states are the 'zero units out of service' state giving maximum available capacity and the '3 units out of service' state giving zero available capacity. All other states in the unit outage table are combinations of the capacity outage table, the '1 unit out of service' state being the combination of the '20 and 30 t/hr outage' states and the '2 units out of service' state being the combination of the '40 and 50 t/hr outage' states.

The principle behind this particular example can be applied to any number of non-identical capacity units. After deducing the final capacity outage table, the appropriate risk index such as expected load loss or expected load curtailment can be evaluated exactly as described in Section 3.3.4.

3.3.8   Non-identical unavailabilities

As stated in the conditions in Section 3.2.1, the binomial distribution is applicable only if each trial has the same probabilities of success and failure. However, in practice not only do units of non-identical capacity exist but also units having different values of unavailability. Consider the case in which all units have the same capacity but with different unavailabilities. If the units had identical capacities and unavailabilities, the system could be represented by the binomial expression of Equation 3.4 as

$$(p+q)^n \tag{3.11}$$

where n = number of units.

The Expression 3.11 could also be written as

$$(p+q)(p+q)\ldots(p+q) \tag{3.12}$$

for which there would be n sets of parentheses, each representing one of the n units.

If now the n units had identical capacities but different unavailabilities, Expression 3.12 would become

$$(p_1+q_1)(p_2+q_2)\ldots(p_i+q_i)\ldots(p_n+q_n) \tag{3.13}$$

where p_i and q_i are the availability and unavailability, respectively, of unit i.

An expansion of Expression 3.13 would produce an equation which is similar in concept to the binomial expansion Equation 3.5. Its application is more difficult because there is no simple and general expression for evaluating the probability of each system state that is equivalent to Equation 3.6 for the binomial case. Expression 3.13 can be expanded and used directly if the number of units is relatively small. Instead the problem can readily be accommodated using the same basic principle as described in Section 3.3.7. Essentially this is a recursive technique which simulates the product, two terms at a time, of Expression 3.13. Using this method, the first step is to combine all identical units, i.e., those units having identical capacities and unavailabilities, using the binomial distribution. Second, to combine, one at a time, these groups of tables using the same combinational technique described in Section 3.3.7.

To illustrate this, reconsider Example 3.10 but this time assume that the 20 t/hr units have an unavailability of 0.1 and that the 30 t/hr unit has an unavailability of 0.15. In this case the combined capacity outage probability is as shown in Table 3.17.

Table 3.17   Combined capacity outage

Capacity out of service, t/hr	Individual probability
0	$0.81 \times 0.85 = 0.6885$
20	$0.18 \times 0.85 = 0.1530$
30	$0.81 \times 0.15 = 0.1215$
40	$0.01 \times 0.85 = 0.0085$
50	$0.18 \times 0.15 = 0.0270$
60	—
70	$0.01 \times 0.15 = 0.0015$
	1.0000

This example illustrates that the unavailability of the different groups of units can be of any value.

3.4   Conclusions

The binomial distribution is an important distribution, which can be used in many combinational problems.

This chapter demonstrates the relationship between the informal approach used in this type of problem as discussed in Chapter 2 and the more formalized approach associated with the use of the binomial distribution.

One of the prerequisites of a system in order to apply the binomial distribution is that all the trials, or in engineering parlance, all the system components must be identical both in their impact on the system and in their probability of failure. This frequently restricts the use of the binomial distribution in engineering applications. It has been shown that the principle of the binomial distribution can be used in conjunction with other rules of probability to solve many engineering problems in which the components are not identical. It has also been shown how reliability indices in the form of expected values or system risk can be evaluated from the concept of capacity outage probability tables obtained using the binomial distribution and an engineering appreciation of the requirements of the system.

Problems

1. What is the probability of getting a total of 8
   (a) exactly three times in four tosses of a pair of dice
   (b) at least twice in four tosses of a pair of dice?
   (c) Draw the probability distribution of the number of times a total of 8 is obtained in four tosses of two dice?
2. The foreman of a casting section in a factory finds that on the average 1 in every 5 castings made is defective. If the section makes 8 castings a day what is the probability that exactly 2 castings will be defective?
3. A system has a continuous load of 80 MW. Find the expected load loss and the expected number of hours that any curtailment will exist if the generation is composed of
   (a) five 20 MW hydro-generating units each with an unavailability of 0.5%.
   (b) nine 10 MW thermal units each with an unavailability of 1.5%.
4. A pumping station has two 20 000 gal/hr pumps and is to have one 40 000 gal/hr pump installed. Draw up a pumping capacity outage probability table for this system given that the unavailabilities for the 20 000 and 40 000 gal/hr pumps are 0.2 and 0.1 respectively.
5. A telephone exchange contains 10 lines. A line can be busy or available for calls and all lines act independently. If the probability that a line will be busy during the noon period is 0.8, what is the probability of there being at least three free lines at any given time during this period? What is the expected number of free lines during this period?
6. The following transformer systems are to be compared:
   (a) 3 transformers each rated at 100% of full load,
   (b) 3 transformers each rated at 90% full load,
   (c) 3 transformers each rated at 50% of full load, and
   (d) 4 transformers each rated at $33\frac{1}{3}\%$ of full load.
   Compare the adequacy of these systems in terms of the expected percent load curtailed and the expected hours of load curtailment, if the transformer unavailability is 0.01.
7. A small manufacturing company is operated by 4 employees. The company can still operate if only 3 are present but the income drops to 60% of the income at full production. If more than one employee is away production stops. It is known that 1 particular employee misses an average of 10 days out of 100 and that each of the others miss an average of 5 days out of 100. Absences are random and independent. The expenses of the company are $500/day when operating and $400 when shut down. The income at full production is $800/day. What is the expected daily profit for the company?

4 Network modelling and evaluation of simple systems

4.1 Network modelling concepts

The previous chapters have considered the application of basic probability techniques to combinational types of reliability assessment. In many types of problems these techniques may be all that is required to assess the adequacy of the system. However, in practice, a system is frequently represented as a network in which the system components are connected together either in series, parallel, meshed or a combination of these. This chapter considers series and parallel network representations (more complicated meshed networks are considered in the next chapter).

It is vital that the relationship between the system and its network model be thoroughly understood before considering the analytical techniques that can be used to evaluate the reliability of these networks.

It must be appreciated that the actual system and the reliability network used to model the system may not necessarily have the same topological structure. This consideration involves the key point discussed previously that, before a reliability assessment of a system can be made, the analyst must be fully conversant with the requirements of the system and be able to phrase these requirements in a form which can be quantitatively assessed.

Definitions of series systems and parallel systems as represented in a reliability network are considered first.

(a) *Series systems*

The components in a set are said to be in series from a reliability point of view if they must *all* work for system success or only *one* needs to fail for system failure.

(b) *Parallel systems*

The components in a set are said to be in parallel from a reliability point of view if only *one* needs to be working for system success or *all* must fail for system failure.

These definitions provide a link between the present discussion and that of Chapter 3 on the use of the binomial distribution. A series system therefore represents a non-redundant system and a parallel system represents a fully redundant system. Reconsider Example 3.7 in which four operating conditions were applied to a four component system. The condition of 'all four components must be working for system success' could be represented by a network in which all four components are connected in series. Similarly, the condition of 'only one component need be working for system success' could be represented by a network in which all four components are connected in parallel. At this stage it appears that the series and parallel network models are simply additional methods for representing non-redundant and fully redundant systems whereas the previous techniques were able to solve such systems and more. Series and parallel network considerations are used extensively in system appreciation, representation and reduction. They are used in a wide range of applications including extremely simple models and complicated systems with complex operational logic. Modelling of these systems using the techniques described in Chapter 3 becomes difficult if not impossible.

The main points in reconsidering Example 3.7 are: (a) there is frequently more than one way of solving the same problem, (b) there are frequently links between one technique and another, and (c) most importantly, a physical system having a defined topological structure may have a considerably different reliability network topology which itself may change when the requirements of the physical system change although the topology of the physical system remains the same.

It remains with the individual analyst to consider the actual requirements of a system and to construct a reliability network from these requirements. The following analytical techniques can then be applied to this reliability network. A reliability network is often referred to as a reliability block diagram.

4.2 Series systems

Consider a system consisting of two independent components A and B connected in series, from a reliability point of view, as shown in Figure 4.1. This arrangement implies that both components must work to ensure system success. Let R_A, R_B = probability of successful operation of components A and B respectively, and Q_A, Q_B = probability of failure of

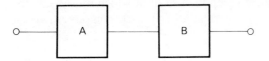

Fig. 4.1 Two component series system

components A and B respectively. Since success and failure are mutually exclusive and complementary,

$$R_A + Q_A = 1 \quad \text{and} \quad R_B + Q_B = 1$$

The requirement for system success is that 'both A and B' must be working. Equation 2.9 can be used to give the probability of system success or reliability as

$$R_S = R_A \cdot R_B \tag{4.1}$$

If there are now n components in series, Equation 4.1 can be generalized to give

$$R_S = \prod_{i=1}^{n} R_i \tag{4.2}$$

This equation frequently is referred to as the product rule of reliability since it establishes that the reliability of a series system is the product of the individual component reliabilities.

In some applications it may be considered advantageous to evaluate the unreliability or probability of system failure rather than evaluating the reliability or probability of system success. System success and system failure are complementary events and therefore for the two component system the unreliability is

$$Q_S = 1 - R_A R_B \tag{4.3}$$

$$= 1 - (1 - Q_A)(1 - Q_B)$$

$$= Q_A + Q_B - Q_A \cdot Q_B \tag{4.4}$$

or for an n component system,

$$Q_S = 1 - \prod_{i=1}^{n} R_i \tag{4.5}$$

Equations 4.3 and 4.5 could have been derived directly from Equation 2.12 since the requirement for system failure is that 'A or B or both' must fail.

Now consider the application of these techniques to some specific problems.

Example 4.1

A system consists of 10 identical components, all of which must work for system success. What is the system reliability if each component has a reliability of 0.95?

From Equation 4.2,

$$R_S = 0.95^{10} = 0.5987$$

This result, although easily derived, establishes an important concept concerning the reliability of series systems. Because of the product rule and the fact that each component has a probability of success that is less than unity, the system reliability is less than the reliability of any one component. It also decreases as the number of components in series increases and as the component reliability decreases. This is illustrated in Figure 4.2 which shows the reliability of series systems containing identical components as a function of the number of series components and the component reliability. It is evident from these results that the system reliability decreases very rapidly as the number of series components increases, particularly for those systems in which the components do not have a very high individual reliability.

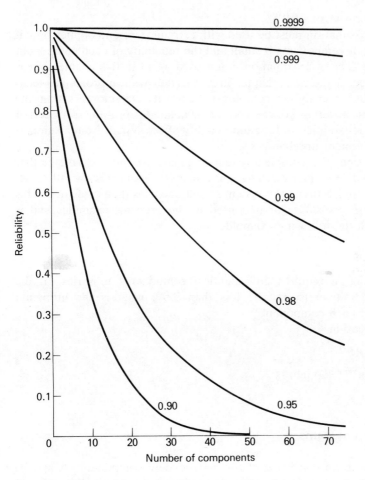

Fig. 4.2 Effects of increasing the number of series components. The numbers represent the reliability of each single component

Example 4.2

A two component series system contains identical components each having a reliability of 0.99. Evaluate the unreliability of the system.

From Equation 4.5, $Q_S = 1 - 0.99^2 = 0.0199$

From Equation 4.4, $Q_S = 0.01 + 0.01 - (0.01 \times 0.01) = 0.0199$

These two results are identical as would be expected. In some system analyses however, Equation 4.4 is used in an approximate form, i.e. the product term which is subtracted from the summation terms is neglected. If this was done in the present example:

$$Q_S \simeq 0.01 + 0.01 = 0.02$$

which gives an error of 0.5%.

This approximation must be used with extreme care and applies only if the number of components is small and the reliability of each component is very high. The approximation is not used again in this chapter but is re-introduced in the next chapter in connection with approximate techniques used for analysing complex systems. Its advantage is that the reliability of a series system can be evaluated from the product of component reliabilities and the unreliability of the system from a summation of component unreliabilities.

In the design of a complex system or plant, a design parameter that may be specified is the overall system reliability. From this overall value, the required reliability of the system's components is then evaluated. This is the inverse procedure of that used in the previous examples and is illustrated in the following example.

Example 4.3

A system design requires 200 identical components in series. If the overall reliability must not be less than 0.99, what is the minimum reliability of each component?

From Equation 4.2

$$0.99 = R^{200}$$

i.e. $R = 0.99^{1/200} = 0.99995$

4.3 Parallel systems

Consider a system consisting of two independent components A and B, connected in parallel, from a reliability point of view as shown in Figure 4.3.

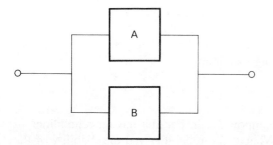

Fig. 4.3   The two component parallel system

In this case the system requirement is that only one component need be working for system success. The system reliability can be obtained as the complement of the system unreliability or by using Equation 2.12 since 'either A or B or both' constitutes success to give

$$R_P = 1 - Q_A \cdot Q_B \tag{4.6}$$

$$= R_A + R_B - R_A \cdot R_B \tag{4.7}$$

or for an n component system:

$$R_P = 1 - \prod_{i=1}^{n} Q_i \tag{4.8}$$

Also

$$Q_P = Q_A \cdot Q_B \tag{4.9}$$

and for an n component system:

$$Q_P = \prod_{i=1}^{n} Q_i \tag{4.10}$$

It follows that the equations for a parallel system are of the same form as those of a series system but with R and Q interchanged. In the case of parallel systems, Equation 4.10 leads to the concept of the product rule of unreliabilities. However, unlike the case of series systems in which, under certain circumstances, Equation 4.4 can be reduced to a simple summation, Equation 4.7 cannot be simplified in this way since the product $(R_A \cdot R_B)$ is, hopefully, always reasonably comparable with the values of R_A and R_B.

In the case of series systems, the system reliability decreased in the number of series components was increased following Equation 4.2. In the case of parallel systems, however, it is the unreliability that decreases as the number of parallel components is increased following Equation 4.10 and hence the reliability increases with the number of components. Increasing the number of parallel components increases the initial cost, weight and volume of the system and increases the required maintenance. Therefore, it must be examined very carefully.

In order to illustrate the application of the equations for parallel systems consider the following examples.

Example 4.4

A system consists of four components in parallel having reliabilities of 0.99, 0.95, 0.98 and 0.97. What is the reliability and unreliability of the system?

From Equation 4.10 $Q_P = (1 - 0.99)(1 - 0.95)(1 - 0.98)(1 - 0.97)$

$$= 3 \times 10^{-7}$$

and from Equation 4.8 $R_P = 0.9999997$

This example also demonstrates the difficulty of physically appreciating the quality of a system in terms of the reliability value R since for many practical systems this numerical value is often a series of 9s followed by another digit or more. It is often more reasonable to state the unreliability as this eliminates the string of 9s and provides a value that is more easily interpreted.

Example 4.5

A system component has a reliability of 0.8. Evaluate the effect on the overall system reliability of increasing the number of these components connected in parallel.

Using Equation 4.10, the value of system reliability is shown in Table 4.1 for systems having 1 to 6 components in parallel. Also shown in Table 4.1 is the increase in reliability obtained by adding each additional component. This is known as incremental reliability. The percentage comparative reliability defined as the change in reliability over that of a

Table 4.1 Reliability results for Example 4.5

Number of components	System reliability	Incremental reliability	Percentage comparative reliability
1	0.800000	—	—
2	0.960000	0.160000	20.00
3	0.992000	0.032000	24.00
4	0.998400	0.006400	24.80
5	0.999680	0.001280	24.96
6	0.999936	0.000256	24.99

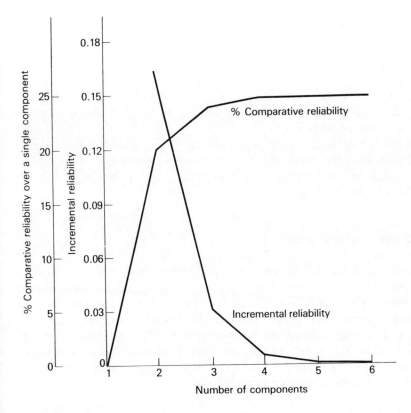

Fig. 4.4 Incremental reliability benefits

single component expressed as a percentage based on the single component reliability is also shown in Table 4.1. The results for incremental
reliability and comparative reliability are also shown in Figure 4.4.

From Figure 4.4 it is evident that the addition of the first redundant
component to the one-component system provides the largest benefit to
the system, the amount of improvement diminishing as further additions
are made.

Since the abscissa axis of Figure 4.4 is related to the cost of the system,
an incremental worth–cost analysis can be performed using diagrams of
incremental reliability such as that shown in Figure 4.4.

Example 4.6

A system is to be designed with an overall reliability of 0.999 using
components having individual reliabilities of 0.7. What is the minimum
number of components that must be connected in parallel?

From Equation 4.10

$$(1 - 0.999) = (1 - 0.7)^n$$
$$0.001 = 0.3^n$$
$$n = 5.74$$

since the number of components must be an integer, the minimum number of components is 6.

It should be noted that increasing the number of parallel elements may actually decrease the reliability of the system if a component failure mode exists which in itself causes a system failure. An example of this is described in Section 5.9.

4.4 Series–parallel systems

The series and parallel systems discussed in the two previous sections form the basis for analysing more complicated configurations. The general principle used is to reduce sequentially the complicated configuration by combining appropriate series and parallel branches of the reliability model until a single equivalent element remains. This equivalent element then represents the reliability (or unreliability) of the original configuration. The following examples illustrate this technique which is generally known as a (network) reduction technique.

Example 4.7

Derive a general expression for the reliability of the model shown in Figure 4.5 and hence evaluate the system reliability if all components have a reliability of 0.9.

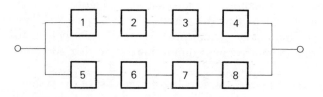

Fig. 4.5   Reliability diagram of Example 4.7

This model could represent, for example, a duplicated control circuit associated with the automatic pilot of an aeroplane. The reduction process is sequential and proceeds as follows.

Combine in series components 1–4 to form an equivalent component 9, combine in series components 5–8 to form an equivalent component 10 and then combine in parallel equivalent components 9 and 10 to form an equivalent component 11 that represents the complete system. This logical step process is illustrated in Figure 4.6.

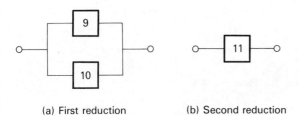

(a) First reduction   (b) Second reduction

Fig. 4.6   Reduction of Example 4.7.

If $R_1, R_2, \ldots, R_8$ are the reliabilities of components $1, 2, \ldots, 8$ respectively then

$$R_9 = R_1 R_2 R_3 R_4$$

$$R_{10} = R_5 R_6 R_7 R_8$$

$$R_{11} = 1 - (1 - R_9)(1 - R_{10})$$

$$= R_9 + R_{10} - R_9 R_{10}$$

$$= R_1 R_2 R_3 R_4 + R_5 R_6 R_7 R_8 - R_1 R_2 R_3 R_4 R_5 R_6 R_7 R_8$$

In deriving expressions of this type, it is possible to produce a number of apparently different equations when the final expression is written in terms of both Rs and Qs. These apparently different versions could all be correct and should reduce to the same one if manipulated and expressed in terms of either R or Q.

Using the data of Example 4.7, then

$$R_{11} = 0.9^4 + 0.9^4 - 0.9^8 = 0.8817$$

Example 4.8

Derive a general expression for the unreliability of the model shown in Figure 4.7 and hence evaluate the unreliability of the system if all components have a reliability of 0.8.

The logical steps for this example are: combine components 3 and 4 to form equivalent component 6, combine components 1 and 2 with equivalent component 6 to give equivalent component 7 and finally combine component 5 with equivalent component 7 to give equivalent component 8 that represents the system reliability. These reduction steps are shown in Figure 4.8.

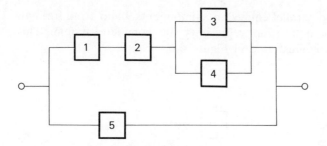

Fig. 4.7 Reliability diagram for Example 4.8

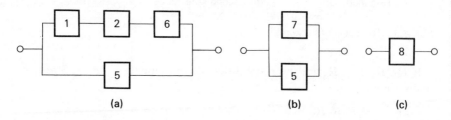

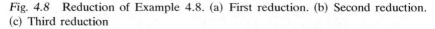

Fig. 4.8 Reduction of Example 4.8. (a) First reduction. (b) Second reduction. (c) Third reduction

If $R_1, \ldots, R_5$ and $Q_1, \ldots, Q_5$ are the reliabilities and unreliabilities of components $1, \ldots, 5$ respectively, then

$$Q_6 = Q_3 Q_4$$

$$Q_7 = 1 - (1 - Q_1)(1 - Q_2)(1 - Q_6)$$

$$= Q_1 + Q_2 + Q_6 - Q_1 Q_2 - Q_2 Q_6 - Q_6 Q_1 + Q_1 Q_2 Q_6$$

$$Q_8 = Q_5 Q_7$$

$$= Q_5(Q_1 + Q_2 + Q_3 Q_4 - Q_1 Q_2 - Q_2 Q_3 Q_4 - Q_3 Q_4 Q_1 + Q_1 Q_2 Q_3 Q_4)$$

For the data given, $R_i = 0.8$ thus $Q_i = 0.2$ and $Q_8 = 0.07712$.

An equivalent expression to the above could have been deduced in terms of R_i.

$$R_6 = R_3 + R_4 - R_3 R_4$$

$$R_7 = R_1 R_2 R_6$$

$$R_8 = R_5 + R_7 - R_5 R_7$$

$$= R_5 + R_1 R_2(R_3 + R_4 - R_3 R_4) - R_5 R_1 R_2(R_3 + R_4 - R_3 R_4)$$

which, for $R_i = 0.8$, gives:

$$R_8 = 0.92288 \quad \text{or} \quad Q_8 = 1 - 0.92288 = 0.07712$$

4.5 Partially redundant systems

The previous sections have been concerned only with series systems (non-redundant) and parallel systems (fully redundant). In many systems, these two extreme situations are not always applicable as there may be some parts of the system that are partially redundant. The concepts of partial redundancy were presented in Chapter 3 in the discussion of the binomial distribution. The techniques described in this chapter for series/parallel systems cannot be used directly for cases involving partial redundancy. The principles that have been described together with the inclusion of binomial distribution concepts can, however, enable any series–parallel system containing regions of partial redundancy to be evaluated.

In order to illustrate this intermingling of the two techniques, consider the following example.

Example 4.9

Derive a general expression for the unreliability of the system whose reliability model is shown in Figure 4.9. Consider the case in which all parallel branches of this system are fully redundant with the exception of that consisting of components 4, 5 and 6 for which any 2 of the branches are required for system success.

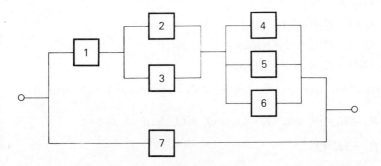

Fig. 4.9 Reliability diagram of Example 4.9

The principle of network reduction applies equally well to this problem, i.e., components 2 and 3 are combined to give equivalent component 8; components 4, 5 and 6 are combined to give equivalent component 9, component 1 and equivalent components 8 and 9 are combined to give equivalent component 10 and finally equivalent component 10 is combined with component 7 to give the system equivalent component 11. These steps are shown in Figure 4.10.

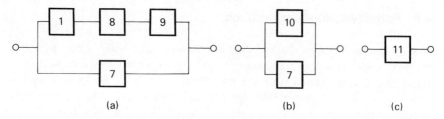

(a)   (b)   (c)

Fig. 4.10 Reduction of Example 4.9. (a) First reduction. (b) Second reduction. (c) Third reduction

The only essential difference between this example and those considered previously in this chapter is that the reliability of equivalent component 9 cannot be evaluated using the equations of Section 4.3 but, instead, must be evaluated from the binomial distribution concepts described in Chapter 3. The binomial distribution can be applied directly if components 4, 5 and 6 are identical. A fundamentally similar approach is used for non-identical components.

If $R_1, \ldots, R_7$ and $Q_1, \ldots, Q_7$ are the reliabilities and unreliabilities of components $1, \ldots, 7$, then

$$Q_8 = Q_2 Q_3$$
$$R_{10} = R_1 R_8 R_9$$
$$Q_{11} = Q_{10} Q_7$$
$$= Q_7 (1 - R_1 R_8 R_9)$$
$$= Q_7 (1 - R_1 (1 - Q_2 Q_3) R_9)$$
$$= Q_7 (1 - R_1 R_9 + R_1 R_9 Q_2 Q_3)$$

R_9 is evaluated by applying the binomial distribution to components 4, 5 and 6.

If $R_4 = R_5 = R_6 = R$ and $Q_4 = Q_5 = Q_6 = Q$, then

$$R_9 = R^3 + 3R^2 Q$$

and $Q_9 = 3RQ^2 + Q^3$

If $R_4 \neq R_5 \neq R_6$ and $Q_4 \neq Q_5 \neq Q_6$, then

$$R_9 = R_4 R_5 R_6 + R_4 R_5 Q_6 + R_5 R_6 Q_4 + R_6 R_4 Q_5$$

and $Q_9 = R_4 Q_5 Q_6 + R_5 Q_6 Q_4 + R_6 Q_4 Q_5 + Q_4 Q_5 Q_6$

In the special case when all components have a reliability of 0.8

$$R_9 = 0.8960, \qquad Q_9 = 0.1040$$

and $Q_{11} = 0.06237$.

4.6   Standby redundant systems

4.6.1   Redundancy concepts

In Section 4.3 it was assumed that a redundant system consisted of two or more branches connected in parallel and that both branches were operating simultaneously.

In some system problems, however, one or more branches of the redundant components may not be continuously operating but remain, in normal operating circumstances, in a standby mode, i.e., they are only switched into an operating mode when a normally operating component fails. The essential difference between these two types of redundancy is illustrated in Figure 4.11.

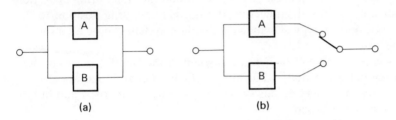

Fig. 4.11   Redundancy modes. (a) Parallel redundancy. (b) Standby redundancy

It is not the purpose of this book to explain which of the two redundancy modes should be used in any specific engineering application but to recognize that both can exist in practice and to explain how each can be analysed. It is however worth mentioning some of the factors involved in deciding which is most appropriate.

In some applications it is physically not possible for both branches to be operating. This could occur for instance when both A and B in Figure 4.11 are used to control some other device. If for some reason A and B produced different outputs, the device would receive opposing instructions. This can be overcome by including a logic gate between the parallel branches and the device so that both A and B may operate but the device receives only one set of instructions and the other is blocked by the gate. In other applications it may be preferable for a component to remain idle unless required to operate following the malfunction of another component because its probability of failure may be insignificant when not operating compared to its probability of failure when in an active and operating mode. This is frequently the case for mechanical devices such as motors and pumps. In such cases, standby redundancy is more appropriate. There are instances in which the failure probability of a component or system is less, when continuously operated, compared with that when it is frequently cycled between an idle and inactive mode and an active mode. This can occur in the case of computer systems and frequently when two or more are used in a redundant process or control application, they are allowed to share the operating duties and each have the ability to pick up the duties of another if the latter should fail during operation. Both modes of redundancy exist in practice and the reader will no doubt be able to compile a list of alternative applications of each.

In the case of standby redundancy, the additional features that exist are the cyclic duty of the redundant component(s) and the necessity of switching from one branch to another.

4.6.2 Perfect switching

Consider the case of a perfect switch, i.e., it does not fail during operation and does not fail in switching from the normal operating position to the standby position. A typical standby redundant system can be as shown in Figure 4.11b.

If it is assumed that B does not fail when in the standby position, then it can only fail given that A has already failed, i.e. B is operating.

Therefore, the failure of this system is given by failure of A and failure of B, given A has failed.

Using the symbolism of Chapter 2, the probability of system failure is

$$Q = Q(A) \cdot Q(B \mid \bar{A})$$

which, if it is assumed that A and B are independent, reduces to:

$$Q = Q_A \cdot Q_B \qquad (4.11)$$

Equation 4.11 appears to be identical to Equation 4.9 and gives the impression that the probability of failure of a standby redundant system is identical to that of a parallel redundant system. This is not true however since the numerical values used in Equations 4.11 and 4.9 are different. Since B is used only for short periods it is not likely that its failure probability will be the same as if it is used continuously. This leads to the necessity of considering time dependent probabilities, whereas up to this point only time independent probabilities have been considered, i.e., it has been assumed that the probabilities do not change with the time for which the component is exposed to failure. Time dependent probabilities are considered in Chapter 7 and the problem of standby redundancy is reconsidered then.

4.6.3 Imperfect switching

Consider the situation in which the switch has a probability of failing to change over from the branch containing component A to that containing component B when A fails. Let the probability of a successful changeover be P_S and the probability of an unsuccessful change over be $\bar{P}_S(=1-P_S)$.

The problem can now be solved using the conditional probability approach discussed in Chapter 2.

P(system failure) = P(system failure *given* successful changeover)

$\quad\quad \times P$(successful changeover)

$\quad\quad + P$(system failure *given* unsuccessful changeover)

$\quad\quad \times P$(unsuccessful changeover)

therefore $Q = Q_A \cdot Q_B \cdot P_S + Q_A \cdot \bar{P}_S$

$\quad\quad = Q_A Q_B P_S + Q_A(1-P_S)$

$\quad\quad = Q_A Q_B P_S + Q_A - Q_A P_S$

$\quad\quad = Q_A - Q_A P_S(1-Q_B)$ (4.12)

The value of Q_B in this equation is affected by the time dependent problem of B being operated for short periods as discussed in Section 4.6.2.

Now consider the situation encountered if the switch can fail in its initial operating position as well as failing to change over when required. Since the failure of the switch in its operating position is likely to be identical whether it is connected to A or to B, it can be considered as a component in series with the parallel branch formed by A and B. This leads to the network model shown in Figure 4.12 in which the switch appears as two components; the first represents its switching mode with a probability of successful changeover of P_S and the second represents its normal operating mode with a reliability of R_S and an unreliability of Q_S.

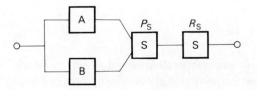

Fig. 4.12   Standby redundancy with imperfect switch

As the second component representation of the switch is in series with the previously considered standby redundant branches, the probability of system failure (or success) can be found by combining its effect with Equation 4.12 to give

$Q = 1 - (1 - (Q_A - Q_B P_S(1-Q_B)))R_S$ (4.13)

or $R = R_S(1 - (Q_A - Q_A P_S(1-Q_B)))$ (4.14)

4.6.4 Standby redundancy calculations

Example 4.10

Consider Figure 4.11b. Evaluate the reliability of this system if A has a reliability of 0.9, B has a reliability given A has failed of 0.96 and,
(a) the switch is perfect,
(b) the switch has a probability of failing to changeover of 0.08, and
(c) as (b) but the switch has an operating reliability of 0.98.

(a) from Equation 4.11, $R = 1 - 0.1 \times 0.04 = 0.996$

(b) from Equation 4.12, $R = 1 - (0.1 - 0.1 \times 0.92(1 - 0.04))$

$$= 0.988$$

(c) from Equation 4.14, $R = 0.98 \times 0.988 = 0.969$

Example 4.11

Consider the system model shown in Figure 4.13 and assume that A, B and S have the reliability indices given in Example 4.10 and part (c). If components C and D have reliabilities of 0.99 and 0.8 respectively, evaluate the reliability of the system.

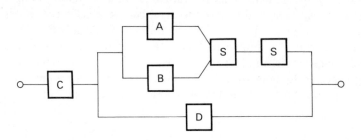

Fig. 4.13 Reliability diagram of Example 4.11

The reliability of this system can be evaluated using the network reduction technique described for series–parallel systems by first evaluating the equivalent component representing A, B and S, combining this with D and finally combining this result with C.

The reliability of the branch containing A, B and S is given in Example 4.10 as

$$R = 0.969$$

The reliability of the system is therefore given by

$$R = R_C(1 - Q_D(1 - 0.969))$$
$$= 0.99(1 - 0.2(1 - 0.969)) = 0.984$$

4.7 Conclusions

This chapter has illustrated network modelling of systems and the reliability evaluation of these networks. The discussion has focused on series, parallel redundant and standby redundant systems as well as combinations of these. More complex arrangements require additional techniques which are described in the next chapter.

In network modelling of systems, the reliability network is frequently not identical to the physical system or network. The analyst must translate the physical system into a reliability network using the system operational logic and a sound understanding of the physical behaviour and requirements of the system.

The examples used in this chapter have shown how an increasing number of series components decreases the system reliability whilst an increasing number of parallel and standby redundant components increases the system reliability. The choice of parallel, or standby redundant systems, must be made by the system designer using engineering knowledge of the performance of the components and devices. The merits of each method are affected by the physical requirements of the system and by the difference in reliability of the component or device in the respective modes of redundancy.

Problems

1. The system shown in Figure 4.14 is made up of ten components. Components 3, 4 and 5 are not identical and at least one component of this group must be available for system success. Components 8, 9 and 10 are identical and for this particular group it is necessary that two out of the three components functions

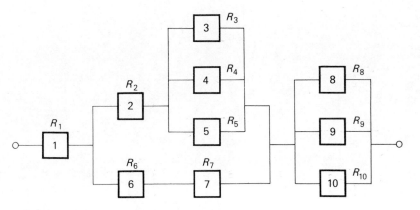

Fig. 4.14

satisfactorily for system success. Write an expression for the system reliability in terms of the R values given. Also evaluate the system reliability if the reliability of each component $= 0.8$.

2   A system consists of four components in parallel. System success requires that at least three of these components must function. What is the probability of system success if the component reliability is 0.9? What is the system reliability if five components are placed in parallel to perform the same function?

3   A system contains two subsystems in series. System 1 has four possible operating levels, and System 2 has three possible operating levels as shown in the following table.

System 1		System 2	
Output	Probability	Output	Probability
100%	0.8	100%	0.7
75%	0.1	50%	0.1
25%	0.05	0%	0.2
0%	0.05		

Develop an operating level probability table for the system.

4   A series system has 10 identical components. If the overall system reliability must be at least 0.99, what is the minimum reliability required of each component?

5   A series system has identical components each having a reliability of 0.998. What is the maximum number of components that can be allowed if the minimum system reliability is to be 0.90?

6   A parallel system has 10 identical components. If the overall system reliability must be at least 0.99, how poor can these components be?

7   A parallel system has identical components having a reliability of 0.5. What is the minimum number of components if the system reliability must be at least 0.99?

5 Network modelling and evaluation of complex systems

5.1 Modelling and evaluation concepts

The techniques described in Chapter 4 are limited in their application to systems and networks that have a series and parallel type of structure. Many systems either do not have this simple type of structure or have complex operational logic. Additional modelling and evaluation techniques are necessary in order to determine the reliability of such systems. A typical system not having a series/parallel structure is the bridge-type network shown in Figure 5.1, a system that is used frequently to demonstrate techniques for complex systems and one that can occur often in many engineering applications.

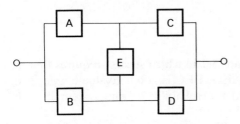

Fig. 5.1 Bridge-type network or system

A visual inspection of the network shown in Figure 5.1 indicates that none of the components is connected in a simple series/parallel arrangement. There are a number of techniques available for solving this type of network, including the conditional probability approach, cut and tie set analysis, tree diagrams, logic diagrams and connection matrix techniques. There are others but they are used less frequently and all problems are usually solvable with one of those already specified.

Most of these more advanced techniques are formalized methods for transforming the logical operation of the system, or the topology of the system, into a structure that consists only of series and parallel components, paths or branches. It should be appreciated that several of the methods are very similar in concept. The main difference between them is in the formal presentation or logic of the method and not the essential underlying concept. The reader should also recognize that the methods discussed in this chapter can also be used for the simple series/parallel systems described in Chapter 4. When performing hand calculations, the method of solution should be as simple and direct as possible. When using digital computers, it can be advantageous to use the same basic program and the same technique for both complex and simple systems.

5.2   Conditional probability approach

One approach which can be used to evaluate the reliability of a complex system is to reduce sequentially the system into subsystem structures that are connected in series/parallel and then to recombine these subsystems using the conditional probability method.

This approach uses Equation 2.19

P(system success or failure) = P(system success or failure if component X is good) · P(X is good) + P(system success or failure if component X is bad) · P(X is bad)   (5.1)

The application of this technique is illustrated by the following examples.

Example 5.1

Consider the system shown in Figure 5.1 in which success requires that at least one of the paths, AC, BD, AED, BEC is good. Evaluate a general expression for system success and the reliability of the system if each component has a reliability of 0.99.

To apply the conditional probability approach it is first necessary to choose the component X which will be considered 'good' and considered 'bad'. Any of the components A to E may be chosen but, for a given system, the 'correct' choice of component can greatly simplify the solution. The best component to choose as X is component E in the present example.

The system shown in Figure 5.1 can now be subdivided into two subsystems, one with E considered good, i.e., it cannot fail and one with E considered bad, i.e., it is always failed. This subdivision is shown in Figure 5.2.

Visual inspection of the two subdivisions identifies that the original system has been decomposed into two subsystems each of which is a simple series/parallel structure. With E considered good, A and B are in parallel, C and D are in parallel and the two parallel branches are in series. With E considered bad, A and C are in series, B and D are in

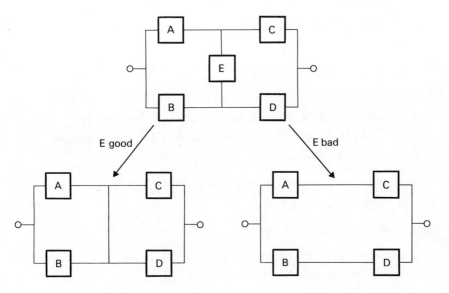

Fig. 5.2 Subdivision of Example 5.1

series and the two series branches are in parallel. These two subsystems are mutually exclusive since neither can exist simultaneously and therefore they can be recombined using the principle of conditional probability.

In some engineering systems, one or more of the subsystems may need further subdivision before a series/parallel structure is obtained. This is only an extension of the technique being discussed since each time a subdivision is made, the two subdivisions must be recombined using the conditional probability approach starting with the two most recent subdivided subsystems, i.e., the lowest hierarchical level. This requirement of further subdivision would be necessary in the present example if any component other than E had been chosen at the first subdivision attempt. An example of this is described in Section 5.4.

After creating a set of subsystems in which all components are connected in series and parallel, the subsystems can be evaluated using the principles of series and parallel systems discussed in Chapter 4 and the overall system reliability evaluated using conditional probability.

In the present example, the overall system reliability will be

$$R_S = R_S(\text{if E is good}) \, R_E + R_S(\text{if E is bad}) \, Q_E$$

(a) *condition*: GIVEN E *is good*

$$R_S = (1 - Q_A Q_B)(1 - Q_C Q_D)$$

(b)   *condition*: GIVEN E *is bad*

$$R_S = 1 - (1 - R_A R_C)(1 - R_B R_D)$$

Therefore, the system reliability is

$$R_S = (1 - Q_A Q_B)(1 - Q_C Q_D)R_E + (1 - (1 - R_A R_C)(1 - R_B R_D))Q_E$$
$$= R_A R_C + R_B R_D + R_A R_D R_E + R_B R_C R_E - R_A R_B R_C R_D$$
$$- R_A R_C R_D R_E - R_A R_B R_C R_E - R_B R_C R_D R_E - R_A R_B R_D R_E$$
$$+ 2R_A R_B R_C R_D R_E \tag{5.2}$$

which, if $R_A = R_B = R_C = R_D = R_E = R$, gives

$$R_S = 2R^2 + 2R^3 - 5R^4 + 2R^5 \tag{5.3}$$

and, if $R = 0.99$, gives:

$$R_S = 0.99979805$$
$$= 0.999798 \text{ (to six decimal places)}$$

The conditional probability approach is a useful tool for reliability evaluation and is frequently used in many applications. It can prove difficult to program on a digital computer for the solution of general network configurations because of the inherent difficulty of generalizing network decomposition. Other methods have been developed which prove more suitable in this respect. However, it is a very useful method which can be used in a wide range of applications.

5.3   Cut set method

5.3.1   Cut set concepts

The cut set method is a powerful one for evaluating the reliability of a system for two main reasons:
(i)   It can be easily programmed on a digital computer for the fast and efficient solution of any general network.
(ii)   The cut sets are directly related to the modes of system failure and therefore identify the distinct and discrete ways in which a system may fail.

A cut set can be defined as follows: *A cut set is a set of system components which, when failed, causes failure of the system.*

In terms of a reliability network or block digram, the above definition can be interpreted as a set of components which must fail in order to disrupt all paths between the input and the output of the reliability network.

The minimum subset of any given set of components which causes system failure is known as a minimal cut set. It can be defined as follows: *A minimal cut set is a set of system components which, when failed, causes failure of the system but when any one component of the set has not failed, does not cause system failure.*

This definition means that *all* components of a minimal cut set must be in the failure state to cause system failure.

Using this definition, the minimal cut sets of the system shown in Figure 5.1 are shown in Table 5.1 assuming the same system requirement as Example 5.1

Table 5.1 Minimal cut sets of Figure 5.1

Number of minimal cut set	Components of the cut set
1	AB
2	CD
3	AED
4	BEC

5.3.2 Application of cut sets

In order to evaluate system reliability (or unreliability), the minimal cut sets identified from the reliability network must be combined. From the definition of minimal cut sets it is evident that all components of each cut must fail in order for the system to fail. Consequently, the components of the cut set are effectively connected in parallel and the failure probabilities of the components in the cut set may be combined using the principle of parallel systems. In addition, the system fails if any one of the cut sets occurs and consequently each cut is effectively in series with all the other cuts.

The use of this principle gives the reliability diagram of Figure 5.3 for the system of Figure 5.1 and the minimal cut sets shown in Table 5.1. Although these cut sets are in series, the concept of series systems cannot be used because the same component can appear in two or more of the cut sets, e.g., component A appears in cuts C_1 and C_3 of Figure 5.3. The concept of union does apply however and if the ith cut is designated as C_i and its probability of occurrence is designated as $P(C_i)$, then the unreliability of the system is given by

$$Q_S = P(C_1 \cup C_2 \cup C_3 \cup \ldots \cup C_i \cup \ldots \cup C_n) \qquad (5.4)$$

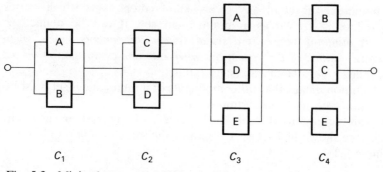

C_1 C_2 C_3 C_4

Fig. 5.3   Minimal cut sets of Example 5.2

Example 5.2

Reconsider Example 5.1 and evaluate the system reliability.
From Equation 5.4 and the reliability diagram of Figure 5.3:

$$Q_S = P(C_1 \cup C_2 \cup C_3 \cup C_4)$$
$$= P(C_1) + P(C_2) + P(C_3) + P(C_4) - P(C_1 \cap C_2)$$
$$- P(C_1 \cap C_3) - P(C_1 \cap C_4) - P(C_2 \cap C_3) - P(C_2 \cap C_4)$$
$$- P(C_3 \cap C_4) + P(C_1 \cap C_2 \cap C_3) + P(C_1 \cap C_2 \cap C_4)$$
$$+ P(C_1 \cap C_3 \cap C_4) + P(C_2 \cap C_3 \cap C_4)$$
$$- P(C_1 \cap C_2 \cap C_3 \cap C_4)$$

where

$$P(C_1) = Q_A Q_B$$
$$P(C_2) = Q_C Q_D$$
$$P(C_3) = Q_A Q_D Q_E$$
$$P(C_4) = Q_B Q_C Q_E$$
$$P(C_1 \cap C_2) = P(C_1)P(C_2) = Q_A Q_B Q_C Q_D$$
$$P(C_1 \cap C_3) = P(C_1)P(C_3) = Q_A Q_B Q_D Q_E$$
$$P(C_1 \cap C_4) = P(C_1)P(C_4) = Q_A Q_B Q_C Q_E$$
$$P(C_2 \cap C_3) = P(C_2)P(C_3) = Q_A Q_C Q_D Q_E$$
$$P(C_2 \cap C_4) = P(C_2)P(C_4) = Q_B Q_C Q_D Q_E$$
$$P(C_3 \cap C_4) = P(C_3)P(C_4) = Q_A Q_B Q_C Q_D Q_E$$
$$P(C_1 \cap C_2 \cap C_3) = P(C_1 \cap C_2 \cap C_4)$$
$$= P(C_1 \cap C_3 \cap C_4)$$
$$= P(C_2 \cap C_3 \cap C_4)$$
$$= P(C_1 \cap C_2 \cap C_3 \cap C_4) = Q_A Q_B Q_C Q_D Q_E$$

therefore

$$Q_S = Q_A Q_B + Q_C Q_D + Q_A Q_D Q_E + Q_B Q_C Q_E - Q_A Q_B Q_C Q_D$$
$$- Q_A Q_B Q_D Q_E - Q_A Q_B Q_C Q_E - Q_A Q_C Q_D Q_E$$
$$- Q_B Q_C Q_D Q_E + 2 Q_A Q_B Q_C Q_D Q_E \qquad (5.5)$$

which may be compared in form with Equation 5.2. If $Q_A = Q_B = Q_C = Q_D = Q_E = Q$, then

$$Q_S = 2Q^2 + 2Q^3 - 5Q^4 + 2Q^5 \qquad (5.6)$$

which may be compared in form with Equation 5.3. If $R = 0.99$ as in Example 5.1, $Q = 1 - 0.99 = 0.01$ and

$$Q_S = 0.00020195$$

and $R_S = 1 - 0.00020195 = 0.99979805$ (as before).

5.3.3 Approximate evaluation

The unreliability, and hence the reliability, of the system was evaluated precisely in the previous section. The calculated value is identical to that obtained in Section 5.2 using the conditional probability approach. This precise evaluation is always theoretically possible, but it can be an exhaustive and time-consuming exercise which can become prohibitive with large systems. To overcome this problem, approximations can be made in the evaluation which, although they reduce precision, permit much faster evaluation. The degree of imprecision introduced is usually negligible and often within the tolerance associated with the data of the component reliabilities for systems which have high values of component reliability. The two required basic approximations are dealt with in turn.

The first approximation assumes that Equation 5.4 can be reduced to a summation of unreliabilities. This was considered in Section 4.2 and gives

$$Q_S = P(C_1) + P(C_2) + \ldots + P(C_i) + \ldots + P(C_n)$$

$$= \sum_{i=1}^{n} P(C_i) \qquad (5.7)$$

Reconsidering Example 5.2, the unreliability of the system is now

$$Q_S = Q_A Q_B + Q_C Q_D + Q_A Q_D Q_E + Q_B Q_C O_E \qquad (5.8)$$

which, if $Q_A = Q_B = Q_C = Q_D = Q_E = Q$ gives

$$Q_S = 2Q^2 + 2Q^3$$

and if $Q = 0.01$:

$Q_S = 0.000202$

and $R_S = 0.999798$

In this example the errors introduced are $+0.02\%$ in the value of Q_S and $-5 \times 10^{-6}\%$ in the value of R_S, i.e., imprecisions of negligible values have been created although the scale of the analysis has been greatly reduced. When this approximation is made, the value of Q_S is always greater than the exact value and exhibits the greatest positive error. Consequently, this approximation is usually referred to [12] as the upper bound of system unreliability. If the second order terms are also included in the analysis, the value of Q_S will be less than the exact value and will exhibit the greatest negative error. In this case, the value is usually referred to as the lower bound of system unreliability.

The second approximation is to neglect cut sets of an order greater than a certain value (the order of a cut set being equal to the number of components comprising that cut set, i.e., a cut set created by two components is known as a cut set of order 2 or a second order cut set). This approximation assumes that high order cut sets are much less probable than low order cut sets. This is valid if all components have reliabilities of similar value but can be invalid if a low order cut set involves components having very high reliabilities while a high order cut set involves components having very low reliabilities. It is evident therefore that this approximation must be treated with care but, if found valid, can again greatly reduce the quantity of analysis that is required.

Again reconsider Example 5.2 and neglect the third order cut sets. The unreliability of the system is now given by

$$Q_S = Q_A Q_B + Q_C Q_D \tag{5.9}$$

which, if $Q_A = Q_B = Q_C = Q_D = Q$ becomes

$$Q_S = 2Q^2 \tag{5.10}$$

and if $Q = 0.01$

$Q_S = 0.000200$　and　$R_S = 0.999800$

In this case the errors introduced in R_S and Q_S are $+2 \times 10^{-4}\%$ and -1% respectively. These are again small and would decrease as component reliabilities increased.

5.3.4   Deducing the minimal cut sets

In the previous discussion it has been assumed that the minimal cut sets can be identified from a visual inspection of the system. In simple systems, visual identification can normally be accomplished with little difficulty. The problem of identification becomes more difficult for larger and more complex systems and there are a number of methods that can be implemented on a digital computer [13–19]. However, it is not within the scope of this book to explain and describe these methods, but two of them can be simplified so that they can be of assistance in the manual identification of the minimal cut sets; these are described briefly as follows.

Most, but not all, of the methods for deducing cuts are based on a knowledge of the minimal paths between input and output. A minimal path can be defined as: *A path between the input and output is minimal if, in that path, no node or intersection between branches is traversed more than once.*

From this definition, the minimal paths of Figure 5.1 are AC, BD, AED, BEC.

(a)   *Method 1*

In this method [13], the steps to be followed are:
 (i)   deduce all minimal paths;
 (ii)   construct an incidence matrix that identifies all components in each path;
 (iii)   if all elements of any column of the incidence matrix are non-zero, the component associated with that column forms a first order cut;
 (iv)   combine two columns of the incidence matrix at a time. If all elements of the combined columns are non-zero, the components associated with those columns form a second order cut. Eliminate any cut containing first order cuts to give the second order minimal cuts;
 (v)   repeat step (iv) with three columns at a time to give the third order cuts; this time eliminating any cuts containing first and second order cuts; and
 (vi)   continue until maximum order of cut has been reached.

Example 5.3

Deduce the minimal cut sets of the network shown in Figure 5.1.
 (i)   Paths are AC, BD, AED, BEC;

(ii)

Path	Component				
	A	B	C	D	E
1	1	0	1	0	0
2	0	1	0	1	0
3	1	0	0	1	1
4	0	1	1	0	1

(iii) no single column exists in which all elements are non-zero. Therefore there are no first order cuts;

(iv) all elements of the following combinations of two columns are non-zero and therefore form second order cuts—AB, CD. Since there are no first order cuts, AB and CD both form second order minimal cuts;

(v) all elements of the following combinations of three columns are non-zero and therefore form third order cuts—ABC, ABD, ABE, ACD, ADE, BCD, BCE, CDE. Eliminating from these those cuts containing AB and CD gives ADE and BCE as the third order minimal cuts; and

(vi) an examination of higher order combinations shows that there are no further minimal cuts.

The minimal cut sets of Figure 5.1 are AB, CD, ADE and BCE, as obtained previously.

(b) *Method 2*

In this method [48], the steps to be followed are:
  (i) deduce all minimal paths
  (ii) deduce all first order cuts of path 1; these being the components in the path
  (iii) deduce all first order cuts of path 2 and combine in all possible ways with all cuts from path 1. Eliminate duplicated combinations, non-minimal cut sets and cut sets of order greater than that required.
  (iv) Take the next path and combine all of its first order cuts with those remaining after step (iii). Eliminate cuts as in step (iii).
  (v) Repeat step (iv) until all paths have been considered.

Example 5.4

Repeat Example 5.3.
  (i) As before the paths are AC, BD, AED, BEC;
  (ii) cut sets of path 1 are A, C;

(iii) the remaining cut sets after combining path 2 with path 1 are AB, AD, BC, CD;

(iv) the remaining cut sets after combining path 3 with the cuts of step (iii) are AB, AD, CD, BCE; and

(v) the remaining cut sets, i.e., system cut sets, after combining path 4 with the cuts of step (iv) are AB, CD, ADE and BCE, i.e., as before.

5.4 Application and comparison of previous techniques

The following example illustrates the application of the conditional probability and cut set techniques to a system other than the classic bridge network.

Example 5.5

Evaluate the reliability of the system shown in Figure 5.4 using conditional probability and cut set methods if each component has a reliability of 0.99.

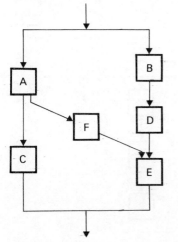

Fig. 5.4 System of Example 5.5

(a) *Conditional probability method*

It was previously noted that any component can be selected to initiate the analysis. Judicious selection can reduce the effort required to obtain a solution. The selection of component F reduces the original system to the two subsystems shown in Figures 5.5b and 5.5c. Although Figure 5.5c now consists of series/parallel components, Figure 5.5b does not, and this

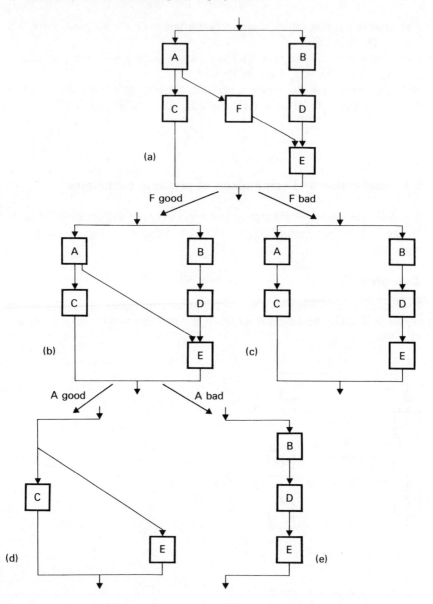

Fig. 5.5 Sequential reduction using conditional probability

subsystem must be further decomposed. The selection of component A to be considered 'good' and 'bad' produces the two subsystems shown in Figures 5.5d and 5.5e. In the case of Figure 5.5d, components B and D do not appear because, when A is 'good', the signal reaches E irrespective whether B and D are good or bad and therefore they become irrelevant.

The reliability of the system can now be deduced as follows:

$$R_S = R_S(\text{if F is good}) \, R_F + R_S(\text{if F is bad}) \, Q_F$$
$$R_S(\text{if F is bad}) = 1 - (1 - R_B R_D R_E)(1 - R_A R_C)$$
$$R_S(\text{if F is good}) = R_S(\text{if A is good}) \, R_A + R_S(\text{if A is bad}) \, Q_A$$
$$R_S(\text{if A is good}) = 1 - Q_C Q_E$$
$$R_S(\text{if A is bad}) = R_B R_D R_E$$

substituting gives

$$R_S = [(1 - Q_C Q_E) R_A + R_B R_D R_E Q_A] R_F$$
$$+ [1 - (1 - R_B R_D R_E)(1 - R_A R_C)] Q_F$$

substituting numerical values gives

$$R_S = 0.999602 \quad \text{and} \quad Q_S = 0.000398$$

(b)   Cut set method

Using visual inspection or one of the two methods described in Section 5.3.4, the minimal cut sets of the network shown in Figure 5.4 are (AB), (AD), (AE), (CE), (BCF) and (CDF). Evaluation of the precise value of system reliability using the rigorous techniques described in Section 5.3.2 becomes very tedious using hand calculations since in the case of this system with 6 cuts, the number of terms in the exact equation is 63. However, it is a useful and logical exercise to deduce all 63 terms and confirm that the result is identical to that obtained using the conditional probability approach. The results obtained using the suggested approximations are as follows:

Consider first the result that will be obtained if only second order events are used and the evaluation is reduced to one of summating the cut probabilities. In this case:

$$Q_S = Q_A Q_B + Q_A Q_D + Q_A Q_E + Q_C Q_E$$
$$= 0.000400$$
$$R_S = 0.999600$$

i.e., an imprecision of +0.5% is introduced in the value of unreliability and −0.0002% is introduced in the value of reliability.

Consider now the result that will be obtained if all of the cuts are used and the evaluation is again limited to one of summating the cut probabilities. In this case

$$Q_S = Q_A Q_B + Q_A Q_D + Q_A Q_E + Q_C Q_E + Q_B Q_C Q_F + Q_C Q_D Q_F$$
$$= 0.000402 \text{ (upper bound to system unreliability)}$$
$$R_S = 0.999598$$

i.e., the imprecisions are +1.0% and −0.0004% in the values of unreliability and reliability respectively.

If the three sets of results are compared, the minimal cut set method, even with the approximations, gives results that are sufficiently precise for most applications. The magnitude of the imprecision decreases significantly as the component reliabilities increase and can be decreased, even in the present example, to a negligible value if the probabilities of two cuts occurring simultaneously, $P(C_1 \cap C_2)$ etc., are included. In the present example this would introduce 15 further terms in the equation of system unreliability and reduce the values of unreliability for the two approximations made to 0.000396 (lower bound to system unreliability) and 0.000398, respectively.

5.5 Tie set method

The tie set method is essentially the complement of the cut set method. It is used less frequently, in practice, as it does not directly identify the failure modes of the system. It has certain special applications and therefore is discussed briefly in this section.

A tie set is a minimal path of the system and is therefore a set of system components connected in series. Consequently, a tie set fails if any one of the components in it fails and this probability can be evaluated using the principle of series systems. For the system to fail however, all of the tie sets must fail and therefore all tie sets are effectively connected in parallel.

Using these concepts, the tie set diagram for the model of Figure 5.1 is shown in Figure 5.6.

It should be noted that although the tie sets are in parallel, the concept of parallel systems cannot be used because the same component can appear in two or more of the tie sets. The concept of union does apply

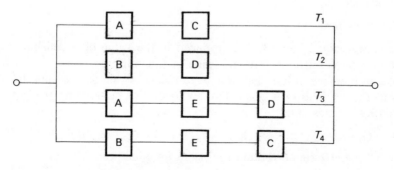

Fig. 5.6 Tie sets of Fig. 5.1

however in a similar manner to that discussed for minimal cut sets in Section 5.3.2.

From the previous concepts of tie sets and Figure 5.6, the reliability of the system shown in Figure 5.1 assuming the same system requirement as Example 5.1 is

$$R_S = P(T_1 \cup T_2 \cup T_3 \cup T_4) \tag{5.11}$$

in which T_i is the ith tie set and its probability of occurrence is $P(T_i)$.

Equation 5.11 can be developed in the same way as Equation 5.4 associated with cut sets was developed to give

$$\begin{aligned}
R_S = {} & P(T_1) + P(T_2) + P(T_3) + P(T_4) - P(T_1 \cap T_2) \\
& - P(T_1 \cap T_3) - P(T_1 \cap T_4) - P(T_2 \cap T_3) - P(T_2 \cap T_4) \\
& - P(T_3 \cap T_4) + P(T_1 \cap T_2 \cap T_3) + P(T_1 \cap T_2 \cap T_4) \\
& + P(T_1 \cap T_3 \cap T_4) + P(T_2 \cap T_3 \cap T_4) \\
& - P(T_1 \cap T_2 \cap T_3 \cap T_4)
\end{aligned} \tag{5.12}$$

where

$$P(T_1) = R_A R_C$$
$$P(T_2) = R_B R_D$$
$$P(T_3) = R_A R_E R_D$$
$$P(T_4) = R_B R_E R_C$$
$$P(T_1 \cap T_2) = P(T_1)P(T_2) = R_A R_B R_C R_D$$
$$P(T_1 \cap T_3) = P(T_1)P(T_3) = R_A R_C R_D R_E$$
$$P(T_1 \cap T_4) = P(T_1)P(T_4) = R_A R_B R_C R_E$$
$$P(T_2 \cap T_3) = P(T_2)P(T_3) = R_A R_B R_D R_E$$
$$P(T_2 \cap T_4) = P(T_2)P(T_4) = R_B R_C R_D R_E$$
$$P(T_3 \cap T_4) = P(T_3)P(T_4) = R_A R_B R_C R_D R_E$$
$$P(T_1 \cap T_2 \cap T_3) = P(T_1 \cap T_2 \cap T_4)$$
$$= P(T_1 \cap T_3 \cap T_4)$$
$$= P(T_2 \cap T_3 \cap T_4)$$
$$= P(T_1 \cap T_2 \cap T_3 \cap T_4) = R_A R_B R_C R_D R_E$$

Equation 5.12 is of the same form as Equation 5.5 but gives the reliability of the system instead of the unreliability, and is expressed in terms of component reliability instead of component unreliability.

If $R_A = R_B = R_C = R_D = R_E = R$, Equation 5.12 would reduce to

$$R_S = 2R^2 + 2R^3 - 5R^4 + 2R^5 \tag{5.13}$$

and if, as in Example 5.1, $R = 0.99$, then

$R_s = 0.99979805$ and $Q_S = 0.00020195$ (as before)

 $= 0.999798$ and $= 0.000202$ (to 6 decimal places)

One of the main disadvantages of the tie set method is that Equation 5.12 cannot be approximated to a set of summation terms as was possible in the case of Equation 5.5. The reasons for this were discussed previously in Section 4.3 and are due to the fact that generally the values of R are very high and all terms in Equation 5.12 are comparable. The scale of the analysis required by tie set evaluation methods is generally much greater than that of cut set methods where approximations can be used.

Tie set methods do have an important role to play in some evaluation situations. Generally, this occurs in those system problems involving sequential logic and/or switching operations. These do not have a physical network structure from which the paths of the system can be obtained topologically. Instead, equivalent system paths are deduced from a knowledge of the sequential logic and/or switching operations using a technique such as event tree analysis. (This method is described in Section 5.7.) At this point it can be stated that, depending on the number of sequences involved, the number of event paths can be extremely large. Also, in many complex systems, a given sequence of events does not necessarily lead to just success or failure but to one of a number of possible outcomes. To restrict the analysis to sensible proportions, the paths leading to one of these outcomes are often neglected; the one being neglected preferably being that having the greatest number of paths. The probability of occurrence of the outcomes for which the paths are not deduced can still be evaluated however if a tie set analysis is performed on those paths that do not lead to this outcome. This is because tie sets are basically the complement of cut sets and paths that do not lead to a particular outcome are basically the complement of those that do. This aspect and its application is described in more detail in Section 5.7 on event trees.

5.6 Connection matrix techniques

In this method, a connection matrix is constructed from the system network or reliability diagram that defines which components are connected between the nodes of the network or diagram. Reconsider Figure 5.1 and label the nodes as shown in Figure 5.7.

From Figure 5.7, the following connection matrix can be constructed in which a zero indicates that there is no connection between two nodes and

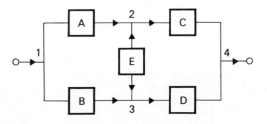

Fig. 5.7 Fig. 5.1 with labelled nodes

unity represents a connection between a node and itself, this being the value of the elements on the principal diagonal.

$$
\begin{array}{c}
\text{to} \\
\text{node} \quad \begin{array}{cccc} 1 & 2 & 3 & 4 \end{array} \\
\text{from} \quad
\begin{array}{c} 1 \\ 2 \\ 3 \\ 4 \end{array}
\begin{bmatrix}
1 & A & B & 0 \\
0 & 1 & E & C \\
0 & E & 1 & D \\
0 & 0 & 0 & 1
\end{bmatrix}
\end{array}
$$

In this example, unidirectional branches (flow is permitted in one direction only) and bidirectional branches (flow is permitted in either direction) are both included. The essence of this method of solution is to transform this basic connection matrix into one which defines the transmission of flow between the input and the output, i.e., between the two nodes of interest. This can be achieved in one of two ways, node removal or matrix multiplication.

(a) *Node removal*

In this method, all nodes of the network that are not input or output are removed by sequential reduction of the basic connection matrix until it is reduced to a 2×2 matrix involving only the input and output nodes. In the present example the matrix must be reduced to one involving only nodes 1 and 4.

To remove a node k from a matrix, each element $N_{ij}(i, j \neq k)$ must be replaced according to

$$
N'_{ij} = N_{ij} + (N_{ik} N_{kj})
$$

where N'_{ij} replaces the old N_{ij}.

In the present example first consider the removal of node 2. The new matrix elements are

$$N_{11} = 1 + A \cdot 0 = 1$$
$$N_{13} = B + A \cdot E = B + AE$$
$$N_{14} = 0 + A \cdot C = AC$$
$$N_{31} = 0 + E \cdot 0 = 0$$
$$N_{33} = 1 + E \cdot E = 1$$
$$N_{34} = D + E \cdot C = D + EC$$
$$N_{41} = 0 + 0 \cdot 0 = 0$$
$$N_{43} = 0 + 0 \cdot E = 0$$
$$N_{44} = 1 + 0 \cdot C = 1$$

which gives the following reduced matrix

$$
\begin{array}{c}
 \\
1 \\
3 \\
4
\end{array}
\begin{array}{ccc}
1 & 3 & 4 \\
\left[\begin{array}{ccc}
1 & B+AE & AC \\
0 & 1 & D+EC \\
0 & 0 & 1
\end{array}\right]
\end{array}
$$

Now consider the removal of node 3. The new elements are

$$N_{11} = 1 + (B + AE) \cdot 0 = 1$$
$$N_{14} = AC + (B + AE)(D + EC) = AC + BD + BEC + AED$$
$$N_{41} = 0 + 0 \cdot 0 = 0$$
$$N_{44} = 1 + 0 \cdot 1 = 1$$

which gives the following reduced matrix

$$
\begin{array}{c}
 \\
1 \\
4
\end{array}
\begin{array}{cc}
1 & 4 \\
\left[\begin{array}{cc}
1 & AC+BD+BEC+AED \\
0 & 1
\end{array}\right]
\end{array}
$$

From this final reduced matrix, the element N_{14} gives the transmission from node 1 (input) to node 4 (output) and, in this case is

$$AC + BD + BEC + AED$$

The deduction and evaluation of the reduced matrices and this transmission involved the application of Boolean algebra. (Many readers will be familiar with this type of algebra but for those who are not, the rules of addition, multiplication, and so on, are summarized in Appendix 1.)

From the rules of Boolean algebra, the above transmission expression can be interpreted as (A and C) or (B and D) or (B and E and C) or (A and E and D). This expression represents all the possible paths that exist between the input and the output of the system and thus are equivalent to the minimal paths or tie sets of the system. The reliability of the system can therefore be evaluated from this point using the evaluation techniques already described in Section 5.5.

(b) *Matrix multiplication*

In this method the basic connection matrix is multiplied by itself a number of times until the resulting matrix remains unchanged. A brief review of matrix techniques is included in Appendix 3 for those unfamiliar with this type of algebra. In the present example, this multiplication process is as follows:

Let

$$
M = \begin{array}{c} \\ 1 \\ 2 \\ 3 \\ 4 \end{array}
\begin{array}{cccc} 1 & 2 & 3 & 4 \\ \left[\begin{array}{cccc} 1 & A & B & 0 \\ 0 & 1 & E & C \\ 0 & E & 1 & D \\ 0 & 0 & 0 & 1 \end{array}\right] \end{array}
$$

then

$$
M^2 = \begin{array}{c} \\ 1 \\ 2 \\ 3 \\ 4 \end{array}
\begin{array}{cccc} 1 & 2 & 3 & 4 \\ \left[\begin{array}{cccc} 1 & A+BE & B+AE & AC+BD \\ 0 & 1 & E & C+DE \\ 0 & E & 1 & EC+D \\ 0 & 0 & 0 & 1 \end{array}\right] \end{array}
$$

$$
M^3 = \begin{array}{c} \\ 1 \\ 2 \\ 3 \\ 4 \end{array}
\begin{array}{cccc} 1 & 2 & 3 & 4 \\ \left[\begin{array}{cccc} 1 & A+BE & B+AE & AC+BD+BEC+AED \\ 0 & 1 & E & C+DE \\ 0 & E & 1 & EC+D \\ 0 & 0 & 0 & 1 \end{array}\right] \end{array}
$$

Further powers of M do not change the resulting matrix and the process can be stopped at this point.

It can be seen from the elements of M^3 that the transmission from node 1 to node 4 is again the same as in the case of the node removal method and the tie set method. The advantage of the multiplication method compared with the node removal method is that it gives the transmission or tie sets between all pairs of nodes simultaneously whereas the node removal method gave the transmission between two nodes of interest only.

Although the connection matrix method is a formal method in its own right, it can also be considered as a means of deducing tie sets. As discussed in Section 5.1, several reliability evaluation methods are essentially the same in concept; the difference is in their formal presentation. This is so in the case of tie sets and connection matrix methods.

5.7   Event trees

5.7.1   General concepts

An event tree is a pictorial representation of all the events which can occur in a system. It is defined as a tree because the pictorial representation gradually fans out like the branches of a tree as an increasing number of events are considered.

The method can be used either for systems in which all components are continuously operating or for systems in which some or all of the components are in a standby mode that involve sequential operational logic and switching. The last type of system is generally associated with safety orientated systems. In practice the event tree method is more widely used for safety orientated systems, as other techniques prove to be more viable for continuously operated systems. The applications of the technique to both types of systems proceed in a similar manner but with two particular differences between them.

The first is that, with continuously operated systems, the events that can occur, i.e., the components that can fail, can be considered in any arbitrary order. With standby systems, or any system in which the operation of a particular component is dependent on the success or failure of another component, the sequence of events must be considered in the chronological order in which they occur.

The second difference is the starting point of the event tree. In the case of continuously operating systems, the starting point is the system operating normally and the event tree is deduced as a sequence of events involving success and failure of the system components. In the case of standby systems and in particular, safety and mission orientated systems, the event tree is used to identify the various possible outcomes of the system following a given initiating event which is generally an unsatisfactory operating event or situation. This latter analysis is similar to decision trees used in business applications in which the initiating event is a particular business decision, not necessarily an adverse one, and the decision tree represents the various possible outcomes of that decision.

5.7.2 Continuously operated systems

(a) *Complete event tree*

In order to illustrate the application of event trees to continuously operated systems, reconsider Example 5.1 and the system shown in Figure 5.1.

The events to be considered in this system are success and failure of the various components. The components can be considered in any order as they do not operate chronologically with respect to each other. Consider them in the order A, B, C, D, E. The event tree for this system is shown in Figure 5.8 in which a vertical line upwards means the component is working or successful and a vertical line downwards means the component is not working or failed.

In this example there are 32 individual paths each of which are numbered in Figure 5.8. Having deduced the event tree it is necessary to deduce the system outcome caused by the occurrence of each path. This can only be done from a knowledge of the operating requirements of the system. In this example the only outcomes are success of the system or failure of the system and these are labelled S for success and F for failure, in Figure 5.8, for which there are 16 paths leading to each. In more complex operational systems there may be several possible outcomes such as total success, total failure and one or more partial success or failure outcomes.

Having deduced the outcome of each path it is a relatively simple arithmetic exercise to evaluate the probability of occurrence of each outcome. The probability of occurrence of each path can be evaluated from the product of the appropriate event probabilities since they must all occur for the path to occur. Since all the paths are mutually exclusive, the probability of a particular system outcome can be evaluated by summating the path probabilities leading to that outcome. Finally, since success and failure are complementary events, the summation of the path probabilities leading to success and the summation of the path probabilities leading to failure must themselves summate to unity.

The reliability of the system can therefore be deduced in the case of this example as

$$R_S = P(P_1) + P(P_2) + P(P_3) + P(P_4) + P(P_5) + P(P_6) + P(P_9)$$
$$+ P(P_{10}) + P(P_{11}) + P(P_{12}) + P(P_{13}) + P(P_{17}) + P(P_{18}) + P(P_{19})$$
$$+ P(P_{21}) + P(P_{22})$$

where $P(P_i) = $ probability of occurrence of path i

and $\quad P(P_1) = R_A R_B R_C R_D R_E$

$\quad\quad P(P_2) = R_A R_B R_C R_D Q_E \quad$ etc.

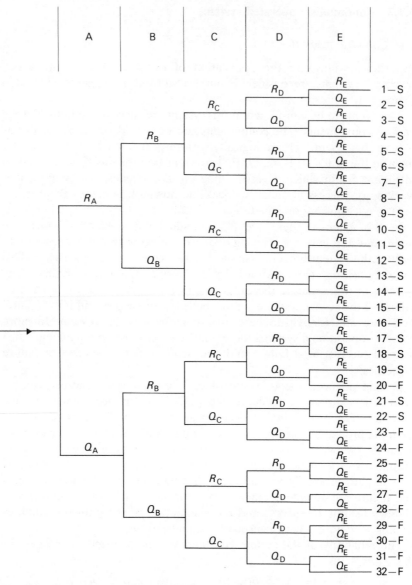

Fig. 5.8   Event tree for Example 5.1

Similarly the unreliability of the system is given by

$$Q_S = P(P_7) + P(P_8) + P(P_{14}) + P(P_{15}) + P(P_{16}) + P(P_{20}) + P(P_{23})$$
$$+ P(P_{24}) + P(P_{25}) + P(P_{26}) + P(P_{27}) + P(P_{28}) + P(P_{29}) + P(P_{30})$$
$$+ P(P_{31}) + P(P_{32})$$

and $R_S + Q_S = 1$.

Evaluating these probabilities for the case where all components have a reliability of 0.99 it can be found that the results are identical to those obtained previously, i.e. $R_S = 0.999798$ and $Q_S = 0.000202$.

(b) Reduced event tree

The number of individual paths of the event tree deduced in the previous example was 32. This was for a 5 component system and it is evident that the number of paths increases dramatically as the components are increased, i.e., the number of paths is 2^n for an n-component system in which each component can reside in one of two states. The number of paths is even greater if some, or all, of the components can reside in more than two states, e.g., success, failure and derated or partial output states.

This problem can be partially overcome by constructing a reduced event tree. This is deduced by considering each component or event in turn as before but, instead of constructing the complete tree before deducing the outcome of each path, the outcome deduction is made before each new component or event is considered. If, at each of these deductions, it is known that a particular outcome is reached by a path irrespective whether subsequent components or events are successful or not, there is no need to consider further development of this event path. For instance, after considering components A, B and C as successful in the present example, the system must be successful irrespective of whether D and E are successful or not. Consequently the path denoted by R_A, R_B and R_C need not be further developed after the consideration of component C. Similarly, after considering components A and B as unsuccessful, the system must always fail irrespective whether components C, D and E are successful or not and this path need not be developed further. This is basically the same as arriving at an outcome conclusion for a particular given condition in the conditional probability approach.

Using this logic the complete event tree shown in Figure 5.8 can be reduced to that shown in Figure 5.9, in which the total number of event paths have been reduced from 32 to 13.

The reliability of the system can be evaluated using the method described for the complete event tree and is given by

$$R_S = R_A R_B R_C + R_A R_B Q_C R_D + R_A Q_B R_C + R_A Q_B Q_C R_D R_E$$
$$+ Q_A R_B R_C R_D + Q_A R_B R_C Q_D R_E + Q_A R_B Q_C R_D$$

which gives if $R_A = R_B = R_C = R_D = R_E = 0.99$

$$R_S = 0.999798 \quad \text{(as before)}$$

Similarly,

$$Q_S = R_A R_B Q_C Q_D + R_A Q_B Q_C R_D Q_E + R_A Q_B Q_C Q_D$$
$$+ Q_A R_B R_C Q_D Q_E + Q_A R_B Q_C Q_D + Q_A Q_B$$

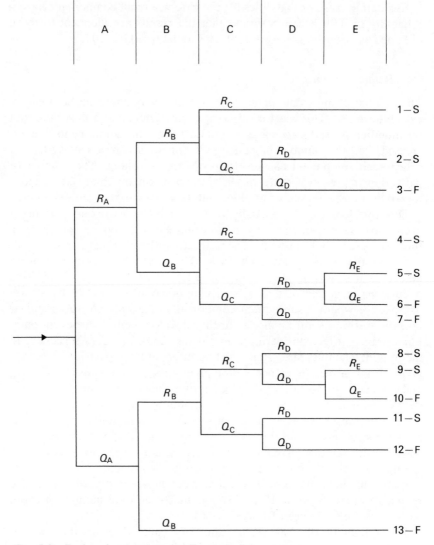

Fig. 5.9   Reduced event tree for Example 5.1

which gives

$$Q_S = 0.000202 = 1 - R_S \quad \text{(as before)}$$

A further reduction in the size of the event tree can be made if only those paths leading to the system outcome of interest are constructed and those paths that are known to lead to other system outcomes are terminated. This has little or no advantage in hand calculations but does have major effects if the events and paths are being stored on a digital computer. Applying this logic to the present example and considering system failure as the outcome of interest, the further reduced event tree is shown in Figure 5.10, in which only 6 paths of the original 32 are now required. A similar event tree can be constructed for system success. The equation for system unreliability can be deduced directly from Figure 5.10 and is, of course, identical to that developed previously. The equation for system reliability cannot be deduced from Figure 5.10 but, with only two mutually exclusive outcomes, can be evaluated as the

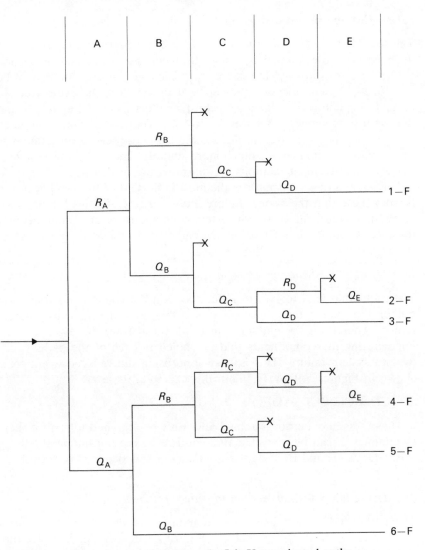

Fig. 5.10 Failure event tree of Example 5.1. X, terminated paths

complement to the value of system unreliability. The reverse situation occurs if a success event tree is constructed.

In the case of systems in which more than two outcomes are possible, this method can be adapted by terminating those paths that lead to only one of the system outcomes, preferably that which will contain the greatest number of paths. In this way the probability of occurrence of each outcome can be evaluated directly from the path probabilities of the event tree or from the complementary value of these probabilities.

5.7.3   Cut and tie set deduction

The cut and tie sets of a system for which a topological structure can be deduced can be evaluated by using the techniques described in Section 5.3 and 5.5 respectively. In systems for which such a structure cannot be developed, the cut and tie sets can be deduced from the event tree. In order to explain this deduction, reconsider the system of Figure 5.1 and the event trees shown in Figures 5.8 to 5.10. There is, of course, no need to construct the event tree to deduce the cut or tie sets of this system as the previous techniques are much more suitable. The use of this system is however a convenient method of confirming the present technique.

The cut sets of the system are the most important of the two because it is from these that the system failure modes can be identified, i.e., which components must fail or which system events must occur simultaneously to cause system failure. These cut sets can be deduced in one of two ways.

(a)   *Using paths leading to system failure*

The paths that lead to system failure contain the components that must fail or the events that must occur together in order to cause system failure. Therefore, the cut sets can be deduced from the event tree by enumerating the components that are failed in each of the paths which lead to system failure. This is best done using the reduced event trees shown in Figures 5.9 and 5.10. In this example, these are

CD, BCE, BCD, ADE, ACD, AB

These sets may be non-minimal and must be searched to reduce them to minimal. It can be seen that BCD and ACD are non-minimal leaving AB, CD, ADE and BCE as the minimal cut sets deduced previously.

(b)   *Using the paths not leading to system failure*

The paths that do not lead to system failure contain the components which must work or the events which must occur together in order that system failure does not occur. Therefore, the tie sets can be deduced from the event tree containing system success paths by enumerating the components that are successful in each of the paths which do not lead to system failure. Again, this is best done using the reduced event tree shown in Figure 5.9 for which the tie sets are

ABC, ABD, AC, ADE, BCD, BCE, BD

These are again non-minimal and can be searched to reduce them to minimal. This reduction gives the minimal tie sets as

AC, BD, ADE and BCE   (as before)

A cut set analysis of either the minimal or non-minimal tie sets using the methods described previously gives AB, CD, ADE and BCE as the minimal cut sets of the system.

The following comments can be made concerning this analysis:
(i)   The cut set method and the event tree method applied to failure events are similar although the formal approaches for their development are different. This is a reasonable deduction because they are both techniques for identifying how a system may fail and therefore both identify the failure states of the system.
(ii) Because the probability of occurrence of both outcomes and the cut sets of the system in a 2-outcome system can be deduced from a knowledge of the paths leading to only one of the outcomes, it is not necessary to deduce and store the paths leading to both outcomes.
(iii) Although the cut set techniques have been described for a 2-outcome system, they can easily be extended to an n-outcome system. The cut sets of each system outcome can be deduced using one of the above methods depending on whether the paths leading to the outcome or not leading to the outcome have been deduced.

5.7.4   Standby and sequential logic systems

Generally all the techniques described in Sections 5.7.2 and 5.7.3 are equally applicable to standby or sequential logic systems. Since the development of the event tree requires slight changes in the logical thought process however, it is of benefit to describe the process in relation to such a system.

Example 5.6

Consider the cooling system of the continuous process plant shown schematically in Figure 5.11 and the sequence of events that may follow a break in the pipe normally used to supply the cooling water (initiating event). When this happens a loss of flow detector D causes both electrically driven pumps P1 and P2 to operate. Consider that both pumps are

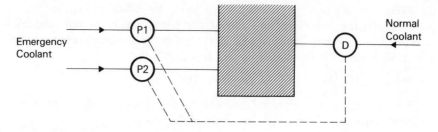

Fig. 5.11 Schematic diagram of Example 5.6

required for 100% system success, 1 pump for 50% system success and that failure occurs if both pumps fail to operate. Deduce the event tree of the system, the probability of each system outcome if all components and subsystems have a success probability of 0.99 and the minimal cut sets leading to partial and complete system failure.

Considering the success and failure of the electric power EP in addition to the effect of D, P1 and P2, the complete event tree is shown in Figure 5.12.

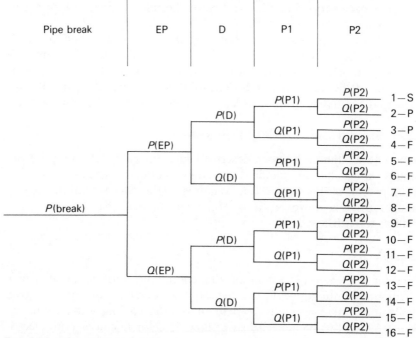

Fig. 5.12 Complete event tree

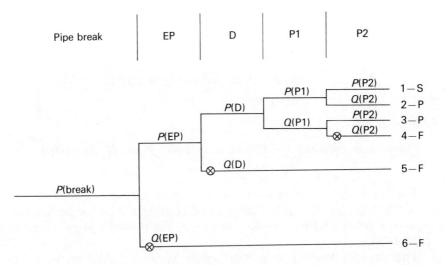

Fig. 5.13   Reduced event tree. X, terminated paths

Since the complete emergency cooling system fails if either the electric power fails or the detector fails, the complete event tree can be reduced to that shown in Figure 5.13 in which only 6 paths of the original 16 are required. A further reduction in storage can be achieved by ignoring those paths leading to complete system failure and terminating the paths at the points shown in Figure 5.13. This leaves only 3 paths to be stored. The system outcome associated with each path whichever tree is constructed must be deduced from an engineering knowledge of the system operational requirements. These outcomes are shown in Figures 5.12 and 5.13 as complete success (S), partial success (P) and complete failure (F).

From Figure 5.13

$$P(\text{system success}) = P(EP) \cdot P(D) \cdot P(P1) \cdot P(P2)$$

which, if all success probabilities are 0.99 gives

$$P(\text{system success}) = 0.99^4 = 0.960596$$

Similarly

$$P(\text{partial success}) = P(EP) \cdot P(D) \cdot P(P1) \cdot Q(P2) + P(EP) \cdot P(D) \cdot Q(P1) \cdot P(P2)$$

which, if all success probabilities are 0.99 gives:

$$P(\text{partial success}) = 2 \times 0.99^3 \times 0.01 = 0.019406$$

Finally

$$P(\text{system failure}) = P(\text{EP}) \cdot P(\text{D}) \cdot Q(\text{P1}) \cdot Q(\text{P2}) + P(\text{EP}) \cdot Q(\text{D})$$
$$+ Q(\text{EP})$$
$$= 0.99^2 \times 0.01^2 + 0.99 \times 0.01 + 0.01$$
$$= 0.019998$$

Alternatively

$$P(\text{system failure}) = 1 - [P(\text{system success}) + P(\text{partial success})]$$
$$= 0.019998$$

The results are the probabilities of the various outcomes given that the pipe break occurs. If required, they could be weighted by the probability of a pipe break and its complement to give the overall system outcome probabilities.

The cut sets leading to partial system success can be deduced by enumerating the failed components in the paths leading to partial system success, i.e. paths 2 and 3 of Figure 5.13. This enumeration gives two first order minimal cut sets for partial system success, these being

P1, P2

The cut sets leading to total system failure can be deduced by analysing the tie sets of the paths leading to system success and partial system success, i.e., paths 1, 2 and 3 of Figure 5.13 or enumerating the failed components in the paths leading to complete system failure, i.e., paths 4, 5 and 6 of Figure 5.13. Either method would give the following minimal cut sets:

EP, D, (P1 and P2)

In Example 5.6, it is assumed that only one detector is used to determine when the normal coolant supply fails. In practice however more than one detector is likely to be used, e.g., one or more flow detectors may be used together with one or more temperature sensors. This does not cause any increase in conceptual complexity although it does increase the amount of analysis. Two methods for solving the problem can be implemented.

The first method considers each component separately and the system event tree is constructed with each component identified in the event tree. This clearly increases the number of sequences considered in the tree and produces a much larger number of system paths. The technique is however identical to that described previously. Whether any given path of this enhanced tree leads to system success, partial success or failure depends on the operational requirements of the detectors, e.g., system success may occur if one detector is successful, if all detectors are required to work or if only a certain number between these extremes are required. In all cases, the appropriate paths can be traced through the tree.

In the second method, the detectors are grouped together to form a subsystem and the event tree is constructed in terms of this subsystem only. The system event tree is therefore identical to that shown in Figures 5.12 and 5.13 but the probability of success of the subsystem representing the detectors must be evaluated as a separate exercise. This can be done either from basic probability laws, from an event tree constructed just for the subsystem being considered or from a fault tree analysis, the latter being the subject of Section 5.8.

The above discussion concerning detectors is equally applicable to any part of the system that contains one or more components, e.g., the electric power supply which may consist of the normal a.c. supply together with standby batteries or emergency generators.

Example 5.7

The single detector in Example 5.6 is replaced by 3 detectors, two monitoring the temperature of the plant and one monitoring the flow. Evaluate the probability of successful operation for the conditions, all must work, two must work (this is known as a 2 out of 3, or in general m-out-of-n, majority-vote system) and one must work using the event tree method and the basic rules of probability method if the success probability for each detector is 0.99.

(a) *Event tree method*

The event tree for this detector system is shown in Figure 5.14.

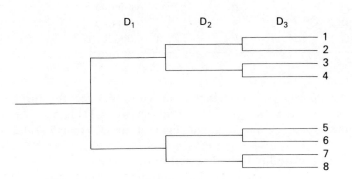

Fig. 5.14 Event tree for Example 5.7

The paths leading to success and failure for each of the operating conditions together with the success probabilities are shown in Table 5.2.

Table 5.2 Results of Example 5.7 using event tree method

Operating condition for success	Success paths of Fig. 5.14	Failure paths of Fig. 5.14	Success probability
All must work (3 out of 3)	1	2–8	0.970299
2 must work (2 out of 3)	1–3, 5	4, 6–8	0.999702
1 must work (1 out of 3)	1–7	8	0.999999

(b) *Basic probability method*

Using the technique described in Section 3.3.8, the states of this system can be expressed as $(R_{D1} + Q_{D1})(R_{D2} + Q_{D2})(R_{D3} + Q_{D3})$ giving the states and probabilities shown in Table 5.3.

Table 5.3 System states and probabilities

| State of | | | Success (S) or failure (F) for | | | |
D1	D2	D3	All must work	2 must work	1 must work	Probability
R_1	R_2	R_3	S	S	S	0.970299
R_1	R_2	Q_3	F	S	S	0.009801
R_1	Q_2	R_3	F	S	S	0.009801
R_1	Q_2	Q_3	F	F	S	0.000099
Q_1	R_2	R_3	F	S	S	0.009801
Q_1	R_2	Q_3	F	F	S	0.000099
Q_1	Q_2	R_3	F	F	S	0.000099
Q_1	Q_2	Q_3	F	F	F	0.000001

Combining the appropriate probabilities in Table 5.3 for the three specified operating requirements gives the results shown in Table 5.2. The following comments can be made in the light of these examples and results.

(i) The values of probability to be inserted in the system event tree of Figures 5.8 to 5.10 would be the appropriate values found in Example 5.7.

(ii) The results found in Example 5.7 should be treated with care since it is seen that a 1-out-of-3 system appears to be more reliable than the others. This is true if a component only operates, or fails to operate, given it has been instructed to operate. In practice, a component may also operate without an instruction, i.e., it operates inadvertently. This has been ignored in this example but if the probability of inadvertent operation is not insignificant, the system can malfunction more times with a 1-out-of-3 system than a 2-out-of-3 system. It is for this reason that majority-vote systems usually require at least 2 devices to operate when instructed to operate.

(iii) A visual inspection of Table 5.3, a table that is often called a truth table, shows that the states enumerated are identical to the event paths shown in the event tree of Figure 5.14. This leads, once again, to the conclusion that several apparently different techniques are very similar in concept, the difference being the formal approach to their deduction and method of presentation. In the cases considered, the state enumeration methods (including the binomial distribution), the event tree methods and truth table methods are all virtually identical.

5.8 Fault trees

The previous section stated that one method for evaluating the probability of failure of a subsystem was using fault trees. This method has been used widely for many years in the reliability evaluation of standby and mission orientated systems. It is very rarely used for the topological type of systems and therefore only the first type of system is considered in this section.

Fault trees use a logic that is essentially the reverse of that used in event trees. In this method a particular failure condition is considered and a tree is constructed that identifies the various combinations and sequences of other failures that lead to the failure being considered.

This method is frequently used as a qualitative evaluation method in order to assist the designer, planner or operator in deciding how a system may fail and what remedies may be used to overcome the causes of failure. The method can also be used for quantitative evaluation, in which case the causes of system failure are gradually broken down into an increasing number of hierarchical levels until a level is reached at which reliability data is sufficient or precise enough for a quantitative assessment to be made. The appropriate data is then inserted into the tree at this hierarchical level and combined together using the logic of the tree to give the reliability assessment of the complete system being studied.

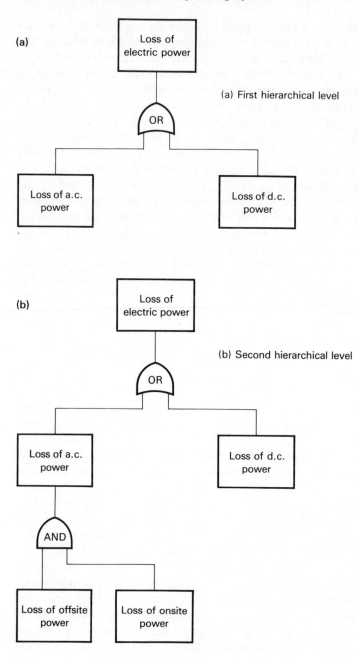

Fig. 5.15 Development of a fault tree. (a) First hierarchical level. (b) Second hierarchical level

In order to illustrate the application of this method, consider the electric power requirements of the system in Example 5.6. In this example, the failure event being considered is 'failure of the electric power'. In practice the electric power requirements may be both a.c. power, to supply energy for prime movers, and d.c. power, to operate relays and contactors, both of which are required to ensure successful operation of the electric power. Consequently the event 'failure of electric power' can be divided into two subevents 'failure of a.c. power' and 'failure of d.c. power'. This is shown in Figure 5.15a with the events being joined by an OR gate as failure of either, or both, causes the system to fail.

If this subdivision is insufficient, both subevents must be divided further. The event 'failure of a.c. power' may be caused by 'failure of offsite power', i.e., the grid supply or by 'failure of onsite power', i.e., standby generators or similar devices. The fault tree of Figure 5.15a can be subdivided as shown in Figure 5.15b with the events joined by an AND gate since both must fail in order to lose the a.c. power. This process can be continued downwards to any required level of subdivision. The logic used requires a thorough engineering understanding of the system being analysed since it is necessary to appreciate the failure events that can occur as well as how they are linked together. The linking process may involve AND and OR gates as shown in Figure 5.15 together with other logic gates such as NOT, NOR, NAND and m-out-of-n gates, i.e., majority-vote components as discussed in Section 5.7.4.

After developing a fault tree, it is necessary to evaluate the probability of occurrence of the upper event by combining component probabilities using basic rules of probability and the logic defined in the fault tree.

In the present example associated with Figure 5.15, let the reliability of the offsite power (R_1) be 0.933, the reliability of the onsite power (R_2) be 0.925 and the reliability of the d.c. power (R_3) be 0.995, then

$$Q(\text{a.c. power}) = (1 - R_1)(1 - R_2)$$
$$= (1 - 0.933)(1 - 0.925)$$
$$= 0.005025$$
$$R(\text{electric power}) = R(\text{a.c. power}) \cdot R_3$$
$$= (1 - 0.005025) \cdot 0.995$$
$$= 0.990000$$

and $Q(\text{electric power}) = 0.010000$

After evaluating this value of probability, it can be inserted into the event tree paths as appropriate.

5.9   Multi-failure modes

In all the preceding discussion, it has been assumed that each component of a system has only one mode of failure and can therefore be represented by two states, one in which it is operating normally and one in which it is failed. There are many examples for which this representation is inadequate. One example was introduced in Section 5.7.4 in which it was suggested that a component could operate as instructed, could fail to operate when instructed and could operate inadvertently even if not instructed to do so. Another example of components for which a two-state representation is inadequate are those components which may suffer both open circuit faults and short circuit faults. This frequently occurs in many electrical components including electronic devices such as diodes and semiconductors and power components such as transformers, cables, etc. In order to obtain correct expressions for the reliability of systems containing such components and a realistic quantitative assessment, these failure modes must be considered. This can be achieved in one of several ways, two of which are described in the following sections using the system of diodes shown in Figure 5.16 as an example.

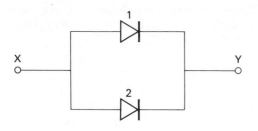

Fig. 5.16   Two diodes connected in parallel

Example 5.8

Derive the expression for the success probability of the system shown in Figure 5.16 if system success is defined as a unidirectional path existing between X and Y. Assume that both diodes have the same probabilities of failure and

P_n = probability of normal operation

P_o = probability of failure due to an open circuit

P_s = probability of failure due to a short circuit

(a) *Using state enumeration*

Considering the application of the binomial distribution (Chapter 3), it can be seen that the states of a system and their associated probabilities can be represented by $(R+Q)^n$ where R and Q are the probabilities of success and failure respectively, R and Q summate to unity and n is the number of components in the system.

In the present example, the component state probabilities are P_n, P_o and P_s, the summation of which must equal unity. Therefore the binomial representation, expressed by Equation 3.4, can be extended such that, with three states for each component, the system states and probabilities can be represented as $(P_n+P_o+P_s)^n$ where n in this example is 2. In the case of a system in which the components have different probabilities, this expression can be modified, similar to Expression 3.12, to

$$(P_{n1}+P_{o1}+P_{s1})(P_{n2}+P_{o2}+P_{s2})\ldots(P_{ni}+P_{oi}+P_{si})\ldots$$

Now

$$(P_n+P_o+P_s)^2 = P_n^2 + P_o^2 + P_s^2 + 2P_nP_o + 2P_nP_s + 2P_oP_s$$
$$\quad\ \ \text{G}\quad\ \text{B}\quad\ \text{B}\qquad\ \text{G}\qquad\ \ \text{B}\qquad\ \ \text{B}$$

At this stage it is necessary to identify which are the good (system success) states and which are the bad (system failed) states. These states are identified in the above expression by G(good) and B(bad) underneath each of the state probabilities. The expression for system reliability R_S can therefore be deduced by summating those terms leading to system success (good states) and the system unreliability Q_S by summating those terms leading to system failure (bad states). Therefore

$$R_S = P_n^2 + 2P_nP_o$$
$$Q_S = P_o^2 + P_s^2 + 2P_nP_s + 2P_oP_s$$

If $P_n = 0.98$ and $P_o = P_s = 0.01$, then:

$$R_S = 0.98, \qquad Q_S = 0.02$$

This result is identical to that if only one diode had been used. The results however are affected by the ratio of open circuit faults to short circuit faults. Consider for example, a constant value of $P_n = 0.98$ with

$$P_o = 0 \quad \text{and} \quad P_s = 0.02 \quad \text{then} \quad R_S = 0.9604$$
$$P_o = 0.02 \quad \text{and} \quad P_s = 0 \quad \text{then} \quad R_S = 0.9996$$

It follows that the system shown in Figure 5.16 is less reliable than a single component system if $P_s > P_o$ but more reliable if $P_o > P_s$.

(b) *Using conditional probability*

From the basic conditional probability equation, Section 5.2

$R_S = P$(system success given 1 is normal)P(1 is normal)

$\quad + P$(system success given 1 is open)P(1 is open)

$\quad + P$(system success given 1 is shorted)P(1 is shorted)

given 1 is normal, P(system success) $= P_n + P_o$

given 1 is open, P(system success) $= P_n$

given 1 is shorted, P(system success) $= 0$

therefore, $R_S = (P_n + P_o)P_n + P_n P_o + 0 \cdot P_s$

$\quad = P_n^2 + 2P_n P_o \quad$ (as before)

The conditional probability equation could have been expressed in terms of system failure in which case the previous expression for Q_S would have been derived. The reader should deduce this complementary expression in order to verify this.

The system failure probability can also be determined by using an intuitive approach and the fundamental concepts of Chapter 2. The system can fail in one of two ways, i.e., either as an open circuit or as a short circuit. These events are therefore mutually exclusive.

P(system failing in the open circuit mode) $= P_o \cdot P_o = P_o^2$

P(system failing in the short circuit mode) $= P_s + P_s - P_s P_s$

$\quad = 2P_s - P_s^2$

P(system failure) $= P_o^2 + 2P_s - P_s^2$

$\quad$ and $Q_s = 0.02$

The principles outlined for evaluating the reliability of a two diode parallel system can be extended to any arrangement of components which may suffer open and short-circuit faults. In order to illustrate this, consider another example involving 3 diodes. The conditional probability approach is used as the main solution technique and the state enumeration method is used to provide a subset of the solution. The problem could be solved completely with the state enumeration method and the reader may like to consider this as a separate exercise.

Example 5.9

Deduce an expression for the reliability of the system shown in Figure 5.17 if the success requirement is that a unidirectional path must exist between X and Y. Assume all diodes have the probabilities given in Example 5.8.

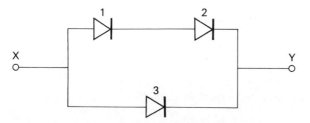

Fig. 5.17   Three diode system for Example 5.9

Let A designate the series combination of diodes 1 and 2. Now

$R_S = P$(system success given A is normal) $\cdot P$(A is normal)

$\quad + P$(system success given A is open) $\cdot P$(A is open)

$\quad + P$(system success given A is shorted) $\cdot P$(A is shorted)

given A is normal, P(system success) $= P_n + P_o$

given A is open, P(system success) $= P_n$

given A is shorted, P(system success) $= 0$

therefore, $R_S = (P_n + P_o)P$(A is normal) $+ P_n P$(A is open) $+ 0 \cdot P$(A is shorted)

The state enumeration method using the principle described in Example 5.8 can be used to evaluate the probability of the 3 states in which A can exist. That is,

$$(P_n + P_o + P_s)^2 = P_n^2 + P_o^2 + P_s^2 + 2P_n P_o + 2P_n P_s + 2P_o P_s$$
$$\text{N}\quad\ \text{O}\quad\ \text{S}\quad\ \ \text{O}\quad\ \ \text{N}\quad\ \ \text{O}$$

This expression is identical to that found in Example 5.8 since it relates to a 2 component system in which each component has 3 states irrespective of the component configuration. The various system states in the expression however must be studied and identified as being good or bad depending on the configuration. For the series system of components 1 and 2, each of the states in the above expression is identified by N(normal), O(open) and S(shorted) underneath the value of state probabilities. Therefore

P(A is normal) $= P_n^2 + 2P_n P_s$

$\quad P$(A is open) $= P_o^2 + 2P_n P_o + 2P_o P_s$

P(A is shorted) $= P_s^2$

and

$$R_S = (P_n + P_o)(P_n^2 + 2P_n P_s) + P_n(P_o^2 + 2P_n P_o + 2P_o P_s) + 0 \cdot P_s^2$$
$$\quad = P_n^3 + 2P_n^2 P_s + 3P_n^2 P_o + P_n P_o^2 + 4P_n P_s P_o$$

A similar expression using the same general principle can be derived for Q_S.

If, as before, $P_n = 0.98$ and $P_s = P_o = 0.01$

$R_S = 0.989702$

Also if P_n is kept constant and equal to 0.98 then

if $P_o = 0$ and $P_s = 0.02$, $R_S = 0.979608$

if $P_o = 0.02$ and $P_s = 0$, $R_S = 0.999208$

Some interesting comparisons can be made between the results of Examples 5.8 and 5.9:

 (i) The reliability of the 3 diode system is greater than that of the 1 or 2 diode systems when the probability of open-circuit faults and short-circuit faults are equal.

 (ii) The reliability of the 3 diode system is greater than that of the 2 diode system but still less than that of the 1 diode system when all the faults are short-circuit faults.

(iii) The reliability of the 3 diode system is less than that of the 2 diode system but greater than that of the 1 diode system when all faults are open-circuit faults.

These results provide an interesting conclusion; it cannot be automatically assumed that increasing the number of parallel components increases the reliability and that increasing the number of components in a series system degrades the reliability. Some faults (in this case short-circuit faults) affect the operational ability of other components. The assumption is only correct in general terms when the failure of a component does not, and cannot, affect the operational ability of another. In this example the assumption is not necessarily true because short-circuit faults and open-circuit faults have distinctly different effects on the remaining healthy components. Care must be exercised in the design of systems containing components which can fail in a multitude of ways and a sound engineering appreciation of these failure modes and their effect on the operation of the system is vital.

5.10 Conclusions

This chapter has presented a variety of methods for evaluating the reliability of complex systems. It also illustrates the relationships and similarities between the various techniques since many of the methods are similar in concept although their formal presentation may seem different. The reader will find in the literature concerned with reliability evaluation, that all these methods are used in one form or another for different purposes. It is not possible to specify which method is most appropriate for a given system problem since most methods can be used for any problem. Furthermore, it is sometimes found that the most suitable solution to a given problem is to employ a mixture of techniques. This is frequently done in safety system analysis [20] in which event trees, fault trees, state enumeration or truth tables are all used in combination. Example 5.9 presented an approach in which conditional probability and state enumeration methods are used within the same problem. The analyst should appreciate that there are a number of alternative techniques available and the first task is to assess the particular problem and to judge which method may be most relevant in order to achieve the required reliability assessment. It is hoped that the numerical examples that have been included in this chapter to illustrate the various techniques will assist the reader and user of these techniques in this assessment and judgement.

Problems

 In the system shown in Figure 5.18a, system success requires that one of the following paths must be available: AD, BD, CE, BE. Write an expression for the reliability of this system. If all the components have a reliability of 0.9, what is the system reliability?

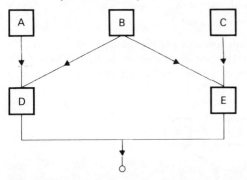

Fig. 5.18a

Compare this with the reliability of the system shown in Figure 5.18b.

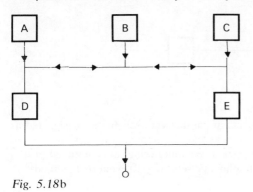

Fig. 5.18b

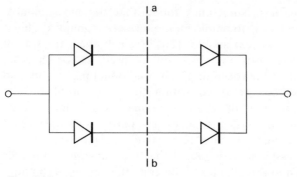

Fig. 5.19

2   For the quad system shown in Figure 5.19, calculate the improvement factor over a single diode. The following data of the system is given:
All diodes are identical.
Probability of normal operation of a diode, $P_n = 0.97$.
Probability of open circuit of a diode, $P_o = 0.01$.
Probability of short circuit of a diode, $P_s = 0.02$.
The improvement factor can be defined as

$$\text{I.F.} = \frac{\text{Probability of failure of one diode}}{\text{Probability of failure of a quad}}$$

Under what conditions would you consider joining the link ab?

3   Develop an expression for the reliability of the system shown in Figure 5.20. Calculate the system reliability if all the individual components have a reliability of 0.9.

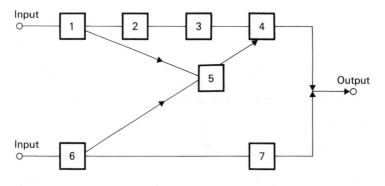

Fig. 5.20

4   A system consists of 3 components in parallel with reliabilities designated as R_1, R_2 and R_3. The system requires at least 1 component to work for system success. Find an expression for system reliability using (a) conditional probability, (b) minimal cuts sets, (c) minimal tie sets, and (d) event tree methods.

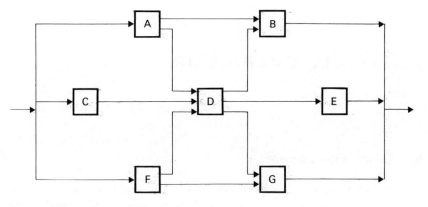

Fig. 5.21

5   Find the minimal cut sets and tie sets of the system shown in Figure 5.21 and
construct the reduced event tree of the system. Calculate the unreliability of
the system if all components are identical with a reliability of 0.95 using the
conditional probability approach and the event tree method. Compare these
values with the upper bound value given by the minimal cut set method.

6 Probability distributions in reliability evaluation

6.1 Distribution concepts

The basic concepts associated with probability distributions were discussed in Chapter 2; terms such as *probability mass function, probability density function, cumulative distribution function, expected* or *mean value, variance* and *standard deviation* were described and illustrated. These concepts were extended in Chapter 3 to a specific distribution, the *binomial distribution*. The fundamental nature and application of the binomial distribution in reliability evaluation was also presented in Chapter 3.

The concept of distributions was deliberately ignored in Chapters 4 and 5 (values of probability used were assumed to be known and fixed) in order that the fundamental evaluation techniques could be introduced without unnecessary complexities.

In practice the parameters that are normally associated with reliability evaluation are described by probability distributions. This can easily be appreciated by considering that all components of a given type, construction, manufacture and operating condition will not all fail after the same operating time but will fail at different times in the future. Consequently, these times-to-failure obey a probability distribution which may, or may not, be known and which describes the probability that a given component fails within a certain specified time or survives beyond a certain specified time. This probability value is a function of the time that is specified or considered. If the construction, or operating condition, changes, or if the components are obtained from a different manufacturer, the distribution describing the times-to-failure is also likely to change causing different values of probability of failure within a given specified time. Similarly, a system that is failed and is being repaired is unlikely to have a constant repair time and the times-to-repair are distributed according to a probability distribution which again may be known, or not known. In all practical cases the appropriate probability distribution cannot be determined from a knowledge of the geometry of the component, device or system but must be deduced from sample testing or from a data collection scheme associated with the operation of the components, devices or systems.

Two main types of distributions were introduced in Chapter 2; discrete and continuous. Discrete distributions represent random variables that can assume only certain discrete values whereas continuous distributions represent random variables that can assume an infinite number of values, albeit within a finite range. The most useful continuous distributions include the normal (or Gaussian), exponential, Weibull, gamma and Rayleigh distributions and the two most important discrete distributions are the binomial and Poisson distributions.

All of these have a wide variety of applications in many fields involving probability and statistics. It is not within the scope of this book to consider all these applications and therefore they are considered only as tools for reliability evaluation of systems. The reader is referred to more general texts on probability and statistics [2–8, 21] for a more detailed discussion and a wider interpretation of their use. This chapter is mainly concerned with the properties of the various distributions and their basic application in reliability problems. The use of some of the distributions in specific system reliability evaluation areas is presented in Chapter 7.

6.2 Terminology of distributions

The terminology and significance of probability distributions was introduced and discussed in Chapter 2 where the meaning and significance of probability density (mass) functions for continuous (discrete) distributions, cumulative distribution functions, expected value or mean and variance or standard deviation was presented. All these properties of distributions are used in reliability evaluation although some of them are usually referred to by alternative names in order to make them more relevant to the reliability property that they describe or represent. The purpose of this section is to familiarize the reader with these more specific terms before introducing the associated mathematical derivations and relationships covered in the following sections.

The cumulative distribution function increases from zero to unity as the random variable increases from its smallest to its largest value. This function increases in discontinuous steps for discrete random variables and as a continuous curve for continuous random variables. In reliability evaluation, the random variable is frequently time. If at $t = 0$, the component or system is known to be operating then its probability of failure at $t = 0$ is zero. As $t \to \infty$ however, the probability of failure tends to unity as it is a certainty that the component or system will fail given that the exposure time to failure is long enough. This characteristic is therefore equivalent to the cumulative distribution function and is a measure of the probability of failure as a function of time (or other random variable being considered). In reliability terminology, this cumulative distribution function is known as the cumulative failure distribution function or more simply, the cumulative failure distribution, designated $Q(t)$.

In many practical examples it is often necessary to evaluate, not the probability of failure in a given period of time, but the probability of surviving that period of time. This is the complementary value of the probability of failure and therefore the complementary function of the cumulative failure distribution. In reliability evaluation this complement is known as the survivor function and designated as $R(t)$ where

$$R(t) = 1 - Q(t) \tag{6.1}$$

The derivative of the cumulative distribution function of a continuous random variable gives the probability density function. In reliability evaluation, the derivative of the cumulative failure distribution, $Q(t)$, therefore gives a function which is equivalent to the probability density function, and this is called the failure density function, $f(t)$, where

$$f(t) = \frac{\mathrm{d}Q(t)}{\mathrm{d}t} = -\frac{\mathrm{d}R(t)}{\mathrm{d}t} \tag{6.2}$$

or

$$Q(t) = \int_0^t f(t)\,\mathrm{d}t \tag{6.3}$$

and

$$R(t) = 1 - \int_0^t f(t)\,\mathrm{d}t \tag{6.4}$$

The total area under the failure density function must be unity and therefore Equation 6.4 may also be written as

$$R(t) = \int_t^\infty f(t)\,\mathrm{d}t \tag{6.5}$$

In the case of discrete random variables, the integrals in Equations 6.3 to 6.5 are replaced by summations.

A hypothetical failure density function is shown in Figure 6.1 in which the values of $Q(t)$ and $R(t)$ are illustrated by the two appropriately shaded areas.

To complete this discussion on terminology there is an additional function, not discussed in Chapter 2, which should be described. This is one of the most extensively used functions in reliability evaluation and one that may be most familiar to readers. However, it is one of the most difficult to describe and interpret. It is best described in general terms as the transition rate although, depending upon the circumstances being considered, it is referred to in particular cases as hazard rate (function),

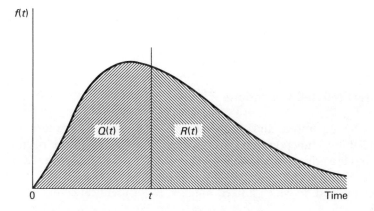

Fig. 6.1 Hypothetical failure density function. $Q(t)$, probability of failure in time t, $R(t)$, probability of surviving beyond time t

failure rate (function), repair rate (function), force of mortality, age specific failure rate, etc. The basic concept of a transition rate is perhaps easiest to explain from a failure point of view and therefore the following discussion concentrates on its significance only in terms of failure. Consequently, it is referred to as the hazard rate, designated $\lambda(t)$. It should be noted that a transition rate has a much wider significance and is used in conjunction with the occurrence of other events such as repair. A more general interpretation is provided in later chapters.

In terms of failure, the hazard rate is a measure of the rate at which failures occur. However, it is not simply the number of failures that occur in a given period of time because this is dependent upon the size of the sample being considered. For example, the number of failures in a 100 component sample is less than that in a 1000 component sample if the same time period is considered and the components are identical, yet the hazard rate should be the same. Similarly, if the number of failures in a given time period is the same for a 100 component sample and a 1000 component sample, in this case the components or the operating conditions being different, the components of the first sample are more failure prone than those of the second sample and the hazard rate should be greater.

This discussion indicates that the hazard rate is dependent on the number of failures in a given time period and the number of components exposed to failure. In order to evaluate the hazard rate, the number of failures must be related per unit to the number of components that are exposed to failure giving the following definition of $\lambda(t)$

$$\lambda(t) = \frac{\text{number of failures per unit time}}{\text{number of components exposed to failure}} \qquad (6.6)$$

This equation is used in the next section to evaluate mathematical descriptions of $\lambda(t)$ and its relationship with the previous reliability functions.

6.3 General reliability functions

The following equations and mathematical relationships between the various reliability functions do not assume any specific form of the functions and are equally applicable to all probability distributions used in reliability evaluation.

Consider the case in which a fixed number N_0 of identical components are tested.

Let $N_s(t) = $ number surviving at time t

$N_f(t) = $ number failed at time t

i.e., $N_s(t) + N_f(t) = N_0$.

At any time t, the reliability or survivor function $R(t)$ is given by

$$R(t) = \frac{N_s(t)}{N_0} \tag{6.7}$$

$$= \frac{N_0 - N_f(t)}{N_0}$$

$$= 1 - \frac{N_f(t)}{N_0} \tag{6.8}$$

Similarly the probability of failure or cumulative failure distribution $Q(t)$ is

$$Q(t) = \frac{N_f(t)}{N_0} \tag{6.9}$$

which follows the previous relationship given in Equation 6.1.

From Equations 6.8 and 6.9

$$\frac{dR(t)}{dt} = \frac{-dQ(t)}{dt} = \frac{-1}{N_0} \cdot \frac{dN_f(t)}{dt} \tag{6.10}$$

As $dt \rightarrow 0$, then following Equation 6.2

$$f(t) = \frac{1}{N_0} \frac{dN_f(t)}{dt} \tag{6.11}$$

Considering Equation 6.6, Equation 6.11 gives the value of the hazard rate when the number of components exposed to failure is N_0, i.e., when $t = 0$. Therefore, the failure density function and hazard rate are identical at $t = 0$ but only at this time.

From Equation 6.6, the general expression for the hazard rate at time t is

$$\lambda(t) = \frac{1}{N_s(t)} \cdot \frac{dN_f(t)}{dt} \tag{6.12}$$

$$= \frac{N_0}{N_0} \cdot \frac{1}{N_s(t)} \cdot \frac{dN_f(t)}{dt}$$

$$= \frac{N_0}{N_s(t)} \cdot \frac{1}{N_0} \frac{dN_f(t)}{dt}$$

$$= \frac{1}{R(t)} \cdot f(t) \qquad \text{from Equations 6.7 and 6.11}$$

$$= \frac{f(t)}{R(t)} \tag{6.13}$$

which from Equation 6.2 gives

$$\lambda(t) = -\frac{1}{R(t)} \cdot \frac{dR(t)}{dt} \tag{6.14}$$

Equation 6.13 is an interesting equation for several reasons. It confirms the comment made above that $\lambda(0) = f(0)$ since at $t = 0$, $R(0) = 1$. In addition, it shows that the hazard rate is a conditional function of the failure density function, the conditional relationship being the survivor function. In physical terms this relationship means that the failure density function permits the probability of failure to be evaluated in any period of time into the future whereas the hazard rate permits the probability of failure to be evaluated in the next period of time given that it has survived up to time t. Mathematically the relationship between $\lambda(t)$ and $f(t)$ can be described as follows.

The hazard rate is equivalent to the failure density function but covering only those times up to the time point of interest. Since the area under this equivalent density function is less than unity, the portion of the failure density function being considered must be normalized back to unity. This can be achieved by dividing the failure density function by the area under the failure density function for times greater than that of interest, that is,

$$\lambda(t) = \frac{f(t)}{\displaystyle\int_t^\infty f(t)\,dt} \qquad \text{for times up to } t$$

$$= \frac{f(t)}{R(t)} \qquad \text{from Equation 6.5}$$

which is the same as Equation 6.13.

Now from Equation 6.14

$$\int_1^{R(t)} \frac{1}{R(t)} \cdot dR(t) = \int_0^t -\lambda(t)\,dt$$

$$\ln R(t) = \int_0^t -\lambda(t)\,dt$$

$$R(t) = \exp\left[-\int_0^t \lambda(t)\,dt\right] \tag{6.15}$$

For the special case in which λ is a constant and independent of time, Equation 6.15 simplifies to

$$R(t) = e^{-\lambda t} \tag{6.16}$$

This special case is known as the exponential distribution and is discussed in detail in Section 6.8.

6.4 Evaluation of the reliability functions

In order to illustrate the procedure for evaluating the various reliability functions described in the previous two sections and to indicate the shape of typical functions that may be deduced from a set of experimental data, an example centred on an equipment initially containing 1000 identical components is analysed in this section. This example is purely hypothetical and the data have been selected only in order to illustrate the relevant concepts.

The complete analysis of these data is shown in Table 6.1. A set of sample calculations is shown below and the computed hazard rate, survivor function (reliability), failure density function and cumulative failure distribution are shown in Figures 6.2 to 6.5 respectively. It should be noted that the area under the failure density function must always be unity as indicated by the summation of the appropriate values in Table 6.1.

(a) Columns 1 and 2 represent the original data which would be obtained experimentally.

(b) Column 3 (cumulative failures, N_f) is obtained by cumulating all the failures in the previous time intervals, e.g., at time 2, $N_f = 140 + 85 = 225$.

(c) Column 4 (number of survivors, N_s) is obtained by subtracting the cumulative number of failures, N_f from the original number of components, i.e. 1000; e.g., at time 3, $N_s = 1000 - 300 = 700$.

(d) Column 5 (failure density function, f) is, from Equation 6.11, the ratio between the number of failures during a time interval and

Table 6.1 Data and results for example of Section 6.4

1	2	3	4	5	6	7	8
Time interval in 100 hrs	Number of failures in each interval	Cumulative failures N_f	No. of survivors N_s	Failure density function f	Cumulative failure distribution Q	Survivor function R	Hazard rate λ
0	140	0	1000	0.140	0	1.000	0.151
1	85	140	860	0.085	0.140	0.860	0.104
2	75	225	775	0.075	0.225	0.775	0.102
3	68	300	700	0.068	0.300	0.700	0.102
4	60	368	632	0.060	0.368	0.632	0.100
5	53	428	572	0.053	0.428	0.572	0.097
6	48	481	519	0.048	0.481	0.519	0.097
7	43	529	471	0.043	0.529	0.471	0.096
8	38	572	428	0.038	0.572	0.428	0.093
9	34	610	390	0.034	0.610	0.390	0.091
10	31	644	356	0.031	0.644	0.356	0.091
11	28	675	325	0.028	0.675	0.325	0.090
12	40	703	297	0.040	0.703	0.297	0.144
13	60	743	257	0.060	0.743	0.257	0.264
14	75	803	197	0.075	0.803	0.197	0.470
15	60	878	122	0.060	0.878	0.122	0.652
16	42	938	62	0.042	0.938	0.062	1.02
17	15	980	20	0.015	0.980	0.020	1.20
18	5	995	5	0.005	0.995	0.005	2.0
19		1000	0		1.000	0.000	
				Sum = 1.000			

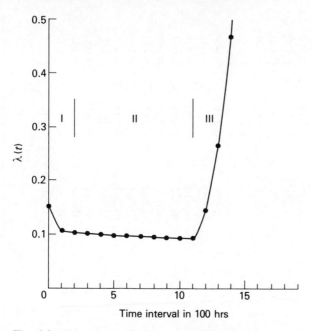

Fig. 6.2 Hazard rate for Example of Section 6.4

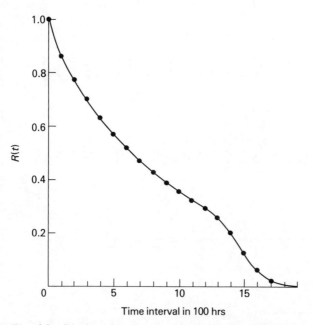

Fig. 6.3 Survivor function for Example of Section 6.4

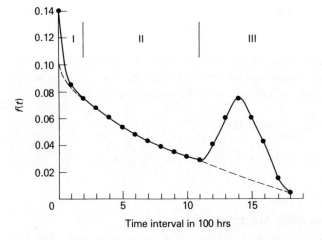

Fig. 6.4   Failure density function for Example of Section 6.4

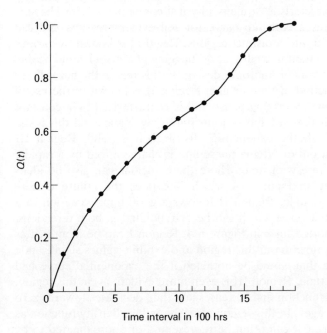

Fig. 6.5   Cumulative failure distribution for Example of Section 6.4

1000; e.g., for the interval between times 2 and 3, $f = 75/1000 = 0.075$.

(e)   Column 6 (cumulative failure distribution, Q) is from Equation 6.9, the ratio between the cumulative number of failures and 1000, e.g., at time 3, $Q = 300/1000 = 0.3$.

(f)   Column 7 (survivor function or reliability, R) is, from Equation 6.7, the ratio between the number of survivors and 1000; e.g., at time 3, $R = 700/1000 = 0.7$.

(g)   Column 8 (hazard rate, λ) is, from Equation 6.12, the ratio between the number of failures in an interval and the average number of survivors for that period; e.g., for the time between 2 and 3,

$$\lambda = \frac{75}{(775 + 700)/2} = 0.102.$$

All the remaining results in Table 6.1 can be evaluated in a similar manner.

6.5   Shape of reliability functions

The hazard rate curve for the previous example, shown in Figure 6.2, has a shape that is characteristic of many physical components, This shape is often referred to as a bath-tub curve for self-evident reasons and can generally be divided into 3 distinct regions. Region I is known by various names, such as the infant mortality or de-bugging phase, and could be due to manufacturing errors or improper design. In this region the hazard rate decreases as a function of time or age. Region II is known as the useful life period or normal operating phase and is characterized by a constant hazard rate. In this region failures occur purely by chance and this is the only region in which the exponential distribution is valid. Region III represents the wearout or fatigue phase and is characterized by a rapidly increasing hazard rate with time. These three regions can also be identified quite readily in Figure 6.4 which illustrates the failure density function for this example. Region II follows a good approximation to a negative exponential curve which can be extrapolated in both directions, as shown by the dotted lines in Figure 6.4. Region I can be identified as the failure density function in this region and exhibits values significantly greater than those that would be obtained if the exponential curve had applied from zero time. Region III is even more evident as, in this region, the failure density function first increases and then decreases towards zero as the component ages. In this region also, the failure density function as illustrated in Figure 6.4 can often be represented or approximated to by the normal distribution. Other distributions such as the gamma and Weibull distributions are often used to represent this region. The reason for this is that these distributions have shaping parameters, the variation of which can create significantly different characteristic shapes. This is discussed in more detail in Sections 6.9 and 6.10.

Although the hazard rate curve shown in Figure 6.2 exhibits all the characteristics of most real sets of data, different types of components can

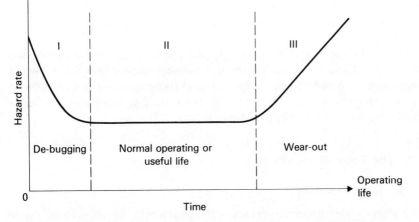

Fig. 6.6   Typical electronic component hazard rate as a function of age

exhibit significant variations on this basic bathtub shape. Two particular examples are shown in Figures 6.6 and 6.7 for typical electronic components and mechanical equipment, respectively. In these two examples which generally cover the two extreme cases, electronic components are usually associated with a relatively long useful life and mechanical components are usually associated with a very brief useful life.

Many components and systems, including power system components and mechanical devices, can be made to remain within their useful life period for the bulk of their economically feasible life by constant and careful preventive maintenance. In this way, the components of the system are not allowed to enter an advanced wearout state before they are replaced. This is an extremely important assumption however, as reliability prediction based on useful life hazard rates, although frequently

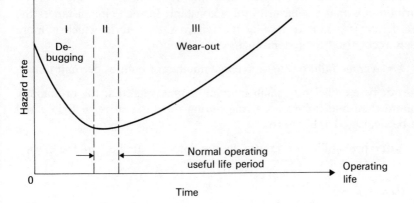

Fig. 6.7   Typical mechanical component hazard rate as a function of age

done because of its analytical simplicity, is invalid and extremely optimistic if the system contains components which are operating within their wearout period.

The remaining sections of this chapter consider particular probability distributions and their application in reliability evaluation. The binomial distribution, considered in Chapter 3, and those distributions considered in this chapter are all important in their own right, and each has a particular role in reliability evaluation.

6.6 The Poisson distribution

6.6.1 General concepts

The Poisson distribution represents the probability of an isolated event occurring a specified number of times in a given interval of time or space when the rate of occurrence (hazard rate) in a continuum of time or space is fixed. The occurrence of events must be affected by chance alone. A particular characteristic feature of the Poisson distribution is that only the occurrence of an event is counted, its non-occurrence is not. This is one of the essential differences between the Poisson and binomial distributions because in the latter, both the occurrence and non-occurrence of an event must be counted. In many practical examples, only the occurrence of an event can be counted, which means that the binomial distribution is inapplicable. Examples of this are
—number of lightning strokes in a period
—number of telephone calls in a period
—number of faults on a system.

6.6.2 Derivation of the Poisson distribution

In Section 6.6.1 it was stated that one requirement of the Poisson distribution is that the hazard rate is constant. In such circumstances the hazard rate is generally termed the failure rate, a term which is more widely recognized by system engineers. Therefore

λ = average failure rate or average number of failures per unit time.

Let dt be a sufficiently small interval of time such that the probability of more than one failure occurring during this interval is negligible and can be neglected. Therefore

$\lambda \, dt$ = probability of failure in the interval dt, i.e., in the period $(t, t + dt)$

(a) *Zero failures*

Let $P_x(t)$ be the probability of failure occurring x times in the interval $(0, t)$, then because:

Probability of zero failures in the interval $(0, t + dt) =$ probability of zero failures in the interval $(0, t) \times$ probability of zero failures in the interval $(t, t + dt)$.

$$P_0(t + dt) = P_0(t)(1 - \lambda \, dt)$$

Assuming event independence

$$\frac{P_0(t + dt) - P_0(t)}{dt} = -\lambda P_0(t)$$

As $dt \to 0$, i.e., it becomes incrementally small

$$\frac{dP_0(t)}{dt} = -\lambda P_0(t)$$

which, by integrating, becomes

$$\ln P_0(t) = -\lambda t + C$$

At $t = 0$, the component is known to be operating. Therefore at $t = 0$, $P_0(0) = 1$, $\ln P_0(t) = 0$ and $C = 0$, giving:

$$P_0(t) = e^{-\lambda t} \tag{6.17}$$

This is the first term of the Poisson distribution and gives the probability of zero failures occurring in a specified time period t. It is probably the best known expression in quantitative reliability evaluation and is identical to Equation 6.16. It is discussed and used in considerable detail in later sections and chapters. It shows that if

$$\lambda(t) = \lambda, \text{ a constant}$$

then, for zero failures

$$R(t) = e^{-\lambda t} \tag{6.18a}$$

$$Q(t) = 1 - e^{-\lambda t} \tag{6.18b}$$

$$f(t) = \frac{-dR(t)}{dt} = \lambda e^{-\lambda t} \tag{6.18c}$$

(b) *Multiple failures*

If $P_x(t)$ is defined as the probability of failure occurring x times in the interval $(0, t)$, then

$$P_x(t + dt) = P_x(t)[P(\text{zero failures in } t, t + dt)]$$
$$+ P_{x-1}(t)[P(\text{one failure in } t, t + dt)]$$
$$+ P_{x-2}(t)[P(\text{two failures in } t, t + dt)] + \dots$$
$$+ P_0(t)[P(x \text{ failures in } t, t + dt)]$$

It is assumed however that the interval dt is sufficiently small that the probability of more than one failure in this interval is negligible. Therefore

$$P_x(t+dt) = P_x(t)[P(\text{zero failures in } t, t+dt)]$$
$$+ P_{x-1}(t)[P(\text{one failure in } t, t+dt)]$$
$$= P_x(t)(1 - \lambda\, dt) + P_{x-1}(t)(\lambda\, dt)$$
$$= P_x(t) - \lambda\, dt[P_x(t) - P_{x-1}(t)]$$

from which,

$$P_x(t) = \frac{(\lambda t)^x e^{-\lambda t}}{x!} \qquad (6.19)$$

Equation 6.19 gives the complete expression for the Poisson distribution, the first term of which $(x = 0)$ can be seen to be identical to Equation 6.17.

One important point to recognize in the application of Equation 6.19 is that the expression recognizes and counts failures but does not include the time taken to repair or replace the component when it does fail. Consequently, the terms in the expression giving the probabilities of two or more failures assume instant replacement. This can be a reasonable assumption for many calculations if the average repair time is very short and negligible compared with the average time to failure. If this assumption cannot be made, then the expression given by Equation 6.19 is not valid for failures other than the first failure and additional techniques such as Markov processes must be applied. These are discussed in Chapters 8 and 9.

(c) *Expected value*

The expected value of a discrete distribution is given by Equation 2.26 as

$$E(x) = \sum_{x=0}^{\infty} x P_x \; = \lambda t$$

where, for the Poisson distribution, $x =$ number of failures and P_x is probability of x failures in the time period of interest.

$$E(x) = \sum_{x=0}^{\infty} x \frac{(\lambda t)^x e^{-\lambda t}}{x!}$$
$$= \sum_{x=1}^{\infty} x \frac{(\lambda t)^x e^{-\lambda t}}{x!} \qquad \text{since the term for } x = 0 \text{ is zero}$$
$$= \lambda t \sum_{x=1}^{\infty} \frac{(\lambda t)^{x-1} e^{-\lambda t}}{(x-1)!}$$
$$= \lambda t \qquad (6.20)$$

since the summation of the probabilities for all x must be unity.

Therefore Equation 6.19 may also be written as

$$P_x(t) = \frac{\mu^x e^{-\mu}}{x!} \tag{6.21}$$

if μ is defined as the expected value $E(x)$.

Example 6.1

In a large system the average number of cable faults per year per 100 km of cable is 0.5. Consider a specified piece of cable 10 km long and evaluate the probabilities of 0, 1, 2, etc., faults occurring in (a) a 20 year period, and (b) a 40 year period.

Assuming the average failure rate data to be valid for the 10 km cable and for the two periods being considered, the expected failure rate λ is,

$$\lambda = \frac{0.5 \times 10}{100} = 0.05 \text{ f/yr.}$$

(a) *for a* 20 *year period,*

$$E(x) = 0.05 \times 20 = 1.0$$

and $P_x = \dfrac{1.0^x e^{-1.0}}{x!}$ for $x = 0, 1, 2, \ldots$

This failure density function is shown in Figure 6.8a and the cumulative failure distribution is shown in Figure 6.8b.

(b) *for a* 40 *year period,*

$$E(x) = 0.05 \times 40 = 2.0$$

and $P_x = \dfrac{2.0^x e^{-2.0}}{x!}$ for $x = 0, 1, 2, \ldots$

The distributions for this case are also shown in Figures 6.8a and 6.8b.

It is evident from the distributions shown in Figure 6.8 that, as would be expected, the probability of a small number of failures decreases and the probability of a large number of failures increases as the time period of interest increases.

The results for Example 6.1 were evaluated by expanding Equations 6.20 or 6.21 and solving for each term of the expansion. The values could also have been obtained from standard probability curves for the Poisson distribution [9, 22].

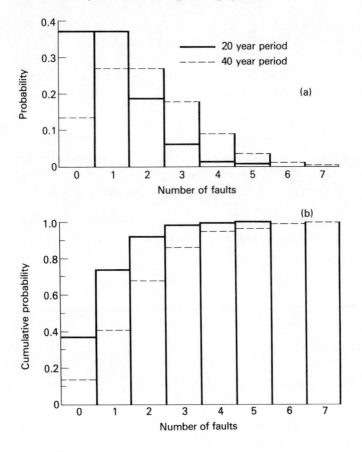

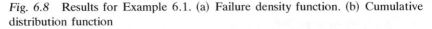

Fig. 6.8 Results for Example 6.1. (a) Failure density function. (b) Cumulative distribution function

6.6.3 Relationship with the binomial distribution

In many engineering statistics books, the Poisson distribution is derived as an approximation to the binomial distribution. This can lead to the invalid assumption that the Poisson distribution is only an approximation whereas it is an important distribution in its own right and has many applications as such. However, it is useful to appreciate that, under certain circumstances, the binomial distribution is related to the Poisson distribution and that the latter can be used as an approximation to simplify calculations. The circumstances in which this relation is valid must however be fully recognized and treated accordingly.

The probability of an event succeeding r times in n trials was given in Chapter 3 as

$$P_r = \frac{n!}{r!\,(n-r)!}\, p^r q^{n-r}$$

If $n \gg r$

$$\frac{n!}{(n-r)!} = n(n-1)(n-2)\ldots(n-r+1)$$

$$\simeq n^r$$

thus, $P_r = \dfrac{n^r}{r!}\, p^r q^{n-r}$

Also, if p is very small and r is small compared to n

$$q^{n-r} \simeq (1-p)^n$$

thus $P_r = \dfrac{(np)^r}{r!}\,(1-p)^n$

$$= \frac{(np)^r}{r!}\left[1 - np + \frac{n(n-1)}{2!}(-p)^2 + \ldots \right]$$

If n is large, $n(n-1) \simeq n^2$

thus $P_r = \dfrac{(np)^r}{r!}\left[1 - np + \dfrac{(np)^2}{2!} + \ldots \right]$

$$= \frac{(np)^r}{r!}\,e^{-np} \tag{6.22}$$

It can be seen that Equation 6.22 is of identical form to Equation 6.19 and is equivalent to it when

$$np = \lambda t \quad \text{and} \quad r = x$$

It must be remembered however that this equality is only valid when n is large, $n \gg r$ and p is very small. In reliability evaluation, the events that are counted are the failure events, and, therefore, p represents the probability of the failure event. In a good system it is hoped that this value is very small. As a guide to the reader, a good approximation between the two distributions is obtained when $n \geqslant 20$ and $p \leqslant 0.05$, and the approximation improves as n increases and p decreases.

The reader should also recall from Chapter 3 that the expected value of a binomial distribution was (np). Under the circumstances in which the binomial distribution and Poisson distribution are equivalent, it is seen, as should be expected, that the expected value of the binomial distribution (np) and the expected value of the Poisson distribution (λt) are identical.

It was also shown in Chapter 3 that the standard deviation of the binomial distribution was

$$\sigma = \sqrt{npq}$$

If it is assumed that the value of p is very small, i.e., the condition which makes the Poisson and binomial distributions equivalent, then $\sqrt{q} \simeq 1$ and $\sigma \simeq \sqrt{np}$.

This is not a rigorous proof, nor is it meant to be, but this relation indicates that the standard deviation of a Poisson distribution is given by

$$\sigma = \sqrt{\lambda t} = \sqrt{E(t)} \tag{6.23}$$

A rigorous proof based on the method described in Chapter 2 will justify Equation 6.23 and show that it is a precise relationship.

Example 6.2

The probability of success in a single trial is 0.1. Calculate the probability that in 10 trials there will be exactly two successes using (a) the binomial distribution, and (b) the Poisson distribution.

(a) $P(2) = {}_{10}C_2 0.1^2 \times 0.9^8$

$$= \frac{10!}{2!\,8!} 0.1^2 \times 0.9^8$$

$$= 0.1937$$

(b) $np = 10 \times 0.1 = 1.0$

therefore, $P(2) = \dfrac{1.0^2}{2!} e^{-1.0}$

$$= 0.1839$$

Example 6.3

Repeat Example 6.2 when the number of trials is 20 and the probability of success in a single trial is 0.005.

(a) $P(2) = \dfrac{20!}{2!\,18!} \times 0.005^2 \times 0.995^{18}$

$$= 0.0043$$

(b) $np = 20 \times 0.005 = 0.1$

therefore, $P(2) = \dfrac{0.1^2}{2!} e^{-0.1}$

$$= 0.0045$$

6.7 The normal distribution

6.7.1 General concepts

The normal probability distribution, sometimes referred to as the Gaussian distribution, is probably the most important and widely used distribution in the entire field of statistics and probability. Although having some important applications in reliability evaluation, it is of less significance in this field than many other distributions.

The probability density function of the normal distribution is perfectly symmetrical about its mean value and the dispersion about the mean is measured and determined by its standard deviation. The precise shape and position of the density function can be specified solely in terms of the mean value and standard deviation. These properties create the possibility for the normal distribution to be misused since all distributions can be characterized by a mean and standard deviation. By specifying only a mean and standard deviation it is possible that a distribution which is non-normal will be assumed to be normal, simply because no information is available other than the mean value and standard deviation. Care must therefore be exercised in interpreting the significance of these two parameters if no other distributional information is available.

One theorem that is widely quoted, and is therefore again likely to be misused, is the *Central Limit Theorem*. The details of this theorem are outside the scope of this book but the essence of it is that if the sample size is very large ($n \to \infty$), the distribution of the sample means approximates to a normal distribution. Again, great care must be exercised in applying the Central Limit Theorem because theoretically n must tend to infinity, i.e., be very large, and it is questionable how large n needs to be in any specific problem area.

6.7.2 Probability density function

The probability density function of a normal distribution may be expressed in general terms as:

$$f(x) = \frac{1}{\beta\sqrt{2\pi}} \exp\left[-\frac{(x-\alpha)^2}{2\beta^2}\right]$$

If the mean value μ and standard deviation σ is evaluated for this expression, it can be shown that

$$\mu = \alpha \quad \text{and} \quad \sigma = \beta$$

Therefore, the expression for the probability density function of a normal distribution is always written as

$$f(x) = \frac{1}{\sigma\sqrt{2\pi}} \exp\left[-\frac{(x-\mu)^2}{2\sigma^2}\right] \tag{6.24}$$

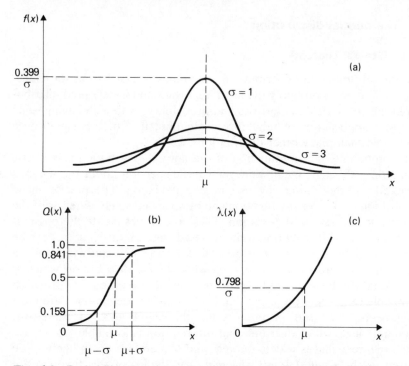

Fig. 6.9 Probability functions of normal distribution. (a) Probability density function. (b) Cumulative distribution function. (c) Hazard rate

Typical normal density function curves are shown in Figure 6.9a for a given value of μ and three values of σ. The characteristic shape of the normal cumulative distribution function is shown in Figure 6.9b. The main feature of this function is that the curve passes through a probability of 0.5 when the random variable has a value μ, i.e. the expected value. This is a particular characteristic of the normal distribution and occurs because of the perfect symmetry of the distribution. The shape of the hazard rate is shown in Figure 6.9c. Since the value of μ determines the position of the curve on the abscissa axis, it is frequently referred to as the location parameter. Similarly since the value of σ determines the amount of spread or dispersion and therefore the shape of the curve, it is referred to as the scale parameter.

The discussion concerning probability density functions in Chapter 2 indicates that for a continuous distribution

$$\int_{-\infty}^{\infty} f(x)\, dx = 1$$

Therefore $\dfrac{1}{\sigma\sqrt{2\pi}} \displaystyle\int_{-\infty}^{\infty} \exp\left[-\dfrac{(x-\mu)^2}{2\sigma^2}\right] dx = 1$

which simply means that the area under the density function between the two infinite limits must enclose all possible values of the random variable x and therefore must be unity.

The probability of the random variable x lying between the two appropriate limits can be evaluated by changing the upper and/or lower limits of the integral.

Unfortunately this integral cannot be expressed in a simple functional form and is not amenable to simple integration techniques. Various alternatives are available however.

Conventional numerical integration techniques such as Simpson's rule can be used on a digital computer. Standard tables [9] which specify the areas under a curve for a large range of possible limits or approximate evaluation techniques can be used for manual calculations. In order to use hand calculation methods it is first necessary to create a standard curve.

The following substitution can be made in Equation 6.24

$$z = \frac{x - \mu}{\sigma} \tag{6.25}$$

to give

$$f(z) = \frac{1}{\sqrt{2\pi}} \exp\left[-\frac{z^2}{2}\right] \tag{6.26}$$

In Equation 6.26, the new random variable is now z, the mean value is zero and the standard deviation is unity. This substitution therefore creates a standard curve in which all deviations of the random variable about the mean are expressed in terms of z.

Tables now can be compiled [9] so that the area under the density function can be found easily for any values of μ and σ (Appendix 2 refers). Its application is demonstrated in Section 6.7.3. The areas and therefore the probabilities are shown in Figure 6.10 for the particular case of integer values of z.

From Figure 6.10 it can be seen that the total area enclosed by the limits of $\pm 3\sigma$ is equal to 0.9972, i.e., it is very close to unity which means that the probability of the random variable being outside these limits is very small. For this reason the limits of $\pm 3\sigma$ are frequently used as confidence limits associated with normal distributions, i.e., it is assumed that these limits enclose all likely values of the variable. This is a reasonable assumption provided rare events are not being considered. However, it is unreasonable to make this assumption for any set of data from which σ has been evaluated without further justification since distributions other than normal distributions can have a significant value of probability outside the $\pm 3\sigma$ limits. There is further discussion on confidence limits in Appendix 5.

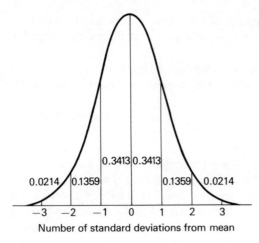

Number of standard deviations from mean

Fig. 6.10 Standard normal density function

6.7.3 Evaluation of probabilities

If tables such as the one shown in Appendix 2 are not available, the area under the normal curve can be found [47] from the following polynomial approximation for $z \geqslant 0$.

Suppose the area $Q(z)$ shown in Figure 6.11 is required. Then

$$Q(z) = y[b_1 t + b_2 t^2 + b_3 t^3 + b_4 t^4 + b_5 t^5] + e(z), \tag{6.27}$$

where $y = f(z) = \dfrac{1}{\sqrt{2\pi}} \exp\left(-\dfrac{z^2}{2}\right)$

$t = \dfrac{1}{1 + rz}$

$r = 0.2316419$

$b_1 = 0.31938153 \qquad b_2 = -0.356563782$

$b_3 = 1.781477937 \qquad b_4 = -1.821255978$

$b_5 = 1.330274429$

and the error is $|e(z)| < 7.5 \times 10^{-8}$ and, therefore, can be neglected. Equation 6.27 is sufficiently accurate for all practical purposes. The expressions are only valid for positive values of z. Since the normal curve is symmetrical, the values of $Q(-z)$ can be found from

$$Q(-z) = Q(z) \tag{6.28}$$

The inverse of this problem, i.e., to find z knowing $Q(z)$, can be

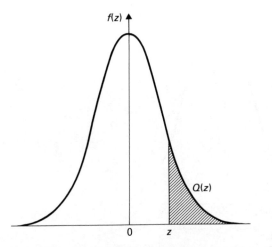

Fig. 6.11   Area under normal density function, $Q(z)$

achieved [47] using

$$z = t - \frac{c_0 + c_1 t + c_2 t^2}{1 + d_1 t + d_2 t^2 + d_3 t^3} + e(Q) \qquad (6.29)$$

where $t = \sqrt{\ln \dfrac{1}{Q^2}}$

$c_0 = 2.515517 \qquad d_1 = 1.432788$

$c_1 = 0.802853 \qquad d_2 = 0.189269$

$c_2 = 0.010328 \qquad d_3 = 0.001308$

and the error is $|e(Q)| < 0.45 \times 10^{-4}$ and again can be neglected.

To illustrate the use of the normal distribution and the application of tables and the above formulae, consider the following numerical examples.

Example 6.4

The Lighting Department of a city installed 2000 electric lamps which have an average life of 1000 burning hours with a standard deviation of 200 hours. How many lamps might be expected to fail in the first 700 burning hours?

The probability density function for this problem is shown in Figure 6.12a in which $\mu = 1000$ and $\sigma = 200$. The required probability is shown by the hatched area in Figure 6.12a.

From Equation 6.25 $z = \dfrac{700 - 1000}{200}$

$$= -1.5$$

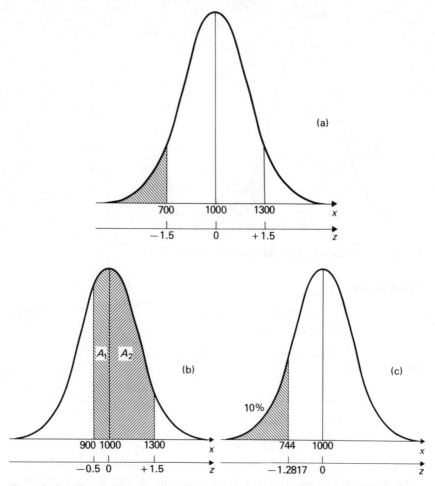

Fig. 6.12 Required areas of normal density function. (a) Example 6.4. (b) Example 6.5. (c) Example 6.6

From the table in Appendix 2, the required area is

$$= 0.5 - 0.4332 = 0.0668$$

From Equation 6.27,

$$Q(1.5) = 0.0668$$

therefore, $Q(-1.5) = 0.0668$

and using either method

expected number of failures $= 2000 \times 0.0668$

$$= 133.6 \equiv 134 \text{ lamps}$$

Example 6.5

In Example 6.4, how many lamps may be expected to fail between 900 and 1300 burning hours?

The required area is shown hatched in Figure 6.12b. This area is divided by the mean value into two sub areas, areas A_1 and A_2.

For area A_1: $z_1 = \dfrac{900 - 1000}{200} = -0.5$

For area A_2: $z_2 = \dfrac{1300 - 1000}{200} = 1.5$

From the table in Appendix 2:

$A_1 = 0.1915$ and $A_2 = 0.4332$

giving the required total area $= 0.1915 + 0.4332$

$$= 0.6247$$

From Equation 6.27: $A_1 = 0.5 - 0.3085 = 0.1915$

$$A_2 = 0.5 - 0.0668 = 0.4332$$

again giving the required total area $= 0.6247$.

therefore, expected number of failures is 2000×0.6247

$$= 1249.4 \equiv 1250 \text{ lamps.}$$

Example 6.6

In Example 6.4, after what period of burning hours would we expect 10% of the lamps to have failed?

The known area in this example is shown in Figure 6.12c and the problem is to determine the value of z that corresponds to this area.

The table in Appendix 2 gives the area under the curve measured from the mean, i.e., $z = 0$. To deduce the value of z from the table, the area $0.5 - 0.1 = 0.4000$ must be identified in the table. This gives $z = -1.2817$ using linear interpolation between tabulated values.

From Equation 6.29, $z = -1.2817$

Therefore, from Equation 6.25 $\dfrac{x - 1000}{200} = -1.2817$

$$x = 743.7 \equiv 744 \text{ hours}$$

6.8 The exponential distribution

6.8.1 General concepts

The exponential, or strictly the negative exponential, distribution is probably the most widely known and used distribution in reliability evaluation of systems. The most important factor for it to be applicable is that the hazard rate should be constant, in which case it is defined as the failure rate λ. This is essentially the same requirement as that of the Poisson distribution and it can be argued that the negative exponential distribution is only a special case of the Poisson distribution, i.e., when considering the probability of the first failure. In practice the negative exponential distribution has a much wider degree of significance than just that of first failure and is extensively used in the analysis of repairable systems in which the components cycle between operating or up states and failure or down states. It is realistic to argue however that the exponential distribution is a special case of the Weibull and gamma distributions as will be seen in Sections 6.9 and 6.10.

The conditions under which the exponential distribution is valid was discussed in Section 6.5. It is applicable only to the useful life or normal operating period of a component.

It is frequently used in system reliability evaluation problems without substantiating that the failure rate is constant or independent of time. There are usually three justifications made for this: First, the analytical techniques, particularly for large systems, are very complex unless simplifications are made. In this case the assumption of constant failure rates and the application of the exponential distribution considerably simplifies the problem. Second, the data used in the evaluation exercise is often very limited and insufficient to verify the correct underlying distribution. Consequently, it is argued that it is unrealistic to use a technique more complicated than the data justifies. Third, it can be shown (Section 12.6) that if the concern is only with limiting state values of system probability then the underlying distribution loses its significance and the results are identical whatever distribution is used. It should be remembered however that this latter justification is inappropriate if time-dependent values of probability are being evaluated. In this case the distribution can cause very marked differences in the system probability values.

6.8.2 Reliability functions

It was shown previously, in Equations 6.16 and 6.18, that the probability of a component surviving for a time t if the hazard rate is constant, i.e., the survivor function, is

$$R(t) = e^{-\lambda t}$$ (6.30)

Therefore the failure density function is

$$f(t) = \frac{-dR(t)}{dt}$$

$$= \lambda e^{-\lambda t}$$ (6.31)

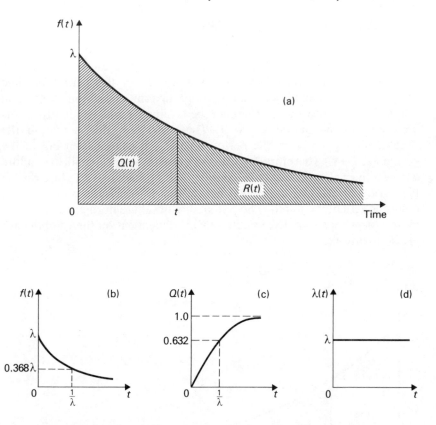

Fig. 6.13 Exponential reliability functions. (a) Areas showing $Q(t)$ and $R(t)$. (b) Failure density function. (c) Cumulative failure distribution. (d) Hazard rate

This density function is shown in Figure 6.13a, in which the areas representing the cumulative failure distribution, $Q(t)$ and the survivor function, $R(t)$ are illustrated. These two areas can be evaluated from the failure density function using the principle of Equations 6.3 and 6.5 to give

$$Q(t) = \int_0^t \lambda e^{-\lambda t}\, dt = 1 - e^{-\lambda t} \tag{6.32}$$

$$R(t) = \int_t^\infty \lambda e^{-\lambda t}\, dt = e^{-\lambda t} \tag{6.33}$$

The failure density function $f(t)$, cumulative failure distribution $Q(t)$ and hazard rate $\lambda(t)$ are shown in Figures 6.13b, c and d, respectively.

6.8.3 A *posteriori* failure probability

Consider a component that has operated for a period of time T as illustrated in Figure 6.14. The requirement is to evaluate the probability of failure in the next interval of time t, i.e., in the period of time $(T, T+t)$. The probability of failure in this next interval of time t is not an *a priori* probability, i.e., it cannot be evaluated independently of its behaviour in the period up to T. The reason for this is that, if the component has failed in the period up to T, it cannot then fail in the period $(T, T+t)$. Therefore, in order to evaluate the probability of failure during t, it is also necessary to consider the probability of failure during the period $(0, T)$, i.e., the period before that in which the probability of failure is actually required. The probability of failure during t is known as an *a posteriori* probability, i.e., its value is dependent on the component's previous history.

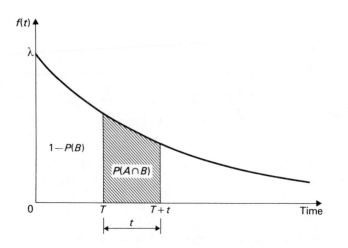

Fig. 6.14   A *posteriori* probability of failure

This problem can be solved using conditional probability since the failure of the component during t is conditional on the component having survived up to time T. From Equation 2.11, the probability of the simultaneous occurrence of two events is given by

$$P(A \cap B) = P(A \mid B) \cdot P(B)$$

or $\quad P(A \mid B) = \dfrac{P(A \cap B)}{P(B)}$

Defining

$$P(A \mid B) = P[\text{failing during time } t \text{ GIVEN that the component has survived up to } T]$$

$$= Q_c(t)$$

$$P(A \cap B) = P[\text{surviving up to } T \text{ AND failing during the time period } (T, T+t)]$$

$$= \int_T^{T+t} \lambda e^{-\lambda t} \, dt$$

$$= e^{-\lambda T} - e^{-\lambda(T+t)}$$

$$P(B) = P[\text{surviving up to time } T]$$

$$= \int_T^{\infty} \lambda e^{-\lambda t} \, dt$$

$$= e^{-\lambda T}$$

then

$$Q_c(t) = \frac{e^{-\lambda T} - e^{-\lambda(T+t)}}{e^{-\lambda T}}$$

$$= 1 - e^{-\lambda t} \tag{6.34}$$

The result expressed by Equation 6.34 is very important since it states that the probability of failure in any constant interval t is independent of the prior operating time and is dependent only on the length of the period being considered, t. It must be noted that this result is applicable only to the exponential distribution and therefore applies only to the useful life or normal operating period. Expressed in a slightly different way, the reliability is constant for equal operating periods throughout the useful life of the component. This important property of the exponential distribution leads to the concept that this distribution is a memory-less distribution; i.e., the probability of failure depends only on the failure time and has no memory of the past.

Therefore, the *a priori* and *a posteriori* probabilities are equal for, and only for, this particular case. Therefore

$$Q(t) = Q_c(t) = 1 - e^{-\lambda t}$$

$$= 1 - \left[1 - \lambda t + \frac{(-\lambda t)^2}{2!} + \frac{(-\lambda t)^3}{3!} + \ldots \right]$$

$$= \lambda t - \frac{(\lambda t)^2}{2!} + \frac{(\lambda t)^3}{3!} - \ldots$$

If $\lambda t \ll 1$

then

$$Q(t) \approx \lambda t \tag{6.35a}$$

and

$$R(t) \approx 1 - \lambda t \tag{6.35b}$$

It must be remembered that Equations 6.35a and b are approximations but ones which make the value of $R(t)$ accurate to at least 4 decimal places if $\lambda t < 0.01$. In some literature however the approximation is made and used without adequate justification and this can be misleading.

It must be emphasized that the *a priori* and *a posteriori* probabilities of failure during an interval t in the future are only equal in the normal operating phase and are not equal in either the debugging period or the wearout region when other probability distributions must be used to describe the operating behaviour of the component. In the wearout region in particular, the probability of failure during a given interval of time in the future is very much dependent upon the prior operating time and can increase rapidly as the prior operating time increases. The *a posteriori* probability can however be evaluated for any period of operation if the appropriate failure density function is known using the principle of Equation 2.11 since, as before:

$$Q_c(t) = \frac{\displaystyle\int_T^{T+t} f(t)\,dt}{\displaystyle\int_T^{\infty} f(t)\,dt} \tag{6.36}$$

6.8.4 Mean value and standard deviation

From Equation 2.27, the expected value of a continuous random variable having a range $(0, \infty)$ is given by

$$E(x) = \int_0^{\infty} x \cdot f(x)\,dx$$

In the case of the failure density function of the exponential distribution, this becomes

$$E(t) = \int_0^{\infty} tf(t)\,dt$$

$$= \int_0^{\infty} \lambda t \cdot e^{-\lambda t}\,dt$$

This can be integrated by parts: Letting

$$u = t \quad \text{and} \quad dv = \lambda e^{-\lambda t}\,dt$$

that is, $v = -e^{-\lambda t}$

then $\displaystyle\int u\,dv = uv - \int v\,du$

that is, $E(t) = [-te^{-\lambda t}]_0^\infty - \int_0^\infty -e^{-\lambda t}\, dt$

$$= [-te^{-\lambda t}]_0^\infty - \left[\frac{1}{\lambda}e^{-\lambda t}\right]_0^\infty$$

$$= 0 + \frac{1}{\lambda}$$

$$E(t) = 1/\lambda \tag{6.37}$$

Similarly, the standard deviation, σ, of the exponential distribution can be found from Equation 2.29.

$$\sigma^2 = \int_0^\infty t^2 \lambda e^{-\lambda t}\, dt - E^2(t)$$

Integrating by parts as before gives

$$\sigma^2 = [-t^2 e^{-\lambda t}]_0^\infty - \int_0^\infty -2te^{-\lambda t}\, dt - E^2(t)$$

$$= 0 + \frac{2}{\lambda} \int_0^\infty \lambda te^{-\lambda t}\, dt - E^2(t)$$

$$= 0 + \frac{2}{\lambda} \cdot \frac{1}{\lambda} - \frac{1}{\lambda^2}$$

thus $\sigma = \dfrac{1}{\lambda}$ $\tag{6.38}$

and the expected value and standard deviation of an exponential distribution are equal.

The expected value of a failure density function is often designated as the *mean time to failure* (MTTF). In the case of the exponential distribution this is equal to the reciprocal of the failure rate λ. Some confusion often arises in this terminology because a slightly different term, *mean time between failures* (MTBF) is sometimes used in the same sense. Conceptually, there is a significant difference between these two terms which becomes fundamentally important in the case of repairable systems. In the latter case the term MTBF is used to indicate the cycle time between failures. This value therefore exceeds the MTTF by a margin which is attributable to the time associated with repair. In the case of most components and systems the repair time is usually very small compared with the operating time and the numerical values of MTTF and MTBF are therefore very close. If the repair time is long however, the two values could be significantly different. This point is discussed further in Chapter 10.

It is also important to recognize that the term *mean time to failure* is usually only applied to the useful life period when the failure rate is constant. The useful life period terminates when the component enters the wearout region and can in practice be relatively short. This leads to an apparent contradiction since a component can be found to have a mean wearout life that is very much less than its MTTF. This can be illustrated by using a numerical example. Consider a component whose mean wearout life is 1000 hours but whose MTTF is 10,000 hours. Although these statements appear contradictory they are in fact not so. The first value, mean wearout life, indicates the average life of the component before it fails in the wearout region. Assuming that the failure density function in the wearout region is normally distributed, the time at which it enters the wearout region depends upon the standard deviation of this distribution. As the standard deviation increases, the useful life period decreases. During the useful life period, failures occur by chance and the failure rate is constant. In the present numerical example, this failure rate has a value of 1/10,000 i.e. 1×10^{-4} failures/hour. The mean time to failure is simply the reciprocal of this failure rate and would be the average failure time if the exponential distribution had continued to be applicable, i.e., if the component had not entered the wearout region. It follows therefore that the MTTF can be very much longer than the mean wearout life.

6.9 The Weibull distribution

The Weibull distribution, in common with a small number of other distributions such as the gamma and lognormal distributions, has one very important property; the distribution has no specific characteristic shape. In fact, depending upon the values of the parameters in its reliability functions, it can be shaped to represent many distributions as well as shaped to fit sets of experimental data that cannot be characterized as a particular distribution other than as a Weibull distribution with certain shaping parameters.

For this reason the Weibull distribution has a very important role to play in the statistical analysis [21] of experimental data. A special type of graph paper known as Weibull probability paper is readily available on which the experimental data can be plotted. This paper is so constructed that the Weibull parameters can be easily deduced from the experimental plots.

The great adaptability of the Weibull distribution can be seen by considering the pertinent functions.

The failure density function of the Weibull distribution is defined as

$$f(t) = \frac{\beta t^{\beta-1}}{\alpha^\beta} \exp\left[-\left(\frac{t}{\alpha}\right)^\beta\right] \tag{6.39}$$

where $t \geqslant 0$, $\beta > 0$ and $\alpha > 0$.

The survivor function is, from Equation 6.5

$$R(t) = \int_t^\infty f(t)\, dt$$

$$= \exp\left[-\left(\frac{t}{\alpha}\right)^\beta\right] \tag{6.40}$$

the cumulative failure distribution is

$$Q(t) = 1 - R(t)$$

$$= 1 - \exp\left[-\left(\frac{t}{\alpha}\right)^\beta\right] \tag{6.41}$$

and the hazard rate is, from Equation 6.13

$$\lambda(t) = \frac{f(t)}{R(t)}$$

$$= \frac{\beta t^{\beta-1}}{\alpha^\beta} \tag{6.42}$$

There are two particular cases that can be deduced from the Weibull distribution; the first is when $\beta = 1$ and the second when $\beta = 2$.

(a) *For $\beta = 1$.*

In this case, Equations 6.39 and 6.42 reduce to

$$f(t) = \frac{1}{\alpha} \exp\left[-\frac{t}{\alpha}\right] \tag{6.43a}$$

and $\lambda(t) = \dfrac{1}{\alpha}$ \hfill (6.43b)

Equations 6.43 are identical to those for the exponential distribution if $\alpha = 1/\lambda$, that is, the value of α represents the mean time to failure (MTTF).

(b)   *For* $\beta = 2$.

In this case, Equations 6.39 and 6.42 reduce to

$$f(t) = \frac{2t}{\alpha^2} \exp\left[-\frac{t^2}{\alpha^2}\right] \tag{6.44}$$

$$\lambda(t) = \frac{2t}{\alpha^2} \tag{6.45}$$

Equations 6.44 and 6.45 are identical to those for the Rayleigh distribution which is described in Section 6.11.

It follows from these two particular cases that the Weibull distribution can be made to fit, or approximate to, a number of distributions. This is a function of its characteristic, that it can be scaled and shaped by varying its shaping parameters. Typical shapes that can be produced for the Weibull distribution including the exponential case are shown in Figure 6.15 for the failure density function, cumulative failure distribution and

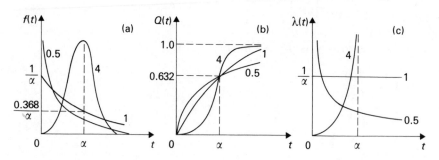

Fig. 6.15   Weibull reliability functions. (a) Failure density function. (b) Cumulative failure distribution. (c) Hazard rate. Parameters = values of β

hazard rate. It is evident from Figure 6.15 that:

$\beta < 1$ represents a decreasing hazard rate or the debugging period,
$\beta = 1$ represents a constant hazard rate or the normal life period, and
$\beta > 1$ represents an increasing hazard rate or the wearout period.

The expected value of the Weibull distribution is given by

$$E(t) = \int_0^\infty t \cdot \frac{\beta t^{\beta-1}}{\alpha^\beta} \exp\left[-\left(\frac{t}{\alpha}\right)^\beta\right] dt$$

$$= \alpha \Gamma\left(\frac{1}{\beta} + 1\right) \tag{6.46}$$

where Γ is the gamma function defined as

$$\Gamma(\gamma) = \int_0^\infty t^{\gamma-1} e^{-t} \, dt \qquad (6.47a)$$

which, for integer values of γ, reduces to $\Gamma(\gamma) = (\gamma - 1)!$ $\qquad$ (6.47b)

The standard deviation of the Weibull distribution is given by

$$\sigma^2 = \int_0^\infty t^2 \cdot \frac{\beta t^{\beta-1}}{\alpha^\beta} \exp\left[-\left(\frac{t}{\alpha}\right)^\beta\right] dt - E^2(t)$$

$$= \alpha^2 \left[\Gamma\left(1 + \frac{2}{\beta}\right) - \Gamma^2\left(\frac{1}{\beta} + 1\right)\right] \qquad (6.48)$$

The conditional or *a posteriori* probability of failure $Q_c(t)$ can be found from Equation 6.36

$$Q_c(t) = \frac{\displaystyle\int_T^{T+t} f(t) \, dt}{\displaystyle\int_T^\infty f(t) \, dt}$$

$$= 1 - \exp\left[-\frac{(T+t)^\beta - T^\beta}{\alpha^\beta}\right] \qquad (6.49)$$

which, for $\beta = 1$, gives the exponential case of

$$Q_c(t) = 1 - e^{-t/\alpha}$$

6.10 The gamma distribution

The gamma distribution has similar properties to those of the Weibull distribution, that is, it is a two parameter distribution having a shape parameter β and a scale parameter α, and by varying these parameters can be made to fit or approximate to a wide range of experimental data.

The failure density function is defined as

$$f(t) = \frac{t^{\beta-1}}{\alpha^\beta \Gamma(\beta)} \exp\left(-\frac{t}{\alpha}\right) \qquad (6.50)$$

where $t \geq 0$, $\alpha > 0$, $\beta > 0$ and $\Gamma(\beta)$ is a gamma function defined by Equation 6.47.

By comparing Equations 6.39 and 6.50, it is seen that there is a degree of similarity between the Weibull and gamma distributions.

The survivor function is from Equation 6.5

$$R(t) = \int_t^\infty \frac{t^{\beta-1}}{\alpha^\beta \Gamma(\beta)} \exp\left(\frac{-t}{\alpha}\right) dt \tag{6.51}$$

and the cumulative failure distribution is

$$Q(t) = \int_0^t \frac{t^{\beta-1}}{\alpha^\beta \Gamma(\beta)} \exp\left(\frac{-t}{\alpha}\right) dt \tag{6.52}$$

If the substitution $z = \dfrac{t}{\alpha}$ and $\alpha\, dz = dt$ is made in Equation 6.52, we obtain

$$Q(t) = \frac{1}{\Gamma(\beta)} \int_0^{t/\alpha} z^{\beta-1} \exp\left(-z\right) dz \tag{6.53}$$

The function $\int_0^{t/\alpha} z^{\beta-1} \exp\left(-z\right) dz$ in Equation 6.53 is known as the incomplete gamma function, i.e., it is an incomplete form of the expression given by Equation 6.47a. Tabulated values of the function have been published [23].

There are two particular and special cases of the gamma distribution. These are when $\beta = 1$ and when β is an integer.

(a)   *For $\beta = 1$*

In this case, Equation 6.50 reduces to

$$f(t) = \frac{1}{\alpha} \exp\left(\frac{-t}{\alpha}\right)$$

i.e., this case is again identical to the exponential distribution when $\alpha = 1/\lambda$, i.e., α is equal to the MTTF.

(b)   *For $\beta = an\ integer$*

In this case the gamma function can be expressed by Equation 6.47b to give

$$f(t) = \frac{t^{\beta-1}}{\alpha^\beta (\beta-1)!} \exp\left(\frac{-t}{\alpha}\right) \tag{6.54}$$

This failure density function is known as the Special Erlangian distribution for which it can be shown that

$$R(t) = \exp\left(\frac{-t}{\alpha}\right) \sum_{j=0}^{\beta-1} \left(\frac{t}{\beta}\right)^j \cdot \frac{1}{j!} \tag{6.55}$$

(This distribution is discussed in Section 12.3.)

It can also be shown that the expected value and standard deviation of a gamma distribution are

$$E(t) = \alpha\beta \tag{6.56}$$

$$\sigma^2 = \alpha^2\beta \tag{6.57}$$

Typical characteristics that can be obtained using the gamma distribution are shown in Figure 6.16. Although a variety of shapes can be

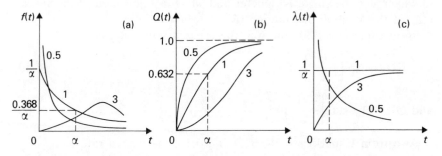

Fig. 6.16   Gamma reliability functions. (a) Failure density function. (b) Cumulative failure distribution. (c) Hazard rate. Parameters = values of β

produced by varying the values of α and β in the gamma distribution in the same way as the Weibull distribution, it is generally, but certainly not universally, accepted that the Weibull distribution is often more suited to reliability evaluation. There are two main exceptions to this: First is the particular example of integer values of β in the gamma distribution which produces the important Special Erlangian distribution. Second is the case when $\alpha = 2$, $\beta = n/2$ and n is an integer. This gives the χ^2 (chi-squared) distribution which is an important distribution used in evaluating confidence limits associated with random variables (Appendix 5 refers).

6.11 The Rayleigh distribution

This distribution was introduced as a special case of the Weibull distribution in Section 6.9. It is however an important distribution in its own right and finds application not only in reliability problems but also in noise problems associated with communications systems. Unlike the Weibull and gamma distributions which are characterized by two parameters, the Rayleigh distribution is a single parameter distribution similar to the exponential distribution.

Recalling Equation 6.44, we have

$$f(t) = \frac{2t}{\alpha^2} \exp\left[\frac{-t^2}{\alpha^2}\right]$$

which indicates that the single parameter is α.

A more general expression for the failure density function is

$$f(t) = kt \exp\left[\frac{-kt^2}{2}\right] \tag{6.58}$$

in which k is the single parameter and which is equivalent to the special case of the Weibull distribution ($\beta = 2$) when $k = 2/\alpha^2$.

From Equations 6.58 and 6.5, the reliability function is

$$R(t) = \exp\left[\frac{-kt^2}{2}\right] \tag{6.59}$$

and $$Q(t) = 1 - \exp\left[\frac{-kt^2}{2}\right] \tag{6.60}$$

Also from Equations 6.58, 6.59 and 6.13, the hazard rate is

$$\lambda(t) = kt \tag{6.61}$$

which is a linearly increasing hazard rate with time. It is this characteristic that gives the Rayleigh distribution its importance in reliability evaluation. The characteristic shape of the failure density function, cumulative failure distribution and the hazard rate are shown in Figure 6.17.

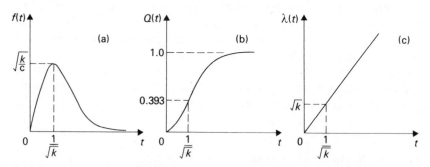

Fig. 6.17 Rayleigh reliability functions. (a) Failure density function. (b) Cumulative failure distribution. (c) Hazard rate

6.12 The lognormal distribution

The lognormal distribution is related to the normal distribution and, likewise, is a two parameter distribution. It does not seem to be particularly suited for the representation of component lifetimes and because of this has not been considered in the past as an important distribution in reliability evaluation. This is still probably true with regard to mission-orientated systems. However, it now appears that the lognormal distribution can be a good fit to the distribution of component repair times and consequently is becoming an important distribution in the assessment of repairable systems.

The failure density function (in practice, because of the above discussion, it is more likely to be a repair density function) is defined as

$$f(t) = \frac{1}{t\sigma\sqrt{2\pi}} \exp\left[-\frac{(\ln t - \mu)^2}{2\sigma^2}\right] \tag{6.62}$$

for $t \geq 0$.

Comparing Equation 6.62 with Equation 6.24 for the normal distribution, it can be concluded that a random variable X has a lognormal distribution with the parameters μ and σ if $\ln X$ is normally distributed with parameters μ and σ. However, it should be noted that, although the values of μ and σ are the mean value and standard deviation of $\ln X$, they are not the mean value and standard deviation of the lognormal distribution, i.e., of X.

The cumulative failure (or probability) distribution of the random variable is given by

$$Q(t) = \int_0^t \frac{1}{t\sigma\sqrt{2\pi}} \exp\left[-\frac{(\ln t - \mu)^2}{2\sigma^2}\right] dt$$

if the substitution $z = \dfrac{\ln t - \mu}{\sigma}$

and $\qquad\qquad dz = \dfrac{dt}{\sigma t}$

is made in the expression for $Q(t)$, we have

$$Q(t) = \frac{1}{\sqrt{2\pi}} \int_{-\infty}^{(\ln t - \mu)/\sigma} \exp\left(\frac{-z^2}{2}\right) dz \tag{6.63}$$

which is identical to the standard normal probability integral that would be obtained by integrating Equation 6.26 to give the cumulative probability distribution. Therefore, the values of $Q(t)$ can be obtained using the table given in Appendix 2 provided the correct limits are used.

The expected value and standard deviation of the lognormal distribution can be shown, using the established techniques (Sections 2.6.3 and 2.6.4) for deriving these values, to be

$$E(t) = \exp\left(\mu + \tfrac{1}{2}\sigma^2\right) \tag{6.64}$$

$$\text{standard deviation} = [\exp\left(2\mu + 2\sigma^2\right) - \exp\left(2\mu + \sigma^2\right)]^{1/2} \tag{6.65}$$

The shapes of the failure (probability) density function, the cumulative failure distribution and the hazard function for the lognormal distribution are shown in Figure 6.18.

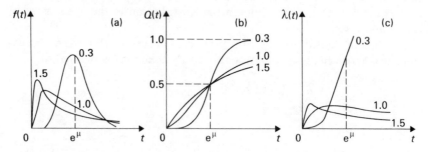

Fig. 6.18 Lognormal reliability functions. (a) Failure density function. (b) Cumulative failure distribution. (c) Hazard rate. Parameters = values of σ

6.13 The rectangular (or uniform) distribution

This is the simplest of all distributions. Its failure density function is shown in Figure 6.19a and can be described mathematically as

$$f(t) = \frac{1}{b-a} \tag{6.66}$$

for $a \leqslant t \leqslant b$.

The distribution can be interpreted as meaning that the random variable can only exist in the range a to b and that the probability of occurrence is directly proportional to the interval length. Equation 6.66 must apply since the total area enclosed by the failure density function must be unity.

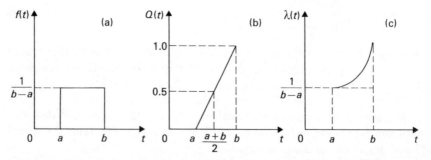

Fig. 6.19 Rectangular (uniform) reliability functions. (a) Failure density function. (b) Cumulative failure distribution. (c) Hazard rate

From Equation 6.66, the survivor function is

$$R(t) = \int_t^b \frac{1}{b-a} \cdot dt$$

$$= \frac{b-t}{b-a} \tag{6.67}$$

the cumulative failure distribution is

$$Q(t) = \int_a^t \frac{1}{b-a} \cdot dt$$

$$= \frac{t-a}{b-a} \tag{6.68}$$

and the hazard rate is

$$\lambda(t) = \frac{f(t)}{R(t)}$$

$$= \frac{1}{b-t} \tag{6.69}$$

These characteristics are also shown in Figure 6.19.
Finally the expected value and standard deviation are

$$E(t) = \int_a^b \frac{t}{b-a} \, dt$$

$$= \frac{a+b}{2} \tag{6.70}$$

$$\sigma^2 = \int_a^b \frac{t^2}{b-a} \cdot dt - E^2(t)$$

$$= \frac{b^3 - a^3}{3(b-a)} - \left[\frac{a+b}{2}\right]^2$$

$$= \frac{(b-a)^2}{12} \tag{6.71}$$

6.14   Summary of reliability functions

It is evident from the discussion in the previous sections of this chapter, that there are a number of probability distributions which are useful and important in reliability problems. For each there are a number of pertinent functions including the failure density function, survivor function, cumulative failure distribution and hazard rate together with the two

Table 6.2 Summary of reliability functions and parameters

Distribution	Range	Failure density function, $f(t)$	Survivor function, $R(t)$	Hazard rate, $\lambda(t)$	Expected value, $E(t)$	Variance σ^2
binomial	$0 \leqslant p \leqslant 1$ $q = 1-p$ $r = 1, 2, \ldots, n$	$_nC_r p^r q^{n-r}$	$1 - \sum_{j=0}^{r} {}_nC_j p^j q^{n-j}$	—	np	npq
Poisson	$0 \leqslant t \leqslant \infty$ $x = 0, 1, 2, \ldots, n$	$\dfrac{(\lambda t)^x e^{-\lambda t}}{x!}$	$1 - \sum_{j=0}^{n} \dfrac{(\lambda t)^j e^{-\lambda t}}{j!}$	—	λt	λt
normal	$-\infty \leqslant t \leqslant \infty$	$\dfrac{1}{\sigma\sqrt{2\pi}} \exp\left[-\dfrac{(t-\mu)^2}{2\sigma^2}\right]$	$\displaystyle\int_t^\infty f(t)\,dt$	$\dfrac{f(t)}{R(t)}$	μ	σ^2
exponential	$t \geqslant 0$	$\lambda \exp(-\lambda t)$	$\exp(-\lambda t)$	λ	$\dfrac{1}{\lambda}$	$\dfrac{1}{\lambda^2}$
Weibull	$t \geqslant 0$ $\beta > 0, \alpha > 0$	$\dfrac{\beta t^{\beta-1}}{\alpha^\beta} \exp\left[-\left(\dfrac{t}{\alpha}\right)^\beta\right]$	$\exp\left[-\left(\dfrac{t}{\alpha}\right)^\beta\right]$	$\dfrac{\beta t^{\beta-1}}{\alpha^\beta}$	$\alpha\Gamma\left(\dfrac{1}{\beta}+1\right)$	$\alpha^2\left[\Gamma\left(1+\dfrac{2}{\beta}\right) - \Gamma^2\left(1+\dfrac{1}{\beta}\right)\right]$
gamma	$t \geqslant 0$ $\beta > 0, \alpha > 0$	$\dfrac{t^{\beta-1}}{\alpha^\beta \Gamma(\beta)} \exp\left[-\dfrac{t}{\alpha}\right]$	$\displaystyle\int_t^\infty f(t)\,dt$	$\dfrac{f(t)}{R(t)}$	$\alpha\beta$	$\alpha^2\beta$
Rayleigh	$t \geqslant 0$	$kt \exp\left[-\dfrac{kt^2}{2}\right]$	$\exp\left[-\dfrac{kt^2}{2}\right]$	kt	$\sqrt{\dfrac{\pi}{2k}}$	$\dfrac{2}{k}\left(1-\dfrac{\pi^2}{4}\right)$
lognormal	$t \geqslant 0$	$\dfrac{1}{t\sigma\sqrt{2\pi}} \exp\left[-\dfrac{(\ln t - \mu)^2}{2\sigma^2}\right]$	$\displaystyle\int_t^\infty f(t)\,dt$	$\dfrac{f(t)}{R(t)}$	$\exp\left(\mu + \dfrac{\sigma^2}{2}\right)$	$\exp(2\mu + 2\sigma^2) - \exp(2\mu + \sigma^2)$
Rectangular	$a \leqslant t \leqslant b$	$\dfrac{1}{b-a}$	$\dfrac{b-t}{b-a}$	$\dfrac{1}{b-t}$	$\dfrac{a+b}{2}$	$\dfrac{(b-a)^2}{12}$

basic parameters that can be used to describe a probability distribution, i.e., expected value and standard deviation (or variance). These functions and parameters are catalogued in Table 6.2 to provide an easy reference source.

6.15 Conclusions

This chapter has presented the most important probability distributions that are likely to be encountered in reliability evaluation problems. It is not meant to be an exhaustive description of these distributions or a detailed discussion of their application in all fields of probability and statistics. For this purpose the reader is referred to more specialized texts [2–8, 21, 24] on probability theory and statistics of which there are a considerable number. Many readers may already be familiar with the concepts and distributions that have been described, in which case the chapter could have been omitted or used only as a reference.

For those who have not been previously exposed to this area, it is intended to provide a basic understanding of the fundamental distributions.

Problems

1 A manufacturer produces 10 items of a special product each year. If the items are not sold within the year they must be discarded. Past experience has indicated that the demand for the product is a Poisson distributed random variable with an expectation of 8. If a profit of $7.00 is made on every item which is sold and a loss of $3.00 results from having to discard an item, calculate the expected profit realized by the supplier on the 10 items that he produces.

2 A highway has a travel rate of 120 vehicles per hour. What is the probability of 0, 1, 2, 3, 4 vehicles passing a certain point during a given 30 second interval?

3 The number of oil tankers arriving at a refinery each day has a Poisson distribution with parameter $np = 2$. Present port facilities can service three tankers arriving in any one day. Tankers in excess of three must be sent to another port.
   (a) On any given day, what is the probability of having to send tankers away?
   (b) How much must present facilities be increased to permit handling all tankers on 90% of the days?
   (c) What is the expected number of tankers arriving per day?
   (d) What is the must probable number of tankers arriving daily?
   (e) What is the expected number of tankers serviced daily?
   (f) What is the expected number of tankers turned away daily?

   (g)   Repeat (a) to (f) if the port facilities can service 2 tankers in any one day.

   (h)   Repeat (a) to (f) if the port facilities can service 4 tankers in any one day.

4   A communication system has on the average 26 component failures per year of the same plug-in element. These elements are replaced from available stock which is replenished every two weeks. How large should the stock be to prevent with a 90% (or greater) probability, the communication system being forced out of service. What should the stock be if the average number of component failures per year is 13?

5   The ABC Auto Supply depot orders stock at the middle of the month and receives the goods at the first of the next month. The average number of requests for fuel pump XY33 is 4 per month. If on April 15, 2 of these fuel pumps are in stock and an additional 5 are ordered (to be received by May 1), what is the probability that the ABC Depot will not be able to supply all the requests for XY33 in the month of May? The demand is completely random. (Requests for pumps are not carried over from one month to the next.)

6   If the diameters of ball bearings are normally distributed with mean 0.6140 inches and standard deviation 0.0025 inches determine the percentage of ball bearings with diameters.

   (a)   Between 0.610 and 0.618 inches.

   (b)   Greater than 0.617 inches.

   (c)   Less than 0.608 inches.

7   The average mark on a final exam is 70 and the standard deviation is 10. The top 10% of the class will receive A's. What is the minimum mark a student must get to receive an A?

8   A machine produces bolts that are 8% defective. Find the probability that in a random sample of 500 bolts produced by the machine,

   (a)   at most 50,

   (b)   between 30 and 50,

   (c)   between 35 and 45,

   (d)   55 or more of the bolts will be defective.

   (Use the normal distribution as an approximation to the binomial).

9   The life of a bearing is normally distributed with an average value of 2000 hours and a standard deviation of 100 hours. What is the probability that the bearing fails sometime between 1964 hrs and 2016 hrs?

10   A component operating during its useful life has a reliability of 90% for a mission of 50 hours. What would the component reliability be for a mission of 100 hours?

11   The variations in the output power of a motor are found to follow a gamma distribution with parameters $\beta = 3$ and $\alpha = 100$ kW. What is

   (a)   the probability that the power output is less than 200 kW?

   (b)   the value of this probability if it is approximated to a normal distribution and then to a lognormal distribution?

12   A large number of identical relays have times to first failure that follow a Weibull distribution with parameters $\beta = 0.5$ and $\alpha = 10$ years. What is the probability that a relay will survive (a) 1 year, (b) 5 years, and (c) 10 years without failure and what is the value of MTTF.

13 What are the conditions for the function shown in Figure 6.20 to be a
    probability density function. Under these conditions evaluate:
    (a) the cumulative failure distribution
    (b) survivor function
    (c) hazard rate
    (d) expected value
    (e) standard deviation
    (f) probability that $\left(a - \dfrac{b}{2} < t \leqslant a + \dfrac{b}{2}\right)$.

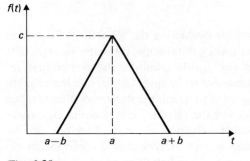

Fig. 6.20

14 The hazard rate of a device is $\lambda(t) = 1/\sqrt{t}$. Deduce
    (a) the probability density function,
    (b) the survivor function,
    (c) the expected value, and
    (d) the variance.

7 System reliability evaluation using probability distributions

7.1 Introduction

A relatively standard procedure for evaluating the reliability of a system is to decompose it into its constituent components, estimate the reliability of each of these components and finally combine the component reliabilities using one or more numerical techniques to estimate the reliability of the complete system. The level to which the decomposition is taken must be such that the reliabilities of the resulting components are known within reasonable and acceptable precision. It may therefore not be necessary to decompose the system into individual real components but into a set of devices or subsystems, the reliabilities of which are known from experience.

The problems of decomposing a system into a form suitable for system reliability evaluation was the subject of Chapters 4 and 5. The basic systems considered were series systems, parallel systems, series/parallel systems, interconnected or meshed systems, majority vote or m-out-of-n systems and standby systems. In Chapters 4 and 5 however, the techniques were described and illustrated assuming that the failure and success probabilities were constant and therefore single-valued.

Chapter 6 showed that this assumption is not usually valid since, in reality, component reliabilities are described by one of many probability distributions. This chapter considers systems of the type described in Chapters 4 and 5 and applies to these the concepts of probability distributions discussed in Chapter 6. This is done mainly in terms of the exponential distribution. The reasons for this are associated with those already stated previously in Section 6.8.1 that a thorough understanding of the technique is best achieved by initially considering a relatively simple distribution such as the exponential. Once this sound foundation has been gained, it is relatively straightforward to extend the concepts to other situations.

Putting aside for the moment the problem of m-out-of-n and standby systems, it was shown in Chapter 5 that systems, irrespective of their complexity, could be decomposed into a reliability diagram consisting of series and parallel components using conditional probability, minimal tie sets, minimal cut sets, connection matrices or tree diagrams. These decomposition techniques also apply when the system reliability is evaluated using probability distributions instead of the constant values of probability assumed in Chapter 5. Consequently, the techniques described in this chapter concerning series and parallel systems can be applied directly to systems that are physically in series, parallel or series/parallel and indirectly to more complex systems provided that these systems are first decomposed into a series/parallel arrangement using one of the techniques described in Chapter 5.

The general aim of this chapter is to provide a set of extended techniques which can be used to evaluate comprehensively the reliability of a real system and includes the system structure, topology and operating logic as well as the underlying probability distributions associated with the components of the system.

7.2 Series systems

The reliability of a 2-component series system is given in Equation 4.1 as

$$R_s = R_1 R_2 \tag{7.1}$$

If time dependent probabilities are now introduced, i.e., the probability of surviving for a period of time t, the equation is now a function of time and is rewritten as

$$R_s(t) = R_1(t) \cdot R_2(t) \tag{7.2}$$

Thus from Equations 6.15 and 7.2

$$R_s(t) = \exp\left[-\int_0^t \lambda_1(t)\,dt\right] \cdot \exp\left[-\int_0^t \lambda_2(t)\,dt\right] \tag{7.3}$$

and for an n-component series system with hazard rates $\lambda_1(t)$, $\lambda_2(t), \ldots, \lambda_n(t)$

$$R_s(t) = \prod_{i=1}^n \exp\left[-\int_0^t \lambda_i(t)\,dt\right] \tag{7.4}$$

Equations 7.3 and 7.4 apply equally well to all failure distributions as there were no distributional assumptions in the derivation of Equation 6.15. These equations also do not assume that all components must have the same distribution and therefore each component of the system can be represented by its correct distribution. Consequently, provided the analytical expression of $\lambda_i(t)$ is known and can be integrated, the evaluation of $R_s(t)$ for any set of series components is readily possible. If the expression of $\lambda_i(t)$ cannot be expressed analytically or the expression is not easy or possible to integrate directly, it is still usually possible to evaluate $R_s(t)$ using numerical integration techniques.

In the special case of the exponential distribution, Equations 7.3 and 7.4 give

for a 2-component series system

$$R_s(t) = \exp(-\lambda_1 t) \exp(-\lambda_2 t)$$
$$= \exp[-(\lambda_1 + \lambda_2)t] \tag{7.5}$$

and for a n-component series system:

$$R_s(t) = \prod_{i=1}^{n} \exp(-\lambda_i t)$$
$$= \exp\left(-\sum_{i=1}^{n} \lambda_i t\right) \tag{7.6}$$

Equations 7.3 to 7.6 hold for any system that can be described as a series system, i.e., any system in which all components must operate for system success.

If a single equivalent component having a hazard rate $\lambda_e(t)$ is considered to represent the complete series system, then from Equations 7.4 and 7.6 we have,

for the general case

$$R_s(t) = \exp\left[-\int_0^t \lambda_e(t)\,dt\right] = \prod_{i=1}^{n} \exp\left[-\int_0^t \lambda_i(t)\,dt\right] \tag{7.7}$$

and for the exponential case

$$R_s(t) = \exp(-\lambda_e t) = \exp\left(-\sum_{i=1}^{n} \lambda_i t\right) \tag{7.8}$$

No simple analytical relationship between $\lambda_e(t)$ and $\lambda_i(t)$ can be deduced from Equation 7.7. Equation 7.8 shows however that, in the case of the exponential distribution, i.e., when the hazard rate is constant

$$\lambda_e = \sum_{i=1}^{n} \lambda_i \tag{7.9}$$

which indicates that the effective failure rate of a series system containing components whose reliabilities follow exponential distributions is simply the summation of the failure rates of the individual series components. This is a very important conclusion and means that the reliability of a series system can be evaluated very rapidly provided the components can be described by exponential distributions.

Example 7.1

A simple electronic circuit consists of 6 transistors each having a failure rate of 10^{-6} f/hr, 4 diodes each having a failure rate of 0.5×10^{-6} f/hr, 3 capacitors each having a failure rate of 0.2×10^{-6} f/hr, 10 resistors each having a failure rate of 5×10^{-6} f/hr and 2 switches each having a failure rate of 2×10^{-6} f/hr. Assuming connectors and wiring are 100% reliable (these can be included if considered significant), evaluate the equivalent failure rate of the system and the probability of the system surviving 1000 hr and also 10 000 hr if all components must operate for system success.

From Equation 7.9

$$\lambda_e = 6 \times (1 \times 10^{-6}) + 4 \times (0.5 \times 10^6) + 3 \times (0.2 \times 10^{-6}) + 10 \times (5 \times 10^{-6})$$
$$+ 2 \times (2 \times 10^{-6})$$

$$= 6.26 \times 10^{-5} \text{ f/hr}$$

$$R_s(1000) = \exp(-6.26 \times 10^{-5} \times 1000)$$

$$= 0.9393$$

$$R_s(10\ 000) = \exp(-6.26 \times 10^{-5} \times 10\ 000)$$

$$= 0.5347$$

Since $\quad Q_s(t) = 1 - R_s(t)$

$$Q_s(1000) = 0.0707$$

and $Q_s(10\ 000) = 0.4653$

7.3 Parallel systems

If Equations 4.6 to 4.10 are adapted for time-dependent probabilities (as for the series systems in Section 7.2) we obtain for a 2-component parallel system

$$Q_p(t) = Q_1(t)Q_2(t) \tag{7.10}$$

$$R_p(t) = 1 - Q_1(t)Q_2(t) \tag{7.11}$$

$$= R_1(t) + R_2(t) - R_1(t)R_2(t) \tag{7.12}$$

and for an n-component parallel system

$$Q_p(t) = \prod_{i=1}^{n} Q_i(t) \tag{7.13}$$

$$R_p(t) = 1 - \prod_{i=1}^{n} Q_i(t) \tag{7.14}$$

Therefore, using Equation 6.15 and considering the n-component system to have hazard rates of $\lambda_1(t), \lambda_2(t), \ldots, \lambda_n(t)$, we have

$$Q_p(t) = \prod_{i=1}^{n} \left(1 - \exp\left[-\int_0^t \lambda_i(t)\, dt\right]\right) \tag{7.15}$$

$$R_p(t) = 1 - \prod_{i=1}^{n} \left(1 - \exp\left[-\int_0^t \lambda_i(t)\, dt\right]\right) \tag{7.16}$$

Equations 7.15 and 7.16 are of the same form as Equation 7.4 for series systems and all the comments made in Section 7.2 in regard to Equation 7.4 apply equally well to Equations 7.15 and 7.16. Consequently, these equations can be solved for any distributional assumptions to give the probability of surviving for a period of time t or alternatively of failing in this period of time.

If we again consider the special case of a constant hazard rate, i.e., the exponential distribution, we obtain, for a 2-component parallel system

$$Q_p(t) = [1 - \exp(-\lambda_1 t)][1 - \exp(-\lambda_2 t)] \tag{7.17a}$$

$$= 1 - [\exp(-\lambda_1 t) + \exp(-\lambda_2 t) - \exp\{-(\lambda_1 + \lambda_2)\}t] \tag{7.17b}$$

and $R_p(t) = \exp(-\lambda_1 t) + \exp(-\lambda_2 t) - \exp[-(\lambda_1 + \lambda_2)t]$ \hfill (7.18)

and for an n-component parallel system

$$Q_p(t) = \prod_{i=1}^{n} [1 - \exp(-\lambda_i t)] \tag{7.19}$$

$$R_p(t) = 1 - \prod_{i=1}^{n} [1 - \exp(-\lambda_i t)] \tag{7.20}$$

It is evident from Equations 7.17 to 7.20 that a single equivalent failure rate cannot be derived to represent the complete parallel system because, unlike Equation 7.8, the system reliability cannot be expressed as a single exponential function but only as a series of exponential functions. It can also be concluded that, although the resulting distribution of a series system comprising exponentially distributed component reliabilities is itself an exponential distribution, the resulting distribution of a parallel system comprising exponentially distributed component reliabilities is non-exponential and the resulting hazard rate is no longer constant but is a function of time.

Example 7.2

Reconsider Example 7.1 and evaluate the probability of surviving 1000 hr and 10 000 hr if (a) two, (b) three identical circuits to those described in Example 7.1 are used in parallel and it is assumed that the system operates successfully if only one of the circuits is successful.

In this example, all the parallel components (each being equivalent to one of the series circuits) are identical and each having a failure rate given by λ_e in Example 7.1, i.e.,

$$\lambda_i = 6.26 \times 10^{-5} \text{ f/hr}$$

(a)   from Equation 7.18

$$R_p(1000) = \exp(-6.26 \times 10^{-5} \times 1000) + \exp(-6.26 \times 10^{-5} \times 1000)$$
$$- \exp(-2 \times 6.26 \times 10^{-5} \times 1000)$$

$$= 0.9963$$

$$R_p(10\ 000) = 2\exp(-6.26 \times 10^{-5} \times 10\ 000)$$
$$- \exp(-2 \times 6.26 \times 10^{-5} \times 10\ 000)$$
$$= 0.7835$$

These results could have been evaluated using the values of R_s and Q_s evaluated in Example 7.1. For example,

$$R_p(10\ 000) = 1 - Q_s(10\ 000)Q_s(10\ 000)$$
$$= 1 - 0.4653^2$$
$$= 0.7835$$

(b) $\quad R_p(1000) = 1 - [1 - \exp(-6.26 \times 10^{-5} \times 1000)]^3$
$$= 0.9998$$

$$R_p(10\ 000) = 1 - [1 - \exp(-6.26 \times 10^{-5} \times 10\ 000)]^3$$
$$= 0.8993$$

or alternatively

$$R_p(10\ 000) = 1 - Q_s^3(10\ 000)$$
$$= 1 - 0.4653^3$$
$$= 0.8993$$

A comparison of the results obtained in Examples 7.1 and 7.2 illustrates, as expected, that the reliability or probability of surviving a given period of time increases as the redundancy in the system is increased and as the mission time or exposure to failure time is decreased.

7.4 Partially redundant systems

Partially redundant systems are frequently known by one of several names such as majority vote systems and m-out-of-n systems. They require some proportion of components between the two extremes of series and parallel systems to operate, whereas series systems require all components to operate and parallel (or fully redundant) systems require only one component to operate. Partially redundant systems were discussed in Chapters 3 and 4.

The techniques described in Chapters 3 and 4 for evaluating the reliability of partially redundant systems can be used again and the success and failure conditions established. The only difference between the application described previously and that required to account for the probability distribution of component failures is in the method used to determine the probability of the success condition and the failure condition.

The application of probability distributions to partially redundant systems can be illustrated by first considering a system with n identical components. The probabilities of each state of this system, i.e., $0, 1, 2, \ldots, n$ components operating can be found from the binomial expansion of $(R + Q)^n$. In Chapter 4 the values of R and Q in this expression were assumed to be constant. In the case of time-dependent probabilities, the values of R and Q are functions of time and the binomial expression is modified to $[R(t) + Q(t)]^n$, in which the values of $R(t)$ and $Q(t)$ can be found, respectively, from the survivor function and cumulative failure distribution described in Chapter 6. The binomial expression is perfectly general and any appropriate distribution can be used for the components.

In the special case of the exponential distribution

$$R(t) = e^{-\lambda t} \tag{7.21}$$

and $Q(t) = 1 - e^{-\lambda t}$ (7.22)

therefore, the binomial expression becomes $[e^{-\lambda t} + (1 - e^{-\lambda t})]^n$.

Example 7.3

Consider a system comprising 4 identical units each having a failure rate of 0.1 f/yr. Evaluate the probability of the system surviving 0.5 yr and 5 yr if at least two units must operate successfully.

Using the binomial expression for $n = 4$ gives

$$[R(t) + Q(t)]^4 = R^4(t) + 4R^3(t)Q(t) + 6R^2(t)Q^2(t) + 4R(t)Q^3(t) + Q^4(t)$$

in which $R(t)$ and $Q(t)$ are given by Equations 7.21 and 7.22. Therefore, the probabilities of system success, if the number of units required for success are 4, 3, 2 and 1, are shown in Table 7.1.

Table 7.1 Probability of system success

Number of units required for success	Probability of system success
4	$e^{-4\lambda t}$
3	$e^{-4\lambda t} + 4e^{-3\lambda t}(1 - e^{-\lambda t})$
2	$e^{-4\lambda t} + 4e^{-3\lambda t}(1 - e^{-\lambda t}) + 6e^{-2\lambda t}(1 - e^{-\lambda t})^2$
1	$e^{-4\lambda t} + 4e^{-3\lambda t}(1 - e^{-\lambda t}) + 6e^{-2\lambda t}(1 - e^{-\lambda t})^2 + 4e^{-\lambda t}(1 - e^{-\lambda t})^3$

Therefore, in this example

$$R(0.5) = e^{-4\lambda t} + 4e^{-3\lambda t}(1 - e^{-\lambda t}) + 6e^{-2\lambda t}(1 - e^{-\lambda t})^2$$

where $\lambda = 0.1$ and $t = 0.5$

thus, $R(0.5) = 0.9996$

Similarly,

$$R(5.0) = 0.8282$$

In the more general case of non-identical units, the probability of each system state can be evaluated from the concept of Section 3.3.8, i.e.:

$$[R_1(t) + Q_1(t)][R_2(t) + Q_2(t)] \ldots [R_n(t) + Q_n(t)]$$

in which the appropriate values of $R_i(t)$ and $Q_i(t)$ can be deduced from a knowledge of the probability distributions of the ith component and the time period of interest. In the particular case of the exponential distribution,

$$R_i(t) = \exp(-\lambda_i t) \quad \text{for} \quad i = 1, 2, \ldots, n$$
$$Q_i(t) = 1 - \exp(-\lambda_i t) \quad \text{for} \quad i = 1, 2, \ldots, n$$

Example 7.4

A control system consists of three separate subsystems, all components of which have reliabilities that are exponentially distributed. The subsystems are (a) a single component having a failure rate of 1×10^{-6} f/hr, (b) two identical components having failure rates of 8×10^{-6} f/hr and for which one component must operate for success and, (c) three components having failure rates of 5×10^{-6} f/hr, 2×10^{-6} f/hr and 10×10^{-6} f/hr and for which two components must operate for success. If all subsystems must be successful for satisfactory system operation, evaluate the probability of surviving for a period of 5000 hr.

$$R(a) = e^{-\lambda t}$$
$$= \exp(-1 \times 10^{-6} \times 5000) = 0.9950$$
$$R(b) = \exp(-\lambda_1 t) + \exp(-\lambda_2 t) - \exp[-(\lambda_1 + \lambda_2)t]$$
$$= 2 \exp(-8 \times 10^{-6} \times 5000) - \exp(-2 \times 8 \times 10^{-6} \times 5000)$$
$$= 0.9985$$
$$R(c) = R_1(t)R_2(t)R_3(t) + R_1(t)R_2(t)Q_3(t) + R_1(t)Q_2(t)R_3(t)$$
$$\quad + Q_1(t)R_2(t)R_3(t)$$
$$= \exp(-\lambda_1 t) \exp(-\lambda_2 t) \exp(-\lambda_3 t) + \exp(-\lambda_1 t) \exp(-\lambda_2 t)$$
$$\quad \times [1 - \exp(-\lambda_3 t)]$$
$$\quad + \exp(-\lambda_1 t) \exp(-\lambda_3 t)[1 - \exp(-\lambda_2 t)]$$
$$\quad + \exp(-\lambda_2 t) \exp(-\lambda_3 t)[1 - \exp(-\lambda_1 t)]$$
$$= 0.9981$$

Therefore, probability of surviving 5000 hrs $= R(a)R(b)R(c)$
$$= 0.9916$$

7.5   Mean time to failure

In Section 6.8.4, the expected value of a probability distribution having a range $(0, \infty)$ was given by

$$E(t) = \int_0^\infty tf(t) \, dt \tag{7.23}$$

It was also noted that, if $f(t)$ is the distribution of times to failure, this expected value was the mean time to failure or MTTF, which can be designated as m.

Recalling Equation 6.2, i.e., $f(t) = \dfrac{-dR(t)}{dt}$ and substituting into Equation 7.23 gives

$$m = -\int_0^\infty t \, dR(t)$$

Integration by parts gives

$$m = [-tR(t)]_0^\infty + \int_0^\infty R(t) \, dt$$

$$= \int_0^\infty R(t) \, dt \tag{7.24}$$

since $R(t) = 1$ at $t = 0$ and it can be shown [25] that $tR(t) \to 0$ as $t \to \infty$.

Equation 7.24 is a very useful alternative method for evaluating the expected value of a distribution and could have been used in Chapter 6 in place of Equation 7.23.

The MTTF of any series or parallel system can therefore be evaluated by using the appropriate system expression for $R(t)$ and integrating between the limits $(0, \infty)$. This is often not a simple task particularly if the system consists of components having different reliability distributions. It can also be done numerically on a digital computer by evaluating $R(t)$ for a suitable step size and obtaining the area under the curve, i.e., integrating, by summating the subsequent intervals.

Consider the particular case of exponential distributions.

(a)   *For a series system*

$$m = \int_0^\infty R_s(t) \, dt$$

$$= \int_0^\infty \exp\left(-\sum_{i=1}^n \lambda_i t\right) \cdot dt \qquad \text{from Equation 7.6}$$

$$= \frac{1}{\sum_{i=1}^n \lambda_i} \tag{7.25a}$$

$$= \frac{1}{\lambda_1 + \lambda_2 + \ldots + \lambda_n} \tag{7.25b}$$

This could be intuitively deduced since it was established in Chapter 6 (Equation 6.37) that the MTTF of an exponential distribution was the reciprocal of the failure rate. Since a series system of components having exponentially distributed reliabilities has an equivalent failure rate of $\sum_{i=1}^{n} \lambda_i$ and the distribution is itself exponential, it would follow that the MTTF of such a series system would be the reciprocal of its equivalent failure rate as Equation 7.25 justifies.

(b)   *For a 2-component parallel system*

In this case the resultant distribution is non-exponential and there is no constant value of equivalent failure rate. Therefore, the MTTF cannot be deduced intuitively. Using Equation 7.24

$$m = \int_0^\infty R_p(t)\, dt$$

$$= \int_0^\infty \{\exp(-\lambda_1 t) + \exp(-\lambda_2 t) - \exp[-(\lambda_1 + \lambda_2)t]\}\, dt$$

from Equation 7.18

$$= \left\{ -\frac{1}{\lambda_1}\exp(-\lambda_1 t) - \frac{1}{\lambda_2}\exp(-\lambda_2 t) + \frac{1}{\lambda_1 + \lambda_2}\exp[-(\lambda_1 + \lambda_2)t] \right\}_0^\infty$$

$$= \frac{1}{\lambda_1} + \frac{1}{\lambda_2} - \frac{1}{\lambda_1 + \lambda_2} \qquad (7.26)$$

(c)   *For an n-component parallel system*

The principle used to derive Equation 7.26 could be applied to a parallel system consisting of any number of components. Such a derivation would show that

$$m = \left(\frac{1}{\lambda_1} + \frac{1}{\lambda_2} + \ldots + \frac{1}{\lambda_n}\right) - \left(\frac{1}{\lambda_1 + \lambda_2} + \frac{1}{\lambda_1 + \lambda_3} + \ldots + \frac{1}{\lambda_i + \lambda_j} + \ldots\right)$$

$$+ \left(\frac{1}{\lambda_1 + \lambda_2 + \lambda_3} + \frac{1}{\lambda_1 + \lambda_2 + \lambda_4} + \ldots + \frac{1}{\lambda_i + \lambda_j + \lambda_k} + \ldots\right) \ldots$$

$$+ (-1)^{n+1}\frac{1}{\sum_{i=1}^{n} \lambda_i} \qquad (7.27)$$

7.6   Standby systems

7.6.1   General concepts

It was shown in the previous sections of this chapter and in Chapters 3 and 4 that parallel redundant or partially redundant systems lead to an increased overall system reliability. In such systems however, all the components are simultaneously in the operating mode. As discussed in Section 4.6.1 this arrangement may not always be feasible or practical, and instead a standby redundant system may be used. In this type of system one or more of the components are in a standby mode ready to take over system operation when the main or normally operating component(s) fail. Such a system may be used when it is impractical to have the main component(s) and the standby component(s) operating simultaneously, e.g., it is impractical to have the main electricity supply connected to a protection system simultaneously with a back-up battery supply. This type of system may also be particularly advantageous when the redundant standby component(s) has a lower failure rate in the standby or idle mode than it has in the operating mode.

The fundamental problem in standby systems is that a failure sensing and changeover device is required to bring the standby unit into operation when the main component fails. These elements are additional items not required in parallel redundant systems and therefore can and do affect the overall reliability of the system. Hence it is not possible to generalize whether standby systems are more reliable or less reliable than parallel redundant systems; each must be analysed separately and the relative merits compared.

A simple and most basic standby system is shown in Figure 7.1 in which A represents the main operating component, B the standby component and S the sensing and changeover switch.

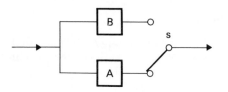

Fig. 7.1 Basic standby system

The general concepts of standby systems were described in Section 4.6 at which point the elementary problems and evaluation techniques were described. It was pointed out however that failure of the standby component B was dependent on the operating or non-operating status of the main component A. The techniques presented in this section indicate how this dependence may be taken into account. In order to do this it is advantageous to make various assumptions which can be modified as the analysis becomes more complex. One assumption which is used throughout is that the components, both normally operating and standby, have a constant hazard rate, i.e., that failures are described by exponential distributions.

7.6.2   Perfect switching

The first case to be considered assumes that the sensing and changeover switch is 100% reliable, that the standby component does not fail while in the standby mode and that the components are identical with a failure rate λ.

(a)   *2-component system*

Consider first a 2 identical component system having a single main component and one standby component.

This arrangement can be regarded as an equivalent single unit which is allowed to fail once. After the first failure of the equivalent unit (failure of A), the standby component (B) takes over for the remainder of the mission and therefore the system does not fail. If there is a second failure of the equivalent unit (failure of B), the system also fails. The logic of this system operation implies that the Poisson distribution can be used to evaluate the probability of system failure since this distribution gives the probability of any number of component failures provided the components are operating in their useful life period. In this case it is necessary to find the probability of not more than one failure. Recalling Equation 6.19

$$P_x(t) = \frac{(\lambda t)^x e^{-\lambda t}}{x!} \tag{7.28}$$

in which $P_x(t)$ denotes the probability that x components fail in time t. Using Equation 7.28

$P[\text{no components fail}] = P_0(t)$

$$= e^{-\lambda t}$$

$P[\text{exactly one component fails}] = P_1(t)$

$$= \lambda t e^{-\lambda t}$$

Therefore, the reliability of the system is

$$R(t) = P_0(t) + P_1(t) = e^{-\lambda t}(1 + \lambda t) \tag{7.29}$$

(b)   *2 standby components*

Now consider one main component and two standby components. The number of failures that can be tolerated in the equivalent unit is two before the system fails. Extending the previous concept gives

$$R(t) = P_0(t) + P_1(t) + P_2(t)$$

$$= e^{-\lambda t}\left[1 + \lambda t + \frac{(\lambda t)^2}{2!}\right] \tag{7.30}$$

(c) *n standby components*

The general principle used to deduce Equations 7.29 and 7.30 can be extended to any number of standby components since the number of failures that can be tolerated is equal to the number of standby components. Therefore, in the general case of n identical standby components

$$R(t) = e^{-\lambda t}\left[1 + \lambda t + \frac{(\lambda t)^2}{2!} + \frac{(\lambda t)^3}{3!} + \ldots + \frac{(\lambda t)^n}{n!}\right] \tag{7.31a}$$

$$= \sum_{x=0}^{n} \frac{(\lambda t)^x e^{-\lambda t}}{x!} \tag{7.31b}$$

i.e., the probability of system failure is given by the sum of the first n terms of the Poisson distribution.

(d) *Mean time to failure*

The values of MTTF for these systems can be evaluated using the principle of Equation 7.24 giving, for a single standby component (case (a)),

$$m = \int_0^\infty e^{-\lambda t}(1 + \lambda t)\,dt$$

$$= \frac{1}{\lambda} + \frac{1}{\lambda}$$

$$= \frac{2}{\lambda} \tag{7.32}$$

and for n standby components (case (c)),

$$m = \int_0^\infty \sum_{x=0}^{n} \frac{(\lambda t)^x e^{-\lambda t}}{x!}$$

$$= \frac{n+1}{\lambda} \tag{7.33}$$

This result is intuitively obvious as the system becomes serial. As one component fails, a second identical component comes into operation. Therefore, the system MTTF is the sum of the individual component MTTF values.

Example 7.5

Compare the reliability of a 2-component system each having a failure rate of 0.02 f/hr after a time of 10 hr if they are (a) parallel redundant and, (b) standby redundant with a 100% reliable sensing and changeover device. Also, compare the MTTFs of the two systems.

(a)   *Parallel system.*

From Equation 7.18

$$R(10) = 2e^{-0.02 \times 10} - e^{-2 \times 0.02 \times 10}$$
$$= 0.967141$$

from Equation 7.26

$$m = \frac{1}{0.02} + \frac{1}{0.02} - \frac{1}{0.02 + 0.02}$$
$$= 75 \text{ hr}$$

(b)   *Standby system.*

From Equation 7.29

$$R(10) = e^{-0.02 \times 10}(1 + 0.02 \times 10)$$
$$= 0.982477$$

from Equation 7.32

$$m = \frac{2}{0.02} = 100 \text{ hr}$$

It can be seen from this example that the reliability of the standby system is greater than that of the parallel redundant system. It should be noted however that this is a general conclusion only when the sensing and changeover device is 100% reliable. This comparison is also reflected in the values of MTTF where the standby system MTTF is significantly longer than that of the parallel redundant system. It should be remembered that the MTTF is only meaningful if the components do not enter the wear-out region before the scheduled end of the mission. This was discussed in Section 6.8.4 where it was noted that the mean wear-out life may be much less than the MTTF.

7.6.3   Imperfect switching

It was assumed in the previous section that the sensing and changeover device was 100% reliable. It can be readily appreciated that this is unlikely, and that the reliability of this device is less than unity. This section includes the effect of the unreliability of these devices and shows the significant effect that they can have on the overall system reliability. This discussion assumes that the reliability of the normally operating component is unaffected by the unreliability of the sensing and switching device.

Define P_s as the probability of successful operation of the sensing and changeover device. Assume it to be a one-shot device, which, if successful, operates when required to do so, i.e., when the normally operating component fails. The value of P_s can be established in practice from a data collection scheme which records the number of successful and failed operations of the device since

$$P_s = \frac{\text{number of successful operations}}{\text{total number of requested operations}} \tag{7.34}$$

The most likely cause for the sensing and changeover device to fail to operate when needed is a failure of the device between the last time it was operated, tested or maintained and the occasion it is required to operate. These faults or failures are frequently termed unrevealed faults since they are not apparent until a subsequent action such as operation, testing or maintenance is performed. Continuously operated components, on the other hand, generally suffer what can be termed revealed faults, since these failures manifest themselves at the time of failure. Once one knows the distribution of idle times and the failure characteristics of the particular device being considered, the mean or expected value of P_s can therefore be evaluated by using the component reliability techniques described in Chapter 6.

Returning to the 2-component standby system in which the switching and sensing device is less than 100% reliable, system success requires that either no failures occur or one failure occurs and the switching device operates. The same logic that was used to derive Equation 7.29 gives

$$P\,[\text{no components fail}] = P_0(t)$$
$$= e^{-\lambda t}$$

$P[\text{exactly one component fails and the}$
$\quad$ sensing and switching device operates$] = P_1(t) \cdot P_s$
$$= P_s \lambda t e^{-\lambda t}$$

which gives

$$R(t) = e^{-\lambda t}(1 + P_s \lambda t) \tag{7.35}$$

This concept can be extended to the case of 2 or more standby components since each term of Equations 7.30 and 7.31 other than that associated with zero failures must be weighted by the value of P_s. A main additional complexity is that the value of P_s may be a function of time, therefore a variable, and different for each term of these equations.

The MTTF of the standby system can again be derived using Equation 7.24 and gives

$$m = \int_0^\infty e^{-\lambda t}(1 + P_s \lambda t)$$
$$= \frac{1 + P_s}{\lambda} \tag{7.36}$$

In order to illustrate the effect of P_s on the reliability of a standby system, consider the following numerical example.

Example 7.6

Reconsider Example 7.5 and evaluate the reliability and MTTF of the standby system for values of P_s between 1.00 and 0.90. The results of these calculations are shown in Table 7.2.

Table 7.2   Results of Example 7.6

P_s	$R(t)$ from Equation 7.35	m (hr) from Equation 7.36
1.00	0.982477	100.0
0.99	0.980839	99.5
0.98	0.979202	99.0
0.97	0.977565	98.5
0.96	0.975927	98.0
0.95	0.974290	97.5
0.94	0.972652	97.0
0.93	0.971015	96.5
0.92	0.969377	96.0
0.91	0.967740	95.5
0.90	0.966102	95.0

Recalling the results for the 2-component parallel system of Example 7.5, the values shown in Table 7.2 compare with $R(t) = 0.967141$ and $m = 75$ hr. It follows therefore that the value of P_s significantly degrades the reliability of the standby system and can cause its reliability to be less than that of the parallel system. The values of MTTF for the standby system, however, still remain significantly greater than that of the parallel system.

7.6.4   Effect of spare components

A mode of system operation which is fundamentally similar to that of standby systems is the case in which a number of identical units are normally operating and one or more similar units are held as spares to replace the function of any of the normally operating units when they fail. This type of system can be evaluated using the same techniques described in the previous sections. In this evaluation, an important assumption is made. This is that the replacement time of a failed component by a spare is sufficiently short that under this condition the system is not considered to be failed. This is often a very valid assumption and, if applicable, considerably simplifies the evaluation of system reliability. An additional assumption is that failed components are not repaired. If repair action is possible then other techniques, such as Markov modelling, must be employed. This is discussed in Chapters 8 and 9.

Consider a system comprising N identical components all of which must operate for system success and consider that there are n spares available to the operating personnel as standby components. It follows that n failures in the system can be tolerated and only the $(n+1)$ failure causes system failure. This logic also indicates that the spare components are themselves not replaced following their use as a normally operating component.

Again, consider the case of exponential distributions and assume that the failure rate of each component is λ.

$$\text{The failure rate of the system} = \sum_{i=1}^{N} \lambda_i$$

$$= N\lambda$$

From Equation 7.31a

$$R(t) = e^{-N\lambda t}\left[1 + N\lambda t + \frac{(N\lambda t)^2}{2!} + \ldots + \frac{(N\lambda t)^n}{n!}\right] \tag{7.37}$$

and from Equation 7.33

$$m = \frac{n+1}{N\lambda} \tag{7.38}$$

Example 7.7

A system contains 50 identical components each of which has a failure rate of 0.001 f/hr. Assuming that system failure occurs when any one component fails, evaluate the system reliability for an operating period of 20 hr and the MTTF when no spares are available and also when a varying number of spares between 1 and 6 are carried as immediate replacements. If the system is to have a minimum reliability of 0.9950, what is the minimum number of spares that must be carried as immediate replacements?

$$\text{System failure rate} = N\lambda$$

$$= 50 \times 0.001 = 0.05 \text{ f/hr}$$

$$R \text{ (no spares available)} = e^{-0.05 \times 20}$$

$$= 0.367879$$

$$R \text{ (n spares available)} = e^{-0.05 \times 20}\left[1 + (0.05 \times 20)\right.$$

$$\left. + \frac{(0.05 \times 20)^2}{2!} + \ldots + \frac{(0.05 \times 20)^n}{n!}\right]$$

Table 7.3   Results for Example 7.7

Number of spares, n	System reliability R(20)	MTTF m, hr
0	0.367879	20
1	0.735759	40
2	0.919699	60
3	0.981012	80
4	0.996340	100
5	0.999406	120
6	0.999917	140

The solution of this equation is shown in Table 7.3 for $n = 0, 1, 2, \ldots, 6$.

Also m (no spares available) $= \dfrac{1}{N\lambda}$

$$= \frac{1}{0.05} = 20 \text{ hr}$$

and m (n spares available) $= \dfrac{n+1}{N\lambda}$

$$= \frac{n+1}{0.05}$$

The solution of this equation is also shown in Table 7.3 for $n = 0, 1, 2, \ldots, 6$.

It can be seen from Table 7.3 that the number of spares should be between 3 and 4 in order to achieve a minimum reliability of 0.9950. Since only an integer number of spares can be carried, the minimum number of spares is 4.

One important conclusion that can be drawn from the results of Example 7.7 is that the provision of a small number of spares in a large system can make a very large difference to the system reliability. The greatest change in reliability is created by the provision of the first spare. The values of MTTF on the other hand continue to increase linearly. It should be remembered however that the wear out region may be reached long before these values of MTTF are obtained.

The question of how many spares should be carried in practice depends on whether it is a safety problem or an availability problem. In the first case, the predominant criterion is achieving an acceptable level of reliability to satisfy the safety requirements, and cost becomes secondary. In the second case, the cost is also of high priority. As the number of spares carried is increased, the capital cost of the system also increases. In order to arrive at the required number of spares it is necessary to make an economic comparison between the increased return due to increased reliability and the required capital invested to achieve this increased reliability. Economic aspects are outside the scope of this book but it clearly is an important factor in deciding the required level of system reliability.

7.6.5 Non-identical components

The preceding sections have assumed that all the components of the standby system are identical. In a real system this is frequently not true and the failure rates of operating and standby components can be different owing to the nature of the components being used. A common example is when a generator is used as the normal operating component of a d.c. supply and a battery is used as the standby component. In this case the failure rates could be very different. Two methods are presented that can be used to evaluate the reliability of standby systems containing non-identical components. The first makes use of the concept of joint probability density functions and is the subject of this section. This method is perfectly general and can be used in conjunction with any probability distribution. It can also be used for identical as well as non-identical components. The resulting equations should however be amenable to integration. This approach is illustrated for the exponential case only. The second method is to use a more direct and intuitive approach which is probably simpler and more appealing than the joint density function method.

In order to illustrate the joint density function approach, consider two components A and B in a standby system and having failure rates λ_a and λ_b respectively. Let A be the normal operating component and B be the standby one. Assume A fails at time t_1 when B takes over instantaneously. Assume B fails at time t. Time to failure of B is then $t_2 = t - t_1$.

$$\text{Failure density function of A, } f_a(t_1) = \lambda_a \exp(-\lambda_a t_1) \tag{7.39}$$

$$\text{Failure density function of B, } f_b(t_2) = \lambda_b \exp(-\lambda_b t_2) \tag{7.40}$$

The joint density function of both components operating is given by

$$
\begin{aligned}
f(t) &= f_a(t_1) \cdot f_b(t_2) \\
&= \lambda_a \exp(-\lambda_a t_1) \cdot \lambda_b \exp(-\lambda_b t_2) \\
&= \lambda_a \exp(-\lambda_a t_1) \cdot \lambda_b \exp[-\lambda_b(t - t_1)]
\end{aligned} \tag{7.41}
$$

There are two time functions, t_1 and t in Equation 7.41. In order to obtain the joint density function in terms of t only, $f(t)$ is integrated with reference to t_1. This gives

$$f(t) = \int_{t_1=0}^{t} \lambda_a \lambda_b \exp(-\lambda_a t_1) \exp[-\lambda_b(t-t_1)] \, dt_1$$

$$= \frac{\lambda_a \lambda_b}{\lambda_a - \lambda_b} [\exp(-\lambda_b t) - \exp(-\lambda_a t)] \tag{7.42}$$

The system reliability can now be evaluated from

$$R(t) = \int_t^{\infty} f(t) \, dt$$

$$= \frac{\lambda_a \lambda_b}{\lambda_a - \lambda_b} \int_t^{\infty} [\exp(-\lambda_b t) - \exp(-\lambda_a t)] \, dt$$

$$= \frac{\lambda_a}{\lambda_a - \lambda_b} \exp(-\lambda_b t) + \frac{\lambda_b}{\lambda_a - \lambda_b} \exp(-\lambda_a t) \tag{7.43}$$

Equation 7.43 can be expressed in the same general form as Equation 7.29 by adding and subtracting $\exp(-\lambda_a t)$ and rearranging to give

$$R(t) = \exp(-\lambda_a t) + \frac{\lambda_a}{\lambda_b - \lambda_a} [\exp(-\lambda_a t) - \exp(-\lambda_b t)] \tag{7.44}$$

The MTTF is given by

$$m = \int_0^{\infty} R(t) \, dt$$

$$= \frac{1}{\lambda_a} + \frac{1}{\lambda_b} \tag{7.45}$$

If the sensing and changeover device is not 100% reliable, Equation 7.44 can be modified in the same way as Equation 7.35 to give

$$R(t) = \exp(-\lambda_a t) + \frac{P_s \lambda_a}{\lambda_b - \lambda_a} [\exp(-\lambda_a t) - \exp(-\lambda_b t)] \tag{7.46}$$

where P_s is as defined in Section 7.6.3.

This approach can be extended to include any number of standby components. Consider a standby system consisting of one normally operating component having a density function $f_1(t_1)$ and $(n-1)$ components in standby having density functions $f_2(t_2), f_3(t_3), \ldots, f_n(t_n)$.

The joint density function is

$$f(t) = \int_{t_{n-1}=0}^{t}, \ldots, \int_{t_2=0}^{t_3} \int_{t_1=0}^{t_2} f_1(t_1) f_2(t_2), \ldots, f_n(t_n) \, dt_1 \, dt_2, \ldots, dt_{n-1} \tag{7.47}$$

where t_1 represents the time of failure of component 1

t_2 represents the time of failure of component 2

$\vdots$

t_n represents the time of failure of component n

and $t_n = t - t_{n-1}$

Equations representing the joint density function, the survivor function and the MTTF can be derived by substituting the appropriate density functions of the components (they need not all be identical functions) into Equation 7.47 and performing sequential integrations.

7.6.6   Failures in the standby mode

It was assumed in the previous developments that the standby components do not fail while in the standby mode. This is not necessarily the case in practice though, in general, the failure rate of a component in the standby mode is less than that when it is operating. This effect can also be included in the reliability evaluation of the system. In addition, the sensing and changeover device may not operate when requested, or may operate, but incorrectly. The following general approach permits all these failure modes and their appropriate failure rates to be taken into account. The examples shown are again limited to the case of constant hazard rates, i.e., the exponential distribution.

In this method all events leading to system success are divided into mutually exclusive events. The expression for system reliability can then be derived by adding the reliability associated with each of these individual mutually exclusive events. This method is perfectly general and involves less effort and computation than the failure density function approach. It is best illustrated using a few simple cases.

(a)   *Case 1*

Consider the case of two non-identical components A and B forming the standby system described in Section 7.6.5 in which the standby component B cannot fail in the standby mode. The events leading to the system success are either

(i)   Component A does not fail for an interval of time 0 to t, or

(ii)   Component A fails at time $t_1 < t$ and component B does not fail in the interval t_1 to t.

Let R_1 and R_2 be the reliabilities associated with these two events respectively, then

$$R_1 = \exp\left(-\lambda_a t\right)$$

$$R_2 = \int_{t_1=0}^{t} (\text{density function for one failure})\, dt_1,$$

$$= \int_{t_1=0}^{t} (\text{probability of one failure in } t_1)$$
$$(\text{probability of no failures in } dt_1)\, dt_1$$

$$= \int_{t_1=0}^{t} [\{\lambda_a \exp[-\lambda_a t_1]\}\{\exp[-\lambda_b(t-t_1)]\}]\, dt_1$$

$$= \lambda_a \exp(-\lambda_b t) \int_{0}^{t} \exp[-(\lambda_a - \lambda_b)t_1]\, dt_1$$

$$= \frac{\lambda_a}{\lambda_a - \lambda_b} \exp(-\lambda_b t)\{1 - \exp[-(\lambda_a - \lambda_b)t]\}$$

$$= \frac{\lambda_a}{\lambda_b - \lambda_a} [\exp(-\lambda_a t) - \exp(-\lambda_b t)]$$

Since the events (i) and (ii) are mutually exclusive

$$R(t) = R_1 + R_2$$
$$= \exp(-\lambda_a t) + \frac{\lambda_a}{\lambda_b - \lambda_a} [\exp(-\lambda_a t) - \exp(-\lambda_b t)] \tag{7.48}$$

which is seen to be identical to Equation 7.44, obtained using the joint failure density approach.

The mutually exclusive contributions R_1 and R_2 can be illustrated in graphical form as shown in Figure 7.2.

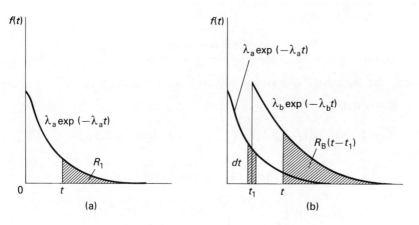

Fig. 7.2 Graphical representation of Case 1. (a) Contribution R_1. (b) Contribution R_2

The contribution R_1 is simply given by the area under the exponential curve associated with component A for times greater than t, i.e., $R_1 = \exp(-\lambda_a t)$.

The contribution R_2 for a given value of t_1 is the area under the exponential curve associated with component B $[R_B(t-t_1)]$ weighted by the probability that component A fails in the time interval dt_1 at t_1.

That is, $R_2(t_1) = R_B(t-t_1) \cdot \lambda_a \exp(-\lambda_a t_1) dt_1$

$$= \exp[-\lambda_b(t-t_1)] \cdot \lambda_a \exp(-\lambda_a t_1) dt_1$$

The value R_2 can then be determined by integrating $R_2(t_1)$ over all values of t_1.

(b)   *Case 2*

Consider now the case of 2 components in a standby system for which λ_1 is the failure rate of the normal operating component, λ_2 is the failure rate of the standby component when operating and λ_3 is its failure rate when in a standby mode.

Using a similar logic to that used in Case 1, the mutually exclusive events leading to system success are
(i)   Component 1 does not fail during the time $(0-t)$,
(ii) Component 1 fails at time t_1 and component 2 is not failed at time t_1 (failure rate λ_3) and component 2 does not fail in the time $(t-t_1)$ (failure rate λ_2).
These events can be tabulated as shown in Table 7.4.

Table 7.4   Events of Case 2

Event	Mode of operation in time domain of Component 1	Component 2
1	good for time t	—
2	fails at time t_1	good for time t_1
		good for time t_1 to t

Using the same logical derivation as in Case 1

$$R_1 = \exp(-\lambda_1 t)$$

$$R_2 = \int_{t_1=0}^{t} \lambda_1 \exp(-\lambda_1 t_1) \exp(-\lambda_3 t_1) \exp[-\lambda_2(t-t_1)] dt_1$$

$$= \lambda_1 \exp(-\lambda_2 t) \int_0^t \exp[-(\lambda_1 + \lambda_3 - \lambda_2)t_1] dt_1$$

$$= \lambda_1 \exp(-\lambda_2 t) \left[\frac{1}{\lambda_1 + \lambda_3 - \lambda_2} - \frac{\exp[-(\lambda_1 + \lambda_3 - \lambda_2)t]}{\lambda_1 + \lambda_3 - \lambda_2} \right]$$

$$= \frac{\lambda_1}{\lambda_1 + \lambda_3 - \lambda_2} \{ \exp(-\lambda_2 t) - \exp[-(\lambda_1 + \lambda_3)t] \}$$

and the system reliability is

$$R(t) = R_1 + R_2$$

$$= \exp(-\lambda_1 t) + \frac{\lambda_1}{\lambda_1 + \lambda_3 - \lambda_2} \{\exp(-\lambda_2 t) - \exp[-(\lambda_1 + \lambda_3)t]\} \quad (7.49)$$

which differs from Equation 7.48 in the second term where the original λ_1 is replaced by $(\lambda_1 + \lambda_3)$ in two of the three locations.

(c)   *Case 3*

Consider the system shown in Figure 7.3 in which components 1 and 2 operate as a parallel redundant system and component 3 is used when both 1 and 2 have failed.

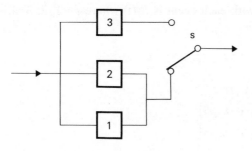

Fig. 7.3   System used for Case 3

In this case assume that the following system data is available:

—all components operate in their useful life period and wear-out can be neglected
—failure rate of component 1 when energized $= \lambda_{1e}$
—failure rate of component 2 when energized $= \lambda_{2e}$
—failure rate of component 3 when energized $= \lambda_{3e}$
—failure rate of component 3 when on standby $= \lambda_{3s}$
—failure rate of the sensing device $= \lambda_s$
—failure rate of changeover device when on standby $= \lambda_{cs}$
—failure rate of changeover device after switching $= \lambda_{ce}$
—probability of successful changeover $= P_s$

Assume that the system is successful if only one of the components is operating and that component 3 is called in after both 1 and 2 have failed. The mutually exclusive events shown in Table 7.5 represent the successful states of the system.

Table 7.5   Events of Case 3

| Event | 1 | 2 | 3 | 3 | Sensing device | Changeover device | | |
			Standby	Energized		Standby	Energized	After switching
1	good/t	good/t						
2	good/t	bad/t						
3	bad/t	good/t						
4	bad/t_1	bad/t_2	good/t_2	good/$t-t_2$	good/t_2	good/t_2	good/one cycle	good/$t-t_2$
5	bad/t_2	bad/t_1	good/t_2	good/$t-t_2$	good/t_2	good/t_2	good/one cycle	good/$t-t_2$

In Table 7.5, $t > t_2 > t_1$.

If the reliability associated with each event is $R_i(t)$ where $i = 1, 2, 3, 4, 5$, then the system reliability is

$$R(t) = \sum_{i=1}^{5} R_i(t)$$

$$R_1(t) = \exp(-\lambda_{1e}t) \exp(-\lambda_{2e}t)$$

$$R_2(t) = \exp(-\lambda_{1e}t)[1 - \exp(-\lambda_{2e}t)]$$

$$R_3(t) = \exp(-\lambda_{2e}t)[1 - \exp(-\lambda_{1e}t)]$$

$$R_4(t) = \int_{t_2=0}^{t} \int_{t_1=0}^{t_2} \lambda_{1e} \exp(-\lambda_{1e}t_1) \cdot \lambda_{2e} \exp(-\lambda_{2e}t_2)$$
$$\times \exp(-\lambda_{3s}t_2) \cdot \exp[-\lambda_{3e}(t-t_2)]$$
$$\times \exp(-\lambda_s t_2) \cdot \exp(-\lambda_{cs}t_2) \cdot P_s \cdot \exp[-\lambda_{ce}(t-t_2)] \, dt_1 \, dt_2$$

$$= \lambda_{2e}P_s \exp[-(\lambda_{3e} + \lambda_{ce})t] \left\{ \frac{1}{\lambda_q}[1 - \exp(-\lambda_q t)] - \frac{1}{\lambda_q + \lambda_{1e}} \right.$$
$$\left. \times \{1 - \exp[-(\lambda_q + \lambda_{1e})t]\} \right\}$$

where $\lambda_q = \lambda_{2e} + \lambda_{3s} + \lambda_s + \lambda_{cs} - \lambda_{3e} - \lambda_{ce}$

similarly,

$$R_5(t) = \lambda_{1e}P_s \exp[-(\lambda_{3e} + \lambda_{ce})t] \left\{ \frac{1}{\lambda'_q}[1 - \exp(-\lambda'_q t)] \right.$$
$$\left. - \frac{1}{\lambda'_q + \lambda_{2e}} \{1 - \exp[-(\lambda'_q + \lambda_{2e})t]\} \right\}$$

where $\lambda'_q = \lambda_{1e} + \lambda_{3s} + \lambda_s + \lambda_{cs} - \lambda_{3e} - \lambda_{ce}$

and $R(t) = R_1(t) + R_2(t) + R_3(t) + R_4(t) + R_5(t)$

7.7 Wearout and component reliability

In most of the reliability calculations made so far, it has been assumed that the components are operating in their useful life period with a constant hazard rate. This therefore implies exponential density functions. The MTTF values have been calculated for several system configurations. It again must be stressed that this time parameter is an average value and assumes that the component continues to operate in its useful life period. Although the useful life period can be extended by careful and regular preventive maintenance and replacement, in practice a component or system may fail owing to wearout long before the MTTF is reached. Therefore, it is not admissible to conclude from a derived MTTF that a system will operate, on average, for this period of time. As discussed in Chapter 6, the failure density function in the wearout region can often be approximated using a normal distribution around the mean life of a component. Recalling Equation 6.24 and designating t as the component age, M as the mean wearout life and σ as the standard deviation of wearout lives around this mean gives the failure density function for the wearout region as

$$f(t) = \frac{1}{\sigma\sqrt{2\pi}} \exp\left(-\frac{(t-M)^2}{2\sigma^2}\right) \tag{7.50}$$

The shapes of the probability functions for the normal distribution shown in Figure 6.9 indicate that the hazard rate increases very rapidly with time unlike the constant value of failure rate associated with the useful life period. Consequently, the values of M can be comparatively very much shorter than the values of MTTF (m).

The most important factor to consider is how the system reliability will be affected if the component is allowed to operate in its wearout region. This effect can be evaluated by considering the cumulative probability of a component surviving both chance events and wearout.

The probability that a component will not fail owing to wearout during the mission time of t from T to $T+t$ is an *a posteriori* probability and can be evaluated using Equation 6.36. If the wearout probabilities are subscripted with w, then

$$R_w(t) = 1 - Q_w(t) = 1 - \frac{\displaystyle\int_T^{T+t} f(t)\,dt}{\displaystyle\int_T^{\infty} f(t)\,dt} = \frac{\displaystyle\int_{T+t}^{\infty} f(t)\,dt}{\displaystyle\int_T^{\infty} f(t)\,dt} \tag{7.51}$$

$$= \frac{R_w(T+t)}{R_w(T)} \tag{7.52}$$

The values required in Equations 7.51 and 7.52 can be obtained from tables using the techniques described in Section 6.7.3. When chance failures are also included, the overall probability of no failures implies that (no failures occur due to chance events and no failures occur owing to wearout) in the interval t from T to $T+t$. If chance events are designated with the subscript c

$$R(t) = R_c(t) \cdot R_w(t)$$

$$= e^{-\lambda t} \cdot \frac{R_w(T+t)}{R_w(T)} \tag{7.53}$$

In the particular case of the life period commencing at zero time, Equation 7.53 becomes

$$R(t) = e^{-\lambda t} \frac{R_w(0+t)}{R_w(0)}$$

$$= e^{-\lambda t} R_w(t) \tag{7.54}$$

since $R_w(0)$ is assumed to be unity, i.e., the component is known to be operating at zero time.

The variation of $R(t)$ with time depends greatly on the relative values of m and M. These differences are illustrated in Figures 7.4a and 7.4b for the cases of $m > M$ and $m < M$, respectively. From Figure 7.4, it is seen that the combined value of reliability follows the exponential curve up to a value T at which time the later occurring wearout failures dominate and the value of $R(t)$ decreases rapidly to zero. From Figure 7.4 it is seen that, when $m < M$, failures occur mainly by chance up to about the MTTF, beyond which the failures are dominated by wearout failures. In the case when $m > M$, the value of T can be much less than m, as shown in Figure 7.4a.

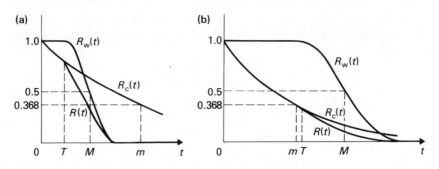

Fig. 7.4 Variation of $R(t)$ with age. (a) $m > M$. (b) $m < M$

High values of system reliability can be achieved, in practice, for extended periods of operation provided proper debugging procedures are adopted to eliminate early or premature failures and strict component replacement schedules are followed during preventive maintenance so that components do not enter their wearout region. This component replacement is essential if reliable system operation is required beyond the component's normal wearout time. Such replacement restores the system to an operational condition of low failure probability. Thus, when good quality preventive maintenance is performed, reliable system operation becomes possible for very long periods. Bad preventive maintenance on the other hand can degrade the system reliability and therefore the skill and quality of the maintenance personnel is a big factor in such situations. The various types of maintenance actions are discussed in the next section. First, consider a numerical example of evaluating system reliability which includes both chance and wearout effects.

Example 7.8

A pump has a useful life failure rate of 100 failures per 10^6 hours, a mean wearout life of 10 000 hr with a standard deviation of 2000 hr. Assuming that the wearout failure distribution is normal, evaluate the reliability of the pump for (a) a 100 hr mission starting at the 9900 hour point of its life cycle and, (b) a similar mission starting 1000 hours later.

(a)   During the useful life period

$$R_c(t) = \exp\left(-100 \times 10^{-6} \times 100\right)$$

$$= 0.990050$$

In Equation 7.52, $T = 9900$, $t = 100$ and $T + t = 10\ 000$. In Equation 7.50, $M = 10\ 000$ and $\sigma = 2000$.

The normal distribution can be used in its standard form as described in Section 6.7.2, Equation 6.25.

For the time $T = 9900$:

$$Z_1 = \frac{9900 - 10\ 000}{2000} = -0.05$$

and for the time $T + t = 10\ 000$:

$$Z_2 = \frac{10\ 000 - 10\ 000}{2000} = 0.0$$

From the tables in Appendix 2

$$R_w(T) = \int_T^\infty f(t)\, dt = 0.5199$$

and $R_w(T + t) = \int_{T+t}^\infty f(t)\, dt = 0.5$

Therefore from Equation 7.52

$$R_w(t) = \frac{0.5}{0.5199} = 0.961723$$

and from Equation 7.54

$$R(t) = R_c(t) \cdot R_w(t)$$
$$= 0.990050 \times 0.961723$$
$$= 0.952154$$

(b) Using the same technique as in (a) above, we can deduce

$R_c(t) = 0.990050$ (unchanged)

$$R_w(t) = \frac{0.3085}{0.3264} = 0.945159$$

and $R(t) = 0.990050 \times 0.945159 = 0.935755$

7.8 Maintenance and component reliability

Maintenance can be classified into two main categories: preventive maintenance and corrective maintenance. Preventive maintenance is performed in order to keep the system in a condition that is consistent with the required levels of performance and reliability. This is achieved by regularly checking all the operating systems, cleaning, adjusting, lubricating, and so on, all the components, replacing the components nearing a wearout condition and checking and repairing failed redundant components. The objective of this maintenance procedure is to keep the system failure rates from increasing above the design levels. Corrective maintenance is necessitated by system in-service failures or malfunction. Its purpose is to restore system operation as soon as possible after failure by replacing, repairing or adjusting the components which have caused interruption or breakdown of the system.

It follows that preventive maintenance can be, and is, performed at regular intervals, but the frequency at which corrective maintenance is performed depends upon the failure rates of the components that cause system failures. On average, the MTTF of a system, m, indicates the average time a system takes to fail, therefore for an operating time t, an average of t/m corrective maintenance actions will have to be performed. The time taken for each of the maintenance actions to be completed depends upon which components of the system have failed.

It was shown in Chapter 4 and also earlier in this chapter that the overall system reliability is increased using parallel redundant components. This improvement in reliability however only results if all the redundant components are checked and repaired, if found to be necessary, before each mission. With such a preventive maintenance policy, the system would fail less frequently than it would without inspection because it ensures that every new operating period or mission phase begins with full redundancy. It follows therefore that the more frequently the system is inspected, the longer is the system's MTTF. If the system is left uninspected and redundant components allowed to remain in a failed state, the MTTF decreases. This relationship between time interval of inspections and MTTF is illustrated in Figure 7.5, from which it can be

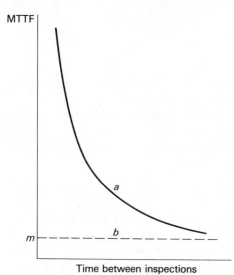

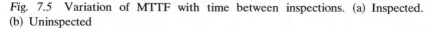

Fig. 7.5   Variation of MTTF with time between inspections. (a) Inspected. (b) Uninspected

observed that, without inspection (i.e., time between inspections becomes infinite) the MTTF reduces to that which would be evaluated for a parallel redundant system if it were left until all components of the system failed. It should be noted however that the improvement which can be created by regular inspections requires careful and skilful maintenance procedures to be adopted. Without this care and skill it is all too easy to leave the system following preventive maintenance in a state that is worse than or little better than before the preventive maintenance action was started.

To illustrate these ideas, consider the following numerical example.

Example 7.9

Consider the following three schemes and compare the maintenance activities for 1000×10 hr missions and the reliabilities of the schemes.

Scheme 1—a single component with a failure rate of 0.01 f/hr.
Scheme 2—a system of 3 components in parallel with identical failure rates of 0.01 f/hr and which is perfectly maintained.
Scheme 3—the same as scheme 2 but left without maintenance until the system fails.

Scheme 1

For a single component with $\lambda = 0.01$ f/hr and a mission time of 10 hr

$$R(t) = e^{-0.01 \times 10} = 0.9048$$

$$m = \frac{1}{0.01} = 100 \text{ hr}$$

$$Q(t) = 1 - 0.9048 = 0.0952$$

These values apply for each mission of 10 hours since, for the mission to commence, the single component must be operative.

For 1000 missions using this scheme there will be, on the average, 95.2 failures which, in integers, implies that there will be 96 failures, 96 corrective maintenance operations and 96 component replacements since one component is replaced at each failure.

Scheme 2

For 3 identical components with $\lambda = 0.01$ f/hr and a 10 hr mission, the following logic is used.

Since perfect maintenance is assumed, each mission commences with all 3 components in a working state and therefore the system fails during a mission only if all 3 components fail during a mission time of 10 hr, i.e.;

$$Q(t) = (1 - e^{-0.01 \times 10})^3$$
$$= (0.0952)^3 = 0.0009$$
$$R(t) = 1 - Q(t) = 0.9991$$

Therefore with perfect maintenance there will be, on average, 0.9 failures in 1000 missions which, in integers, implies 1 failure per 1000 missions.

Consider now the number of maintenance actions and number of component replacements. Since the components are identical, the binomial distribution can be used to determine the number of component failures during each mission of 10 hrs. These components will be replaced between missions and, therefore, each new mission will start with 3 operative components. The results of the binomial expansion are shown in Table 7.6.

The results shown in Table 7.6 indicate that there will be, on average in 1000 missions, 286 component replacements and 260 corrective maintenance actions. In addition, the scheme must be checked before each

Table 7.6   Results for scheme 2 of Example 7.9

Number of failures in each mission	Probability of occurrence	Expected number of component replacements in 1000 missions	Number of maintenance actions in 1000 missions
0	$e^{-3\lambda t}$ $= 0.7408$	—	—
1	$3e^{-2\lambda t}(1-e^{-\lambda t}) = 0.2337$	233.7	233.7
2	$3e^{-\lambda t}(1-e^{-\lambda t})^2 = 0.0246$	49.2	24.6
3	$(1-e^{-\lambda t})^3$ $= 0.0009$	2.7	0.9
	1.0000	285.6	259.2

mission starts and therefore there will also be 1000 preventive maintenance actions for 1000 missions. The expected number of component replacements could have been obtained more directly by multiplying the 95.2 value obtained in Scheme 1 by 3, i.e., 285.6 components.

Scheme 3

If 3 units are used in parallel redundancy and no preventive maintenance is performed, the system will again only fail when all 3 components fail. In this case however the condition of the components is not checked between missions and therefore component failures are detected only when all 3 components have failed. The MTTF of this system can be calculated using Equation 7.27 for parallel redundant systems to give

$$m = \frac{3}{0.01} - \frac{3}{0.01+0.01} + \frac{1}{0.01+0.01+0.01}$$

$$= 300 - 150 + 33.3$$

$$= 183.3 \, hr$$

This value of MTTF implies that 1 system failure occurs in 18.33×10 hr missions or there are

1000/18.33 = 54.56 system failures in 1000 missions

54.56 ($\equiv 55$) corrective maintenance actions

$3 \times 55 = 165$ component replacements since 3 components must be replaced at each system failure.

Also, the average probability of mission failure,

$$Q(t) = 54.56/1000$$

$$= 0.0546$$

and $R(t) = 1 - Q(t)$

$$= 0.9454$$

The results for each of these schemes are shown in Table 7.7 for a total of 1000 missions. It can be seen that Scheme 2 has the highest value of reliability and the lowest number of system failures as may be reasonably expected. This increased reliability is achieved however by a considerable increase in maintenance activity and by replacing a considerably greater number of components, i.e., it is achieved by increased capital and operating costs. The most appropriate scheme to choose is therefore dependent upon system requirements, e.g., whether failures can be tolerated, and an economic appraisal of the schemes.

Table 7.7 Summary of results for Example 7.9

Scheme	Mission reliability	Total number of maintenance actions	Number of components replaced	Number of mission failures
1	0.9048	96	96	96
2	0.9991	1260	286	1
3	0.9454	55	165	55

7.9 Conclusions

This chapter has been concerned with evaluating the reliability of series, parallel and standby systems when the times to failure obey a probability distribution. Although much of the discussion has centred on exponential distributions, this is not an inherent limitation and the techniques apply equally well to any other distribution of times to failure. The only essential difference is that the integration for some distributions is rather complex or even impossible analytically and additional numerical integration techniques must be used. This can make the evaluation tedious or too difficult for hand calculations and digital computer solutions are then required. The only significant limitation of the techniques described in this chapter is that they generally assume instantaneous replacement. This is usually valid for mission-oriented systems particularly when it is the probability of the first failure that is required. The techniques are reasonably valid for repairable systems provided the repair, or down time, is very small compared to the operating, or up time. If this is not a valid assumption, techniques such as the Markov approach presented in Chapters 8 and 9 must be used. These additional techniques frequently limit the analysis to only exponential distributions unless additional complex techniques are included.

Problems

1. A system consists of three black boxes A, B and C. These may be arranged in any one of the four configurations shown in Figure 7.6. The individual

(a)   (b)

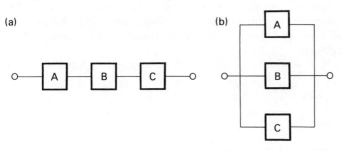

(c)   (d)

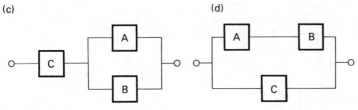

Fig. 7.6

component reliabilities are

$$R_A(t) = e^{-\alpha t}$$
$$R_B(t) = e^{-\beta t}$$
$$R_C(t) = e^{-\gamma t}$$

Write an expression for the system reliability in each of the four cases.

2. The system shown in Figure 7.7 has the following assumed average failure rates

	f/1000 hr
Signal Supply	0.010
Transmission Link 1	0.015
Transmission Link 2	0.027
Receiver	0.011

Transmission Link 1

Transmission Link 2

Signal supply

Receiver

Fig. 7.7

This circuit is left operating for a period of 1000 hr. What is the probability of it still operating at the end of this time? If transmission link 2 is removed from service, what is the probability of the system operating at the end of a 1000 hr period?

3   A system contains a series string of components for which $\sum \lambda = 0.005$ f/hr. What is the reliability of this system for a mission time of 10 hours? If a similar system is placed in parallel what is the reliability of the configuration for a 10 hr mission?

4   For the stand-by system shown in Figure 7.8, mission success requires at least

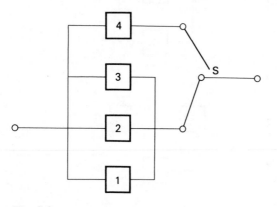

Fig. 7.8

two components. Components 1, 2 and 3 are in parallel and component 4 is in stand-by. Assuming 100% reliable sensing and changeover arrangement, develop the expression for the system reliability. Assume constant failure rates, λ_1, λ_2, λ_3 and λ_4 for components 1, 2, 3 and 4 respectively.

5   Calculate the reliability of the system shown in Figure 7.9 for a 100 hr

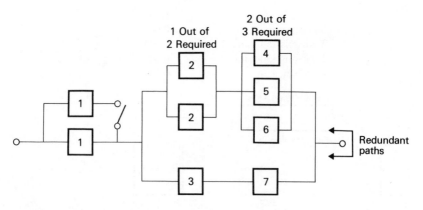

Fig. 7.9

mission.

$$\lambda_1 = 12 \times 10^{-5} \text{ f/hr}$$
$$\lambda_2 = 2 \times 10^{-4} \text{ f/hr}$$
$$\lambda_3 = 1 \times 10^{-5} \text{ f/hr}$$
$$\lambda_4 = \lambda_5 = 10 \times 10^{-5} \text{ f/hr}$$
$$\lambda_6 = 5 \times 10^{-5} \text{ f/hr}$$
$$\lambda_7 = 10 \times 10^{-5} \text{ f/hr}$$

6 (a) Calculate the reliability of the system shown in Figure 7.10 for a

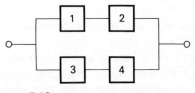

Fig. 7.10

1000 hr mission.

$$\lambda_1 = 1 \times 10^{-5} \text{ f/hr}; \qquad \lambda_2 = 10 \times 10^{-5} \text{ f/hr};$$
$$\lambda_3 = 2 \times 10^{-4} \text{ f/hr}; \qquad \lambda_4 = 5 \times 10^{-5} \text{ f/hr}.$$

(b) What is the mean time to failure for this system.
(c) Repeat part (a) but with the following additional data.

Component	1	2	3	4
Mean wearout time, hr	800	1600	5000	6000
Standard deviation, hr	400	600	200	1000

The mission starts at $T = 1000$ hr in the life of the system.

7 Derive an expression for the reliability of the system shown in Figure 7.11.

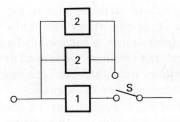

Fig. 7.11

Applicable rates λ_{1e} (1, energized mode)

λ_{2e} (2, energized mode)

λ_{se} (switch, energized mode)

λ_{ss} (switch, standby mode)

8 Discrete Markov chains

8.1 Introduction

Chapter 7 described and illustrated several analytical techniques for evaluating the reliability of systems. Although these techniques can be applied to both non-repairable and repairable systems, in the latter case they assume that the repair process is instantaneous or negligible compared with the operating time. This is an inherent restriction and additional techniques are required if this assumption is not valid. One very important technique that overcomes this problem and which has received considerable attention and use during the past few years is known as the Markov approach or Markov modelling. Several excellent texts [4, 25–27] are available on the subject of the application of Markov chains to reliability analysis.

The Markov approach can be applied to the random behaviour of systems that vary discretely or continuously with respect to time and space. This discrete or continuous random variation is known as a stochastic process. Not all stochastic processes can be modelled using the basic Markov approach although there are techniques available for modelling some additional stochastic processes using extensions of this basic method. These additional techniques will be discussed in Chapter 12.

In order for the basic Markov approach to be applicable, the behaviour of the system must be characterized by a lack of memory, that is, the future states of a system are independent of all past states except the immediately preceding one. Therefore the future random behaviour of a system only depends on where it is at present, not on where it has been in the past or how it arrived at its present position. In addition, the process must be stationary, sometimes called homogeneous, for the approach to be applicable. This means that the behaviour of the system must be the same at all points of time irrespective of the point of time being considered, i.e., the probability of making a transition from one given state to another is the same (stationary) at all times in the past and future. It is evident from these two aspects, lack of memory and being stationary, that the Markov approach is applicable to those systems whose behaviour can be described by a probability distribution that is characterized by a constant hazard rate, i.e., Poisson and exponential distributions, since only if the hazard rate is constant does the probability of making a transition between two states remain constant at all points of time. If this probability is a function of time or the number of discrete steps, then the process is non-stationary and designated as non-Markovian.

In the general case of Markov models, both time and space may either be discrete or continuous. In the particular case of system reliability evaluation, space is normally represented only as a discrete function since this represents the discrete and identifiable states in which the system and its components can reside, whereas time may either be discrete or continuous. This text only considers these two cases. The discrete case, generally known as a Markov chain, is discussed in this chapter. The continuous case, generally known as a Markov process, is discussed in Chapter 9. The reader may be primarily interested in the continuous case, but should also be familiar with the concepts and techniques described in this chapter before reading Chapter 9.

The reader should recognize that, although this chapter was initially introduced by the problem that repair was not included in the techniques of Chapter 7, and could be overcome by the use of the Markov approach, the techniques described in this and subsequent chapters are applicable to both repairable and non-repairable systems including all those discussed in Chapter 7. The only requirements needed for the technique to be applicable are that the system must be stationary, the process must lack memory and the states of the system must be identifiable.

8.2 General modelling concepts

The basic concepts of Markov modelling can be illustrated by considering the simple system shown in Figure 8.1. In this system two system states are identifiable, being designated 1 and 2. The probabilities of remaining in or leaving a particular state in a finite time are also shown in Figure 8.1, and these probabilities are assumed to be constant for all times into the future.

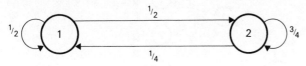

Fig. 8.1 A two state system

This is a discrete Markov chain since the system is stationary and the movement between states occurs in discrete steps.

Consider the first time interval and assume that the system is initially in state 1. The system can remain in state 1 with a probability of 1/2 or it

Number of time intervals

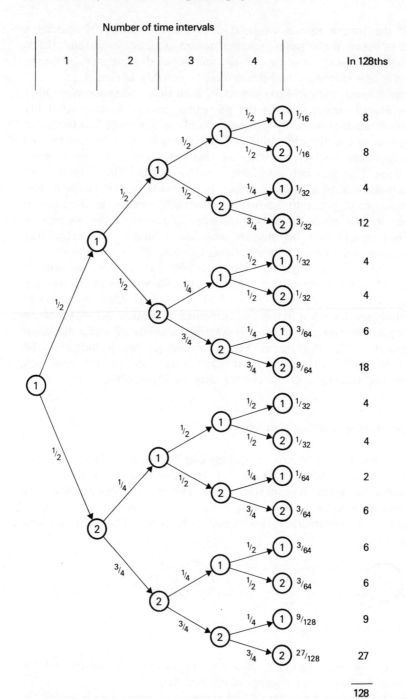

Fig. 8.2 Tree diagram of the two state system

can move (make a transition) into state 2 with a probability of 1/2. It is important to recognize that the sum of these probabilities must be unity, i.e., the system must either remain in the state being considered or move out of the state. This principle applies equally to all systems no matter what degree of complexity exists or how many ways there are of moving out of a given state, the sum of the probabilities of remaining in or moving out of a state must be unity.

Once the system shown in Figure 8.1 is in state 2, it can remain in it with a probability of 3/4 or it can make a transition back to state 1 with a probability of 1/4 during the next time interval.

The behaviour of this system can be easily illustrated by the tree diagram (*see* Section 5.7) shown in Figure 8.2. This figure assumes the system starts in state 1, shows the states in which the system can reside after each step or time interval and considers up to 4 such time intervals. Using the concepts described in Section 5.7, the probability of following any one branch of this tree can be evaluated by multiplying the appropriate probabilities of each step of this branch. The probability of residing in a particular state of the system after a certain number of time intervals is then evaluated by summating the branch probabilities that lead to that state after the number of time intervals being considered. The branch probabilities are also shown in Figure 8.2 for the situation that arises after 4 time intervals. If all these probabilities are summated it is again found that they add up to unity, this being a necessity and a useful check of accuracy. If those branch probabilities leading to state 1 are summated, the probability of residing in state 1 after 4 time intervals is 43/128 whereas a similar sum would show that the equivalent probability of residing in state 2 is 85/128.

If the same technique is used to evaluate the branch probabilities and state probabilities after each time interval, the state probabilities shown in Table 8.1 are obtained.

The results shown in Table 8.1 are represented in graphical form in Figure 8.3. These characteristics are known as the transient behaviour or time-dependent values of the state probabilities. It is evident from Figure

Table 8.1 State Probabilities of the 2-state system

| Time interval | State probability | |
	State 1	State 2
1	1/2 = 0.5	1/2 = 0.5
2	3/8 = 0.375	5/8 = 0.625
3	11/32 = 0.344	21/32 = 0.656
4	43/128 = 0.336	85/128 = 0.664
5	171/512 = 0.334	341/512 = 0.666

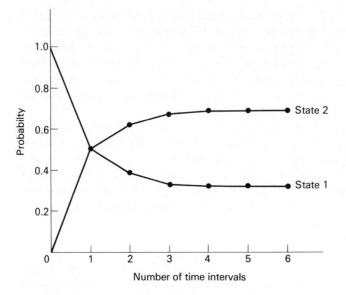

Fig. 8.3 System transient behaviour

8.3, that as the number of time intervals is increased, the values of state probabilities tend to a constant or limiting value. This is characteristic of most systems which satisfy the conditions of the Markov approach, and these limiting values of probability are known as the limiting-state or time-independent values of the state probabilities.

In this example, it was assumed that the system started in state 1 and the transient behaviour was evaluated as time increased. The state of the system at step 0 or zero time is known as the initial conditions. In most reliability evaluation problems these initial conditions are known, and the problem centres around evaluating the system reliability as time extends into the future. The transient behaviour is very dependent on the initial conditions and the reader is left to evaluate a similar graph to that shown in Figure 8.3 for the case when the system initially resides in state 2 rather than state 1. This evaluation provides a very interesting and important conclusion. This is that, although the transient behaviour is very dependent on the initial conditions, the limiting values of the state probabilities are totally independent of the initial conditions and both will tend to the same limiting-state values shown in Figure 8.3. This is a very important conclusion and one that is used again in subsequent discussions. A system or process for which the limiting values of state probabilities are independent of the initial conditions is known as ergodic. Not all systems are characterized by ergodicity. For a system to be ergodic it is essential that every state of a system can be reached from all other states of the system either directly or indirectly through intermediate states. If this is not possible and a particular state or states, once entered cannot be left, the system is not ergodic and the relevant states are known as absorbing states. This problem will be discussed in Section 8.6. The initial discussion will consider only ergodic systems.

Although the limiting or steady-state probabilities for the states of any ergodic system are independent of the initial conditions, the rate of convergence to the limiting-state value can be dependent on the initial conditions and is very dependent on the probabilities of making transitions between the states of the system.

The tree diagram method is a useful technique for illustrating the concepts of Markov chains but it is totally impractical for large systems and a large number of time intervals in even very small systems. Therefore other solution techniques are required and these are the subject of the remaining sections of this chapter.

8.3   Stochastic transitional probability matrix

Matrix solution techniques are used frequently in a variety of system analyses when other, more basic, techniques would be totally intractable. System reliability evaluation is no exception and one example of this was described in Section 5.6 in order to deduce the path connections between the input and output of a network.

Matrix algebra and matrix manipulation is used several times in both this and subsequent chapters. For those readers unfamiliar with these techniques, a description of elementary matrix algebra has been included in Appendix 3.

In order to apply matrix techniques to system reliability evaluation, it is necessary to deduce a matrix which represents the probabilities of making a transition from one state to another in a single step or time interval.

Again consider the system shown in Figure 8.1, these transition probabilities can be represented by the following matrix P

$$P = \begin{bmatrix} P_{11} & P_{12} \\ P_{21} & P_{22} \end{bmatrix} = \begin{bmatrix} 1/2 & 1/2 \\ 1/4 & 3/4 \end{bmatrix} \tag{8.1}$$

where P_{ij} = probability of making a transition to state j after a time interval given that it was in state i at the beginning of the time interval.

Applying this concept to the system shown in Figure 8.1 for the first time interval means that $P_{11} = 1/2$, $P_{12} = 1/2$, $P_{21} = 1/4$ and $P_{22} = 3/4$ as shown in Equation 8.1.

The definition of P_{ij} indicates that the row position of the matrix is the state from which the transition occurs and the column position of the matrix is the state to which the transition occurs. Consequently, for an n-state system the general form of the matrix, which must always be square, is shown in Equation 8.2.

$$
\begin{array}{c}
\rightarrow \quad \text{to state} \\[4pt]
\begin{array}{cccccc}
 & 1 & 2 & 3 & \ldots & n
\end{array}
\end{array}
$$

$$
\begin{array}{ll}
\text{from} & 1 \\
\text{state} & 2 \\
\downarrow & 3 \\
\boldsymbol{P} =
\end{array}
\quad
n
\begin{bmatrix}
P_{11} & P_{12} & P_{13} & \ldots & P_{1n} \\
P_{21} & P_{22} & P_{23} & \ldots & \cdot \\
P_{31} & P_{32} & P_{33} & \ldots & \cdot \\
\cdot & \cdot & \cdot & \cdot & \cdot \\
\cdot & \cdot & \cdot & \cdot & \cdot \\
\cdot & \cdot & \cdot & \cdot & \cdot \\
P_{n1} & \cdot & \cdot & & P_{nn}
\end{bmatrix}
\tag{8.2}
$$

This matrix is known as the *stochastic transitional probability matrix* for the system, since it represents, in matrix form, the transitional probabilities of the stochastic process. It should be noted that the summation of the probabilities in each row of the matrix must be unity since row i represents the complete and exhaustive ways in which the system can behave in a particular time interval given that it is in state i at the beginning of that time interval.

8.4   Time dependent probability evaluation

In order to illustrate the evaluation of the transient behaviour of a system using the stochastic transitional probability matrix, reconsider the simple two-state system shown in Figure 8.1. The stochastic transitional probability matrix for this system is shown in Equation 8.1. Now multiply this matrix by itself (see Appendix 3), i.e., square it. This gives

$$
\begin{aligned}
\boldsymbol{P}^2 &= \begin{bmatrix} P_{11} & P_{12} \\ P_{21} & P_{22} \end{bmatrix} \begin{bmatrix} P_{11} & P_{12} \\ P_{21} & P_{22} \end{bmatrix} \\[6pt]
&= \begin{bmatrix} (P_{11}P_{11}+P_{12}P_{21}) & (P_{11}P_{12}+P_{12}P_{22}) \\ (P_{21}P_{11}+P_{22}P_{11}) & (P_{21}P_{12}+P_{22}P_{22}) \end{bmatrix}.
\end{aligned}
\tag{8.3}
$$

If the values of $P_{11}, P_{12}, P_{21}, P_{22}$ are substituted into Equation 8.3

$$
\boldsymbol{P}^2 = \begin{bmatrix} 3/8 & 5/8 \\ 5/16 & 11/16 \end{bmatrix}
\tag{8.4}
$$

Recalling the principle of Equation 8.2, the first element of row 1 (3/8) is the probability of being in state 1 after a time interval given that it started in state 1. Similarly the second element of row 1 (5/8) is the probability of being in state 2 after a time interval given that it started in state 1. Similar reasoning can be applied to the second row.

If the values in row 1 are now compared with those shown in Table 8.1, it will be seen that they are identical to the state probabilities that were evaluated after two time intervals given that the system commenced in state 1. A similar comparison could be made between the values in row 2 and the probabilities that would have been evaluated after two time intervals if the system had started in state 2. It follows from this reasoning that the elements of $\boldsymbol{P}^2$ give all the state probabilities of the system after two time intervals, both those when starting in state 1 and those when starting in state 2.

The principle illustrated by this example can be extended to any power of $\boldsymbol{P}$ and the matrix $\boldsymbol{P}^n$ can be defined as the matrix whose element P_{ij}^n represents the probability that the system will be in state j after n time intervals given that it started in state i.

It is suggested that the reader finds the values of higher orders of $\boldsymbol{P}$ in order to confirm the technique and the values given in Table 8.1. This approach should also be used to obtain similar values for the case of starting in state 2. These results should be plotted on top of those in Figure 8.3.

Equations 8.3 and 8.4 for this particular two-state system and similar equations for more complex systems and other time intervals permit the probability of residing in any state to be evaluated provided it is known for certain in which state the system started, i.e., the probability of starting in a particular state is unity and the probability of starting in all others is zero. Frequently this is the case in practice because, at time zero, the deterministic state of the system is known. If however it is required to evaluate these state probabilities when the initial conditions are not known with this degree of certainty, then the matrix $\boldsymbol{P}^n$ can be premultiplied by the initial probability vector $\boldsymbol{P}(0)$ which represents the probability of being in each of the system states at the start of the mission. The values of probability contained in this vector must themselves summate to unity.

If the system shown in Figure 8.1 starts in state 1, this initial probability vector is

$$\boldsymbol{P}(0) = \begin{matrix} 1 & 2 \\ [1 & 0] \end{matrix} \tag{8.4a}$$

since the probability of being in state 1 at zero time is unity and the probability of being in state 2 is zero. If, on the other hand, it is known that the system is equally likely to start in state 1 or state 2, then this initial probability vector becomes

$$\boldsymbol{P}(0) = \begin{matrix} 1 & 2 \\ [1/2 & 1/2] \end{matrix} \tag{8.4b}$$

In the first case, the probability vector representing the state probabilities after two time intervals is

$$P(2) = P(0)P^2$$

$$= [1 \quad 0]\begin{bmatrix} 3/8 & 5/8 \\ 5/16 & 11/16 \end{bmatrix}$$

$$\begin{array}{cc} 1 & 2 \end{array}$$

$$= [3/8 \quad 5/8] \tag{8.5a}$$

as given in Table 8.1 for this set of initial conditions.

In the second case, the probability vector representing the state probabilities after two time intervals is

$$P(2) = P(0)P^2$$

$$= [1/2 \quad 1/2]\begin{bmatrix} 3/8 & 5/8 \\ 5/16 & 11/16 \end{bmatrix}$$

$$\begin{array}{cc} 1 & 2 \end{array}$$

$$= [11/32 \quad 21/32] \tag{8.5b}$$

This principle can again be extended to give

$$P(n) = P(0)P^n \tag{8.5c}$$

From the foregoing discussion, it is evident that the state probabilities can be readily evaluated at any time interval, simply by multiplying the stochastic transitional probability matrix by itself the relevant number of times. If this process is continued sequentially, the transient behaviour can be deduced. The limiting or steady-state values of state probabilities can be derived by continuing the multiplication process a sufficient number of times.

8.5 Limiting state probability evaluation

The steady-state or limiting values of state probabilities of an ergodic system can be evaluated using the matrix multiplication technique described in Section 8.4. If the transient behaviour is also required, it may be sensible to use this technique. If on the other hand, only the limiting state probabilities are required, matrix multiplication can be tedious and time-consuming. A very efficient alternative method is described in this section for evaluating these limiting probabilities.

The principle of this technique is that, once the limiting state probabilities have been reached by the matrix multiplication method, any further multiplication by the stochastic transitional probability matrix does not change the values of the limiting state probabilities, i.e., if α represents the limiting probability vector and P is the stochastic transitional probability matrix, then

$$\alpha P = \alpha \tag{8.6}$$

This principle can be applied to the simple two state system shown in Figure 8.1. Define P_1 and P_2 as the limiting probabilities of being in states 1 and 2 respectively, then

$$[P_1 \quad P_2] P = [P_1 \quad P_2]$$

or

$$[P_1 \quad P_2] \begin{bmatrix} 1/2 & 1/2 \\ 1/4 & 3/4 \end{bmatrix} = [P_1 \quad P_2]$$

from which

$$\tfrac{1}{2}P_1 + \tfrac{1}{4}P_2 = P_1$$
$$\tfrac{1}{2}P_1 + \tfrac{3}{4}P_2 = P_2$$

rearranging gives

$$-\tfrac{1}{2}P_1 + \tfrac{1}{4}P_2 = 0 \tag{8.7}$$

$$\tfrac{1}{2}P_1 - \tfrac{1}{4}P_2 = 0 \tag{8.8}$$

It is evident that Equations 8.7 and 8.8 are identical and, therefore, to solve for the two unknowns, P_1 and P_2, a third equation which is independent of Equations 8.7 and 8.8 is needed. This additional equation is

$$P_1 + P_2 = 1 \tag{8.9}$$

With systems of any size, one of the equations developed from Equation 8.6 will always be redundant and therefore any one of the equations so developed must be replaced by one of the form of Equation 8.9.

If Equations 8.7 and 8.9 are used as the two independent equations, they can be expressed in matrix form as

$$\begin{bmatrix} -1/2 & 1/4 \\ 1 & 1 \end{bmatrix} \begin{bmatrix} P_1 \\ P_2 \end{bmatrix} = \begin{bmatrix} 0 \\ 1 \end{bmatrix} \tag{8.10}$$

which is of the form $AX = b$, the solution for X being given by $X = A^{-1}b$ where A^{-1} is the inverse matrix of A. For those readers who are unfamiliar with the inversion of matrices, there is a useful method called Cramer's Rule, which is suitable for hand calculations provided the order of the matrix is small. This rule is explained in Appendix 3 and is used in the present example. However, it should be noted that this method is not particularly suited for digital computer solution as it can lead to precision errors. In such cases other techniques [28] are available.

Equation 8.10 can be solved using Cramer's rule to give

$$P_1 = \frac{(1 \times 0) - (1/4 \times 1)}{\begin{vmatrix} -1/2 & 1/4 \\ 1 & 1 \end{vmatrix}} = \frac{-1/4}{-3/4}$$

$$= 0.333$$

$$P_2 = \frac{(-1/2 \times 1) - (1 \times 0)}{-3/4} = \frac{-1/2}{-3/4}$$

$$= 0.667$$

these being the values which the characteristics shown in Figure 8.3 would approach asymptotically.

8.6 Absorbing states

In Section 8.1 it was stated that some states of a system may be absorbing states, i.e., states which, once entered, cannot be left until the system starts a new mission. These can readily be identified in terms of mission oriented systems as the catastrophic failure event states into which the probability of entering must be minimized to ensure safe operation of the mission. In such cases, one requirement of the reliability analysis is to evaluate the average number of time intervals in which the system resides in one of the non-absorbing states or, expressed another way, for how many time intervals does the system operate on average before it enters one of the absorbing states.

The principle behind such a system can also be applied to repairable systems in order to evaluate the average number of time intervals the system will operate satisfactorily before entering an undesirable state or states. In this case the states may not be real absorbing states because they can be left following a repair action. The principle of absorbing states can be used however in order to deduce the average number of time intervals by defining them as absorbing states.

The following technique for evaluating the number of time intervals can be used for both mission oriented and repairable systems.

Reconsider the two state system shown in Figure 8.1, it can be seen from the tree diagram in Figure 8.2, that, if the system starts in state 1, the probability of continuing to reside in this state without ever entering state 2 becomes progressively smaller as the number of time intervals increases, i.e., provided the number of time intervals is allowed to become great enough, the system must eventually enter state 2.

Mathematically this is because

$$\lim_{n \to \infty} \left(\frac{1}{2}\right)^n = 0 \tag{8.11}$$

where n is the number of time intervals and $(1/2)$ is the probability of remaining in state 1. If in this example, state 2 is defined as an absorbing state, it follows that eventually this state must be entered. This applies to all systems unless the probability of residing in a state is unity, which is most improbable. The problem is to evaluate the average value of time intervals before the absorbing state is reached.

If P is the stochastic transitional probability matrix of the system, a truncated matrix Q can be created by deleting the row(s) and column(s) associated with the absorbing state(s). In the case of P shown by Equation 8.1, this truncation will create a matrix Q having one element only, namely $[P_{11}]$ if state 2 is defined as the absorbing state. This truncated matrix Q represents the transient set of states and it is necessary to evaluate the expected number of time intervals for which the system remains in one of the states represented in this matrix.

The principle of mathematical expectation was given in Chapter 2 as

$$E(x) = \sum_{i=1}^{\infty} x_i P_i \tag{8.12}$$

This principle not only applies to single probability elements P_i but also to multi-probability elements represented by matrix Q. Therefore if N is the expected number of time intervals

$$N = 1 \cdot I + 1 \cdot Q + 1 \cdot Q^2 + \ldots + 1 . Q^{n-1} \tag{8.13}$$

where I is the identity (or unit) matrix (See Appendix 3).

The principle of Equation 8.13 can be explained as follows. The identity matrix represents the probability of all possible initial conditions i.e., the unity in row 1 represents the contribution to the expectation of the system starting in state 1, the unity in row 2 represents the contribution of the system starting in state 2, and so on. Each of the unity digits in Equation 8.13 represents one further time interval, i.e., these are equivalent to x_i in Equation 8.12. The first time interval occurs with probability I, the second with probability Q, the third with probability Q^2, and so on, the nth time interval being the one that enters the absorbing state. Equation 8.13 is therefore an explicit form of Equation 8.12.

From Equation 8.13

$$N = I + Q + Q^2 + \ldots + Q^{n-1} \tag{8.14}$$

Equation 8.14 is not readily evaluated. Instead consider the following identity

$$[I - Q][I + Q + Q^2 + \ldots + Q^{n-1}] = I - Q^n \tag{8.15}$$

Equation 8.15 can easily be verified by multiplying out the left hand side.

Following Equation 8.11

$$\lim_{n \to \infty} Q^n = 0$$

therefore, as $n \to \infty$

$$I - Q^n \to I$$

and Equation 8.15 becomes

$$[I - Q][I + Q + Q^2 + \ldots + Q^{n-1}] = I$$

or

$$I + Q + Q^2 + \ldots + Q^{n-1} = [I - Q]^{-1} I$$
$$= [I - Q]^{-1} \qquad (8.16)$$

Therefore, from Equations 8.14 and 8.16,

$$N = [I - Q]^{-1} \qquad (8.17)$$

which is readily evaluated compared with Equation 8.14. An example using Equation 8.17 is given in the next section.

If, using the simple 2 state system, state 2 is defined as the absorbing state then, as stated previously, $Q = P_{11} = 1/2$.

Therefore $N = [1 - 1/2]^{-1} = 2$ time intervals on average before state 2 is entered, if the system commences in state 1.

8.7 Application of discrete Markov techniques

Two particular numerical examples can be considered in order to illustrate the application of the techniques described in the previous section of this chapter.

Example 8.1

Consider the 3-state system shown in Figure 8.4 and the transition probabilities indicated. Evaluate (a) the limiting state probabilities as-

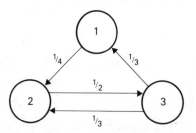

Fig. 8.4 System used in Example 8.1

sociated with each state and, (b) the average number of time intervals spent in each state if state 3 is defined as an absorbing state.

(a)   The stochastic transitional probability matrix for this system is

$$\boldsymbol{P} = \begin{matrix} & 1 & 2 & 3 \\ 1 \\ 2 \\ 3 \end{matrix} \begin{bmatrix} 3/4 & 1/4 & 0 \\ 0 & 1/2 & 1/2 \\ 1/3 & 1/3 & 1/3 \end{bmatrix}$$

If the limiting state probabilities are P_1, P_2 and P_3 respectively, then from Equation 8.6

$$[P_1 \quad P_2 \quad P_3] \begin{bmatrix} 3/4 & 1/4 & 0 \\ 0 & 1/2 & 1/2 \\ 1/3 & 1/3 & 1/3 \end{bmatrix} = [P_1 \quad P_2 \quad P_3]$$

giving the following explicit equations

$$3/4 P_1 \qquad\qquad + 1/3 P_3 = P_1 \tag{8.18}$$

$$1/4 P_1 + 1/2 P_2 + 1/3 P_3 = P_2 \tag{8.19}$$

$$1/2 P_2 + 1/3 P_3 = P_3 \tag{8.20}$$

One of these equations must be deleted and replaced by

$$P_1 + P_2 + P_3 = 1 \tag{8.21}$$

Deleting Equation 8.20, rearranging the remaining three equations and putting into matrix form gives

$$\begin{bmatrix} -1/4 & 0 & 1/3 \\ 1/4 & -1/2 & 1/3 \\ 1 & 1 & 1 \end{bmatrix} \begin{bmatrix} P_1 \\ P_2 \\ P_3 \end{bmatrix} = \begin{bmatrix} 0 \\ 0 \\ 1 \end{bmatrix}$$

Using Cramer's Rule (Appendix 3)

$$P_1 = \frac{\begin{vmatrix} 0 & 0 & 1/3 \\ 0 & -1/2 & 1/3 \\ 1 & 1 & 1 \end{vmatrix}}{\begin{vmatrix} -1/4 & 0 & 1/3 \\ 1/4 & -1/2 & 1/3 \\ 1 & 1 & 1 \end{vmatrix}} = 4/11$$

similarly $P_2 = 4/11$ and $P_3 = 3/11$.

(b)   If state 3 is the absorbing state, the truncated matrix Q becomes

$$Q = \begin{array}{c} 1 \\ 2 \end{array}\begin{bmatrix} 3/4 & 1/4 \\ 0 & 1/2 \end{bmatrix}$$

$$[I - Q] = \begin{bmatrix} 1 & 0 \\ 0 & 1 \end{bmatrix} - \begin{bmatrix} 3/4 & 1/4 \\ 0 & 1/2 \end{bmatrix}$$

$$= \begin{bmatrix} 1/4 & -1/4 \\ 0 & 1/2 \end{bmatrix}$$

$$[I - Q]^{-1} = \frac{\begin{bmatrix} 1/2 & 1/4 \\ 0 & 1/4 \end{bmatrix}}{\begin{vmatrix} 1/4 & -1/4 \\ 0 & 1/2 \end{vmatrix}}$$

$$= 8\begin{bmatrix} 1/2 & 1/4 \\ 0 & 1/4 \end{bmatrix}$$

$$= \begin{bmatrix} 4 & 2 \\ 0 & 2 \end{bmatrix}$$

therefore, from Equation 8.17

$$N = \begin{array}{c} 1 \\ 2 \end{array}\begin{array}{cc} 1 & 2 \end{array}\begin{bmatrix} 4 & 2 \\ 0 & 2 \end{bmatrix}$$

or $N_{11} = 4$, $N_{12} = 2$, $N_{21} = 0$, $N_{22} = 2$.

These values indicate that the average number of time intervals spent in state 1 given the system started in state 1 is 4 ($= N_{11}$), the average number of time intervals spent in state 2 given the system started in state 1 is 2 ($= N_{12}$), and so on.

One of these values, N_{21}, is zero and this indicates that the system spends zero time intervals in state 1 given that it starts in state 2. The reason for this is that there is no direct transition from state 2 to state 1, the only way of going from state 2 to state 1 being through state 3, the absorbing state.

Example 8.2

A man either drives his car to work or catches a train. Assume that he never takes the train two days in a row but if he drives to work, then the next day he is just as likely to drive again as he is to catch the train. Evaluate (a) the probability that he drives to work after (i) 2 days (ii) a long time, (b) the probability that he drives to work after (i) 2 days, (ii) a long time if on the first day of work he tosses a fair die and drives to work only if a 2 appears.

The stochastic probability matrix for this Markov process is

$$P = \begin{matrix} & t & d \\ t \\ d \end{matrix} \begin{bmatrix} 0 & 1 \\ 1/2 & 1/2 \end{bmatrix}$$

in which t denotes his taking a train to work and d denotes his driving. The elements of P can be deduced as follows. Row 1 represents the probability of taking the train and driving the day after (next time interval) he caught the train. Since he never takes the train on two consecutive days, the elements of this row must be zero and unity respectively. Row 2 represents the probability of taking the train and driving the day after he drove. These have equal probabilities and are therefore 1/2 each.

(a) (i) The transition probabilities after 2 days, i.e., 2 time intervals, are given by P^2

$$P^2 = \begin{bmatrix} 0 & 1 \\ 1/2 & 1/2 \end{bmatrix}\begin{bmatrix} 0 & 1 \\ 1/2 & 1/2 \end{bmatrix}$$

$$= \begin{matrix} & t & d \\ t \\ d \end{matrix}\begin{bmatrix} 1/2 & 1/2 \\ 1/4 & 3/4 \end{bmatrix}$$

Suppose first that, on the first day of work, he takes the train. In this case the initial vector of probabilities $P(0)$ is

$$\begin{matrix} t & d \end{matrix}$$
$$P(0) = [1 \quad 0]$$

and the state probabilities after 2 days are

$$P(2) = [1 \quad 0]\begin{bmatrix} 1/2 & 1/2 \\ 1/4 & 3/4 \end{bmatrix}$$

$$\begin{matrix} t & d \end{matrix}$$
$$= [1/2 \quad 1/2]$$

i.e., if he takes the train on the first day, he is as likely to catch the train as to drive two days later. Suppose that he drove to work on the first day. In this case the initial vector of probabilities is

$$\begin{matrix} t & d \end{matrix}$$
$$P(0) = [0 \quad 1] \quad \text{and}$$

$$P(2) = [0 \quad 1]\begin{bmatrix} 1/2 & 1/2 \\ 1/4 & 3/4 \end{bmatrix}$$

$$\begin{matrix} t & d \end{matrix}$$
$$= [1/4 \quad 3/4]$$

Therefore, the probability that he drives to work is 3/4, i.e., he is 3 times more likely to drive than he is to catch the train.

(a) (ii) To evaluate the probabilities after a long time, we need to evaluate the limiting state probabilities. Let these limiting probabilities be P_t and P_d for catching the train and driving respectively, then

$$[P_t \quad P_d]\begin{bmatrix} 0 & 1 \\ 1/2 & 1/2 \end{bmatrix} = [P_t \quad P_d]$$

That is,

$$1/2P_d = P_t$$

also

$$P_t + P_d = 1$$

A straightforward evaluation of these 2 simultaneous equations gives

$$P_d = 2/3 \quad \text{and} \quad P_t = 1/3$$

Therefore, in the long run, he will drive to work 2/3 of the time.

(b) (i) The probability of getting a 2 in a single throw of a fair die $= 1/6$. Therefore the initial vector of probabilities in this case is

$$\begin{array}{cc} t & d \\ P(0) = [5/6 & 1/6] \end{array} \quad \text{and}$$

$$P(2) = [5/6 \quad 1/6]\begin{bmatrix} 1/2 & 1/2 \\ 1/4 & 3/4 \end{bmatrix}$$

$$\begin{array}{cc} t & d \\ = [11/24 & 13/24] \end{array}$$

Hence, the probability that he drives two days later is 13/24.

(b) (ii) Since this problem is an ergodic problem, the limiting values of probability do not depend on the initial conditions. The results for this case, which the reader may like to verify, are identical therefore to case (a), (ii), i.e.,

$$P_d = 2/3 \quad \text{and} \quad P_t = 1/3$$

8.8 Conclusions

This chapter has presented the essential and basic concepts of Markov modelling in terms of system problems that are discrete in space and time. Most reliability problems are concerned with systems that operate continuously with time and for this reason the reader may find the next chapter more applicable. It should be noted however that the underlying techniques used for continuously operated systems are based on the principles described in this chapter and therefore, before progressing to Chapter 9, the reader should become familiar with the techniques expounded in the previous sections of this chapter.

Further and more detailed applications of Markov modelling and evaluation of discrete systems are given in Feller [4] and Kemeny and Snell [27].

Problems

1 A man's exercise habits are as follows. If he does his exercise one day, he is 70% sure not to do them the next day. On the other hand, if he does not do his exercises one day he is 60% sure not to do them the next day. In the long run, how often does he do his exercises?

2 A tax consultant has a contract for three cities: X, Y and Z. He never stays in any city more than one day. If he visits city X, then the next day he visits city Y. If, however, he visits either Y or Z, then the next day he is twice as likely to visit city X as the other city. In the long run, how often does he visit each city?

3 A discrete process has the state diagram shown in Figure 8.5. Find the probabilities of being in each of the three states after three steps using a tree diagram given that the process started in State 1. Determine the limiting state probabilities and the mean number of steps to enter State 3 if the process starts each time in State 2.

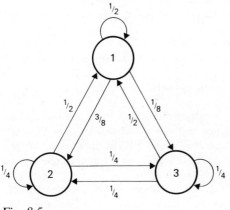

Fig. 8.5

4 A player has 3 dollars. At each play of a game, he loses a dollar with a probability of 3/4 but wins 2 dollars with probability of 1/4. He stops playing if he has lost his 3 dollars or he has won at least 3 dollars. Find the transient probability matrix of the Markov chain. What is the probability that there are at least 4 plays of the game?

5 A gambler's luck follows a pattern: If he wins a game, the probability of winning the next game is 0.8. However if he loses a game, the probability of losing the next game is 0.7. There is an even chance that he wins the first game.
   (a) What is the probability that he wins the second game?
   (b) What is the probability that he wins the third game?
   (c) In the long run how often does he win?

6 Each year a man trades his car for a new car. If he has a Chrysler he trades for a Plymouth. If he has a Plymouth he trades it for a Ford. However, if he has a Ford, he is just as likely to trade it in for a Chrysler or a Plymouth. In 1977 he bought his first car which was a Ford.
   (a) Find the probability that he has a
      (i) 1979 Ford
      (ii) 1979 Chrysler
      (iii) 1980 Plymouth.
   (b) In the long run how often will he have a Ford?

7 A psychologist makes the following assumptions concerning the behaviour of mice subjected to a particular feeding schedule. For any particulat trial 80% of the mice that went right on the previous experiment will go right on this trial and 60% of those mice that went left on the previous experiment will go right on this trial. If 50% went right on the first trial, what would he predict for
   (a) the second trial
   (b) third trial
   (c) the thousandth trial.

8 There are 2 white marbles in urn A and 3 red marbles in urn B. At each step of the process a marble is selected from each urn and the two marbles selected are interchanged. If the state a_i designates the number of i red marbles in urn A,
   (a) Find the transitional probability matrix of the process.
   (b) What is the probability that there are 2 red marbles in urn A after 3 steps?
   (c) In the long run what is the probability that there are 2 red marbles in urn A?

9 Two boys, b_1, b_2 and girls g_1, g_2 are throwing a ball from one to another. Each boy throws the ball to the other boy with a probability 0.5 and to each girl with a probability 0.25. On the other hand, each girl throws the ball to a boy with probability 0.5 and never to the other girl. In the long run how often does each receive the ball?

10 A man's smoking habits are as follows. If he smokes filter cigarettes this week, he switches to non-filter ones the next week with a probability of 0.2. On the other hand if he smokes non-filter ones this week there is 0.7 probability that he will smoke non-filter cigarettes the next week. In the long run how often does he smoke filter cigarettes?

9 Continuous Markov processes

9.1 Introduction

Reliability problems are normally concerned with systems that are discrete in space, i.e., they can exist in one of a number of discrete and identifiable states, and continuous in time; i.e., they exist continuously in one of the system states until a transition occurs which takes them discretely to another state in which they then exist continuously until another transition occurs. The techniques described in this chapter pertain to systems that can be described as stationary Markov processes i.e., the conditional probability of failure or repair during any fixed interval of time is constant. This implies that the failure and repair characteristics of the components are associated with (negative) exponential distributions. In the case of a single component, or in systems composed of statistically independent components, the limiting or steady-state probabilities are not dependent on the state residence time distributions, only upon their mean values. This is discussed further in Chapter 12. It must be stressed however, that very considerable differences can exist in the values of the time-dependent state probabilities as these are very dependent on the distributional assumptions.

Given that the conditions described above are applicable, the Markov approach can be used for a wide range of reliability problems including systems that are either non-repairable or repairable and are either series-connected, parallel redundant or standby redundant.

9.2 General modelling concepts

9.2.1 Transition rate concepts

Consider the case of a single repairable component for which the failure rate and repair rate are constant, i.e. they are characterized by the exponential distribution. The state transition diagram for this component is shown in Figure 9.1.

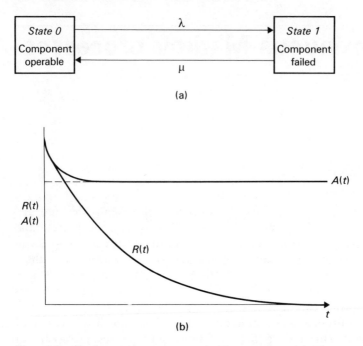

(a)

(b)

Fig. 9.1 Single component repairable system. (a) State space diagram. (b) Variation of reliability and time-dependent availability

Define:

$P_o(t)$ = probability that the component is operable at time t

$P_1(t)$ = probability that the component is failed at time t

λ = failure rate

μ = repair rate.

The failure density function for a component with a constant hazard rate of λ was given in Equation 6.31 as

$$f(t) = \lambda e^{-\lambda t}$$

The density functions for the operating and failed states of the system shown in Figure 9.1a are therefore

$f_o(t) = \lambda e^{-\lambda t}$ and $f_1(t) = \mu e^{-\mu t}$, respectively.

The parameters λ and μ are referred to as state transition rates since they represent the rate at which the system transits from one state of the system to another.

In Chapter 7 the failure rate λ was found to be the reciprocal of the mean time to failure, MTTF, with the times to failure counted from the moment the component begins to operate to the moment it fails. Similarly, the repair rate μ is the reciprocal of the mean time to repair, MTTR, with these times counted from the moment the component fails to the moment it is returned to an operable condition. The correct interpretation of state residence time is an important point, as the failure and repair rates are sometimes incorrectly evaluated by counting the number of failures or repairs in a given period of time, and dividing by the elapsed time. The correct time value to use in the denominator is the portion of time in which the component was in the state being considered. This is less than the actual elapsed period of time unless no transitions occurred from the state. Consequently

$$\lambda = \frac{\text{number of failures of a component in the given period of time}}{\text{total period of time the component was operating}}$$

(9.1a)

$$\mu = \frac{\text{number of repairs of a component in the given period of time}}{\text{total period of time the component was being repaired}}$$

(9.1b)

This concept of a transition rate leads to the definition

transition rate = number of times a transition occurs from a
given state/time spent in that state   (9.1c)

This point is discussed further in Chapter 10.

9.2.2 Evaluating time dependent probabilities

The relevant state space diagram for the simple single component is shown in Figure 9.1a. In Chapter 8 the transitions in these diagrams were represented by the value of transitional probability. In the case of continuous Markov processes they are usually represented by a transition rate as shown in Figure 9.1a, i.e., by the transitions λ and μ from the operating and failed states respectively.

Consider now an incremental interval of time dt which is made sufficiently small so that the probability of two or more events occurring during this increment of time is negligible. This concept was first used in Chapter 6 in connection with the Poisson distribution.

The probability of being in the operating state after this time interval dt, i.e., the probability of being in state 0 of Figure 9.1a at time $(t + dt)$ is

[Probability of being operative at time t AND of not failing in time dt]

+[probability of being failed at time t AND of being repaired in time dt].

Using a similar approach to that used to develop the Poisson distribution in Chapter 6

$$P_o(t+dt) = P_o(t)(1 - \lambda \, dt) + P_1(t)(\mu \, dt) \tag{9.2}$$

Similarly,

$$P_1(t+dt) = P_1(t)(1 - \mu \, dt) + P_o(t)(\lambda \, dt) \tag{9.3}$$

from Equation 9.2

$$\frac{P_o(t+dt) - P_o(t)}{dt} = -\lambda P_o(t) + \mu P_1(t)$$

as $dt \to 0$

$$\frac{P_o(t+dt) - P_o(t)}{dt}\bigg|_{dt \to 0} = \frac{dP_o(t)}{dt} = P_o'(t)$$

thus,

$$P_o'(t) = -\lambda P_o(t) + \mu P_1(t) \tag{9.4a}$$

similarly, from Equation 9.3

$$P_1'(t) = \lambda P_o(t) - \mu P_1(t) \tag{9.4b}$$

Equations 9.4 may be expressed in matrix form as

$$[P_o'(t) \quad P_1'(t)] = [P_o(t) \quad P_1(t)]\begin{bmatrix} -\lambda & \lambda \\ \mu & -\mu \end{bmatrix} \tag{9.4c}$$

The coefficient matrix in Equation 9.4c is not a stochastic transitional probability matrix (see Section 8.3) because the rows of this coefficient matrix summate to zero whereas those of the stochastic transitional probability matrix summate to unity.

Equations 9.4a and 9.4b are linear differential equations with constant coefficients. There are a number of ways in which such equations can be solved but one of the easiest and most widely used is by Laplace transforms (Appendix 4 refers). To illustrate this consider Equation 9.4a. The Laplace transform of this is (see Appendix 4)

$$sP_o(s) - P_o(0) = -\lambda P_o(s) + \mu P_1(s) \tag{9.5}$$

where $P_i(s)$ is the Laplace transform of $P_i(t)$ and $P_o(0)$ is the initial value of $P_o(t)$. Rearranging Equation 9.5 gives

$$P_o(s) = \frac{\mu}{s+\lambda} P_1(s) + \frac{1}{s+\lambda} P_o(0) \tag{9.6a}$$

Similarly Equation 9.4b can be transformed into

$$P_1(s) = \frac{\lambda}{s+\mu} P_o(s) + \frac{1}{s+\mu} P_1(0) \tag{9.6b}$$

where $P_1(0)$ is the initial value of $P_1(t)$.

Equations 9.6a and 9.6b can now be solved for $P_o(s)$ and $P_1(s)$ as linear simultaneous equations using a straightforward substitution method or using the matrix solution techniques of Appendix 3. In either case

$$P_o(s) = \frac{\mu}{\lambda + \mu}\left[\frac{P_o(0) + P_1(0)}{s}\right] + \frac{1}{\lambda + \mu} \cdot \frac{1}{s + \lambda + \mu}[\lambda P_o(0) - \mu P_1(0)]$$

$$(9.7a)$$

$$P_1(s) = \frac{\lambda}{\lambda + \mu}\left[\frac{P_o(0) + P_1(0)}{s}\right] + \frac{1}{\lambda + \mu} \cdot \frac{1}{s + \lambda + \mu}[\mu P_1(0) - \lambda P_o(0)]$$

$$(9.7b)$$

Equations 9.7a and 9.7b must now be transformed back into the real time domain using inverse Laplace transforms (as shown in Appendix 4). The inverse transform of $1/s$ is 1 and $1/(s+a)$ is e^{-at}, which gives

$$P_o(t) = \frac{\mu}{\lambda + \mu}[P_o(0) + P_1(0)] + \frac{e^{-(\lambda + \mu)t}}{\lambda + \mu}[\lambda P_o(0) - \mu P_1(0)] \quad \text{and} \quad (9.8a)$$

$$P_1(t) = \frac{\lambda}{\lambda + \mu}[P_o(0) + P_1(0)] + \frac{e^{-(\lambda + \mu)t}}{\lambda + \mu}[\mu P_1(0) - \lambda P_o(0)] \quad (9.8b)$$

The term $P_o(0) + P_1(0) = 1$ for all initial conditions and therefore Equations 9.8 become

$$P_o(t) = \frac{\mu}{\lambda + \mu} + \frac{e^{-(\lambda + \mu)t}}{\lambda + \mu}[\lambda P_o(0) - \mu P_1(0)] \quad (9.9a)$$

$$P_1(t) = \frac{\lambda}{\lambda + \mu} + \frac{e^{-(\lambda + \mu)t}}{\lambda + \mu}[\mu P_1(0) - \lambda P_o(0)] \quad (9.9b)$$

In practice the most likely state in which the system starts is state 0, i.e. the system is in an operable condition at zero time. In this case

$$P_o(0) = 1 \quad \text{and} \quad P_1(0) = 0$$

and Equations 9.9 reduce to the frequently quoted equations for the time-dependent probabilities of a single repairable component given by

$$P_o(t) = \frac{\mu}{\lambda + \mu} + \frac{\lambda e^{-(\lambda + \mu)t}}{\lambda + \mu} \quad (9.10a)$$

$$P_1(t) = \frac{\lambda}{\lambda + \mu} - \frac{\lambda e^{-(\lambda + \mu)t}}{\lambda + \mu} \quad (9.10b)$$

The probabilities $P_o(t)$ and $P_1(t)$ are the probabilities of being found in the operating state and failed state respectively as a function of time given that the system started at time $t = 0$ in the operating state.

9.2.3   Evaluating limiting state probabilities

The limiting state or steady-state probabilities will be non-zero for a continuous Markov process provided the system is ergodic, as in the case of a discrete Markov chain. In the case of the single repairable component represented by the state space diagram shown in Figure 9.1a, the limiting probabilities can be evaluated from Equations 9.10 by letting $t \to \infty$. If these values of limiting state probabilities are defined as P_o and P_1 for the operating state and the failed state, respectively, then from Equations 9.10 as $t \to \infty$

$$P_o = P_o(\infty) = \frac{\mu}{\lambda + \mu} \tag{9.11a}$$

$$P_1 = P_1(\infty) = \frac{\lambda}{\lambda + \mu} \tag{9.11b}$$

These limiting state probability expressions are applicable irrespective of whether the system starts in the operating state or in the failed state. This can be seen from Equation 9.9 where the second term in each case goes to zero as $t \to \infty$ for all values of $P_o(0)$ and $P_1(0)$.

It was shown in Chapter 6 that, for the exponential distribution, the mean time to failure,

$$\text{MTTF} = m = 1/\lambda \tag{9.12a}$$

Similarly the mean time to repair,

$$\text{MTTR} = r = 1/\mu \tag{9.12b}$$

Substituting Equations 12 into Equations 11 gives

$$P_o = \frac{m}{m + r} \tag{9.13a}$$

$$P_1 = \frac{r}{m + r} \tag{9.13b}$$

The values of P_o and P_1 are generally referred to as the steady-state or limiting availability A and unavailability U of the system respectively. The time dependent availability $A(t)$ of the system is given by Equation 9.10a, i.e.,

$$A(t) = P_o(t) = \frac{\mu}{\lambda + \mu} + \frac{\lambda}{\lambda + \mu} e^{-(\lambda + \mu)t}$$

As noted earlier, this is the probability of *being found* in the operating state at some time t in the future given that the system started in the operating state at time $t = 0$. This is quite different from the reliability

$R(t)$ as given by

$$R(t) = e^{-\lambda t}$$

This is the probability of *staying* in the operating state as a function of time given that the system started in the operating state at time $t = 0$.

A similar conceptual relationship exists between the unavailability $U(t)$ and the unreliability $Q(t)$. The relationship between $A(t)$ and $R(t)$ is shown in Figure 9.1b.

The limiting state probabilities could have been evaluated directly and simply from the differential equations represented by Equations 9.4 without actually solving them. The approach is to evaluate the state probabilities as t tends to infinity. Under this condition $P_0'(t)$ and $P_1'(t)$ both tend to zero and Equations 9.4 reduce to

$$-\lambda P_0 + \mu P_1 = 0 \tag{9.14a}$$

$$\lambda P_0 - \mu P_1 = 0 \tag{9.14b}$$

One of these equations must be declared redundant as they are both identical. As in the case of discrete Markov chains considered in Chapter 8 it is always possible to write the following equation

$$P_0 + P_1 = 1 \tag{9.14c}$$

Using the two simultaneous equations given in 9.14a and 9.14c

$$P_0 = \frac{\mu}{\lambda + \mu} \quad \text{and} \quad P_1 = \frac{\lambda}{\lambda + \mu}$$

9.3 State space diagrams

9.3.1 General concepts

In order to facilitate the solution of continuous or discrete Markov processes it is desirable first to construct the appropriate state space diagram and insert the relevant transition rates. All relevant states in which the system can reside should be included in such a diagram and all known ways in which transitions between states can occur should be inserted. There are no basic restrictions on the number of states or the type and number of transitions that can be inserted.

It is not possible to illustrate in this book all possible variations that can occur in practice and only a selected number of examples are shown. This phase of the problem solution is very important. It translates the analyst's knowledge of the operation of the system into a mathematical model that can be solved by using Markov techniques. It must be stressed that there are no mathematical models, nor should there be, that eliminate the need to exercise engineering judgement and the requirement of a thorough and exhaustive understanding of the physical and logical operation of the system. The techniques presented both in this chapter and throughout this book are tools by which the analyst, having understood the problem, can then evaluate the system reliability.

The analyst must therefore first translate the operation of the system into a state space diagram recognizing both the states of the system, the way these states communicate and the values of the transition rates. It is relatively easy to formulate state space diagrams for small system models. Larger applications require a certain amount of experience and prior application. Several illustrative examples are presented in the following subsections.

9.3.2 Single repairable component

Figure 9.1a shows a state space diagram for a single repairable component which is assumed to exist in one of two states, the operating, or up, state and the failed, or down, state. In some practical situations, a single component may be best represented by more than two states. For example, a pump in good working order may be able to deliver full output, under certain conditions may only be able to deliver partial output (known as a partial output or derated state) and when failed is unable to deliver any output. This therefore gives three states as shown in Figure 9.2. In a given practical application, additional derated states may exist and it is necessary for the analyst to appreciate these additional states and represent them in the diagram.

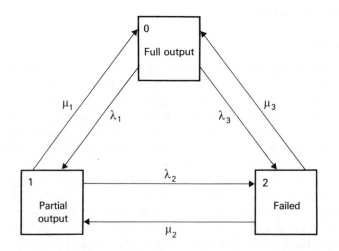

Fig. 9.2 State space diagram of component with partial output state

The diagram shown in Figure 9.2 includes all possible transition rates. Some of these may not physically exist in practice, in which case they should be omitted from the diagram. One of the most likely transitions not to exist is the rate μ_2, since it is probable that, once failed, the repair process will return it to the full output state.

9.3.3 Two repairable components

If the system consists of two repairable components, there are four possible states in which the system can exist. If λ_1, μ_1 and λ_2, μ_2 are the failure and repair rates of components 1 and 2 respectively, the state space diagram including the relevant transition rates is shown in Figure 9.3.

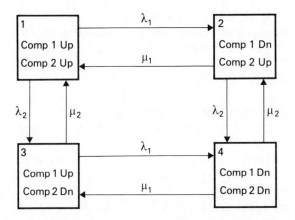

Fig. 9.3 State space diagram for two component system

One important feature to recognize in this particular example is that the state space diagram shown in Figure 9.3 is the same irrespective of whether the two components are in series or are parallel redundant.

In the case of a series system, state 1 is the system up state and states 2, 3 and 4 are the system down states. In the case of a parallel redundant system, states 1, 2 and 3 are the system up states and state 4 is the system down state. Therefore if P_1, P_2, P_3 and P_4 are the probabilities of being in states 1–4 respectively, then

for the series system $P_{up} = A = P_1$

$$P_{down} = U = P_2 + P_3 + P_4$$

for the parallel redundant system $P_{up} = A = P_1 + P_2 + P_3$

$$P_{down} = U = P_4$$

and these equations apply for both the time-dependent and limiting state probabilities.

As in the case of the single repairable component of Section 9.3.2, additional states can be added to the diagram of Figure 9.3 to represent partial output or derated states.

Certain transitions in the state space model may not be physically possible and should be deleted and others should perhaps be added. As an example, if both components of the system have failed, repair of component 2 may never be started until component 1 has been repaired in which case the transition μ_2 from state 4 to state 2 would not exist. It may also be possible for both components to fail simultaneously in which case a transition between state 1 and state 4 will exist. This transition implies a common mode, or common cause, failure and is not considered further in this chapter. It is an important factor however and will be discussed in Chapter 11. The physical transition from state 1 to state 4 caused by a common mode failure should not be confused with the simultaneous occurrence of two independent failures. The latter case is not possible if the interval dt is incrementally small. One failure would precede the other in which case the transition from state 1 to state 4 would be via state 2 or 3.

In some practical situations, the state space diagram shown in Figure 9.3 can be simplified and reduced. For example, it may be known that when one of the components fails in a series system, the other component is no longer operating and its failure rate in these circumstances becomes zero. In this case, state 4 does not exist leaving only states 1–3 and the transition rates between these 3 states.

If both of the components are identical, states 2 and 3 are also identical and may be combined to give a reduced 3-state system as shown in Figure 9.4. The 2λ and 2μ terms in Figure 9.4 indicate that two components are

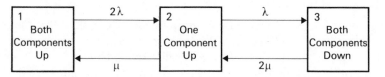

Fig. 9.4   State space diagram for two identical components

available for failure or repair respectively in the next increment of time and that one of the two can fail or be repaired, but not both in that interval.

9.3.4   Three component system

The maximum number of states in a three component system, where each component can exist in two states, is 2^3 or 8. This is shown in Figure 9.5 in which λ_i, μ_i represents the failure rate and repair rate of component i,

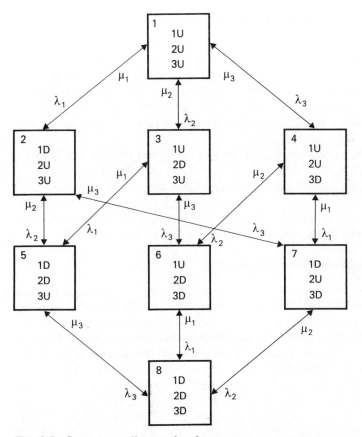

Fig. 9.5 State space diagram for three component system

and U and D indicate that the component is up or down respectively.

This diagram can be modified by further knowledge of the system it is meant to represent, e.g., whether some states and transitions are inappropriate and whether derated states are also necessary.

As in the case of the two component system described in Section 9.3.3, the state space diagram may under certain conditions be valid for a range of physical systems. The reader should be able to identify that for a series system, parallel redundant system and a 2-out-of-3 partial redundant system, the states to be combined for system success and failure are

series system	success = state 1
	failure = states 2, 3, 4, 5, 6, 7, 8
parallel redundant system	success = states 1, 2, 3, 4, 5, 6, 7
	failure = state 8
2-out-of-3 system	success = states 1, 2, 3, 4
	failure = states 5, 6, 7, 8

9.3.5 Large number of components

The number of states in the state space diagram increases as the number of system components increases and as the number of states in which each system component can reside increases. If all states are represented, the number of states in the diagram is 2^n for an n-component system in which each component is represented as a 2-state model and 3^n if each component has a derated state. The model can therefore become unmanageable for large systems.

Two solutions are possible in these circumstances. The first involves state truncation. This approach utilizes engineering judgement based on experience to reduce the number of possible system states by neglecting those that have a very low probability of occurrence. The second solution involves approximate solution techniques based on Markov modelling. These techniques are described in Chapter 11.

9.3.6 Standby redundant systems

The state space diagrams described and discussed in Sections 9.3.2 to 9.3.5 assume that all the system components are continuously operating either in series, parallel or series/parallel. The important class of systems known as standby systems can also be modelled and analyzed using state space diagrams and Markov techniques. The most important aspect in the representation of these systems is to recognize and identify the states in which the system can reside and the transitions that can occur between these states. In order to illustrate the construction of state space diagrams reconsider the two component standby system shown in Figure 7.1 in

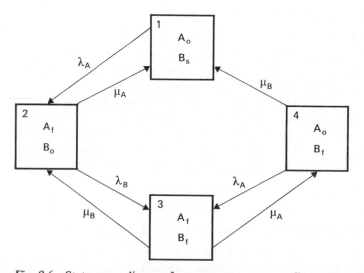

Fig. 9.6 State space diagram for two component standby system

which the switch was assumed to be perfect. The state space diagram of this system is shown in Figure 9.6. In this diagram the subscripts o, f and s represent operating, failed and stand-by respectively. As in Section 7.6.1, it is assumed that component A is the normally operating component.

The diagram shown in Figure 9.6 is not meant to be a rigorous or exhaustive representation. It assumes that, whenever A is operable, it will replace B as the operating component. In circumstances when A and B are identical, it may be operating policy to leave B operating and place A on standby to give a state equivalent to state 1 with the status of the components reversed. If the switch is not perfect, each state of the diagram must include the status of not only A and B but also of the switch itself which results in a greater number of states.

9.3.7 Mission orientated systems

In Sections 9.3.2 to 9.3.6, it was assumed that the components of the system are repairable. State space diagrams can however be constructed for non-repairable or mission orientated systems in exactly the same way and can be solved using Markov techniques. The only difference between these systems and repairable systems is that the repair transitions of non-repairable components do not exist. The state space diagram of Figure 9.4 for a system having two identical components is modified to that shown in Figure 9.7 if the components are non-repairable.

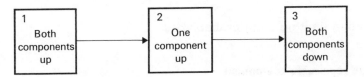

Fig. 9.7 State space diagram for two identical non-repairable components

In this case, the system is no longer ergodic since not all states can communicate and one state is an absorbing state. The time dependent probabilities of non-repairable systems can be evaluated by using Markov process techniques in the same way as for repairable systems. The limiting state probabilities, however, do not have any significance since, in the limit, the probability of residing in the absorbing state is unity and the probability of residing in all non-absorbing states is zero.

9.4 Stochastic transitional probability matrix

In the case of discrete Markov chains, a matrix defined as the stochastic transitional probability matrix (see Section 8.3) was introduced which presents the probabilities of making a transition from one state of the system to another. This is relatively easy to appreciate in the case of discrete Markov chains as each step in the chain represents an equal interval of time and the probability of transition in each interval is constant. A similar stochastic transitional probability matrix can be derived for a continuous Markov process. The basic difference is that in this case, a discrete interval of time is not part of the problem specification. An incremental interval of time Δt can be introduced as in Section 9.2.2 which is sufficiently small that the probability of two or more transitions occurring in the interval is negligible. A stochastic transitional probability matrix can be derived in terms of this discretized form of the continuous process since the probability of occurrence of a transition in this interval of time is equal to the transition rate times the time interval. If the failure rate of a component is λ then the probability of a failure transition in time $\Delta t = \lambda \, \Delta t$ and the probability of not failing in time $\Delta t = 1 - \lambda \, \Delta t$.

In the case of the single repairable component represented by the state space diagram shown in Figure 9.1a, the stochastic transitional probability matrix P is

$$P = \begin{array}{c} 1 \\ 2 \end{array} \begin{bmatrix} \overset{\displaystyle 1}{1 - \lambda \, \Delta t} & \overset{\displaystyle 2}{\lambda \, \Delta t} \\ \mu \, \Delta t & 1 - \mu \, \Delta t \end{bmatrix} \qquad (9.15)$$

9.5 Evaluating limiting state probabilities

9.5.1 Single repairable component

It was shown in Section 8.5 that the stochastic transitional probability matrix was ideally suited for the evaluation of limiting state probabilities. The approach used was to define α as the limiting state probability vector which remained unchanged when multiplied by the stochastic transitional probability matrix, that is,

$$\alpha P = \alpha \qquad (9.16)$$

If α is given by $[P_o \quad P_1]$ for the single repairable component, then from Equations 9.14 to 9.15

$$[P_o \quad P_1] \begin{bmatrix} 1 - \lambda \, \Delta t & \lambda \, \Delta t \\ \mu \, \Delta t & 1 - \mu \, \Delta t \end{bmatrix} = [P_o \quad P_1] \qquad (9.17)$$

which when written in explicit form, gives

$$(1 - \lambda \, \Delta t)P_o + \mu \, \Delta t \, P_1 = P_o \qquad (9.18a)$$

$$\lambda \, \Delta t \, P_o + (1 - \mu \, \Delta t)P_1 = P_1 \qquad (9.18b)$$

Rearranging Equations 9.18 gives

$$-\lambda \, \Delta t \, P_o + \mu \, \Delta t \, P_1 = 0 \tag{9.19a}$$

$$\lambda \, \Delta t \, P_o - \mu \, \Delta t \, P_1 = 0 \tag{9.19b}$$

In Equations 9.19 the value of Δt, provided it is non-zero and finite, disappears to give

$$-\lambda P_o + \mu P_1 = 0 \tag{9.20a}$$

$$\lambda P_o - \mu P_1 = 0 \tag{9.20b}$$

which are identical to Equations 9.14 and will therefore again give

$$P_o = \frac{\mu}{\lambda + \mu} \quad \text{and} \quad P_1 = \frac{\lambda}{\lambda + \mu}$$

The Δt terms disappear in Equations 9.20. It is convenient therefore to omit them entirely in formulating the initiating matrix and express the transition probabilities strictly in terms of the transition rates. In this case the stochastic transitional probability matrix given in Equation 9.15 would appear as

$$\boldsymbol{P} = \begin{array}{c} \\ \\ \end{array} \begin{matrix} 1 & 2 \\ \begin{bmatrix} 1 - \lambda & \lambda \\ \mu & 1 - \mu \end{bmatrix} \end{matrix} \tag{9.21}$$

It should be stressed that Equation 9.21 is not the complete form of the stochastic transitional probability matrix as λ and μ are not strictly probabilities. It is, however, convenient when developing equations for the limiting probability values. The time increment Δt must be included if the discrete matrix is to be used to obtain an approximation of the time dependent probabilities using the matrix multiplication approach.

9.5.2 Two identical repairable components

In this case the state space diagram is shown in Figure 9.4. The stochastic transitional probability matrix in the form given by Equation 9.21 is

$$\boldsymbol{P} = \begin{matrix} 1 \\ 2 \\ 3 \end{matrix} \begin{bmatrix} \begin{matrix} 1 & 2 & 3 \end{matrix} \\ \begin{matrix} 1 - 2\lambda & 2\lambda & 0 \\ \mu & 1 - \lambda - \mu & \lambda \\ 0 & 2\mu & 1 - 2\mu \end{matrix} \end{bmatrix} \tag{9.22}$$

Therefore, if the limiting state probability vector is $[P_1 \ \ P_2 \ \ P_3]$, Equation 9.16 gives

$$[P_1 \ \ P_2 \ \ P_3] \begin{bmatrix} 1 - 2\lambda & 2\lambda & 0 \\ \mu & 1 - \lambda - \mu & \lambda \\ 0 & 2\mu & 1 - 2\mu \end{bmatrix} = [P_1 \ \ P_2 \ \ P_3] \tag{9.23}$$

which, in explicit form, gives

$$P_1(1-2\lambda)+P_2\mu = P_1 \tag{9.24a}$$

$$P_1 2\lambda + P_2(1-\lambda-\mu)+P_3 2\mu = P_2 \tag{9.24b}$$

$$P_2\lambda + P_3(1-2\mu) = P_3 \tag{9.24c}$$

rearranging gives

$$-2\lambda P_1 + \mu P_2 = 0 \tag{9.25a}$$

$$2\lambda P_1 - (\lambda+\mu)P_2 + 2\mu P_3 = 0 \tag{9.25b}$$

$$\lambda P_2 - 2\mu P_3 = 0 \tag{9.25c}$$

and $$P_1 + P_2 + P_3 = 1 \tag{9.25d}$$

The limiting state probabilities can be obtained by using straightforward substitution methods or matrix techniques, and are

$$P_1 = \frac{\mu^2}{(\lambda+\mu)^2} \qquad P_2 = \frac{2\lambda\mu}{(\lambda+\mu)^2} \qquad P_3 = \frac{\lambda^2}{(\lambda+\mu)^2} \tag{9.26}$$

(a) *Series connected components*

In the case of two identical components connected in series, the up state of the system is state 1 and the down state is states 2 and 3, therefore

availability, $A = P_1$

$$= \frac{\mu^2}{(\lambda+\mu)^2} \tag{9.27a}$$

unavailability, $U = P_2 + P_3$

$$= \frac{2\lambda\mu + \lambda^2}{(\lambda+\mu)^2} \tag{9.27b}$$

(b) *Parallel connected components*

In the case of two identical components connected in parallel, state 2 also becomes an up state giving

availability, $A = P_1 + P_2$

$$= \frac{\mu^2 + 2\lambda\mu}{(\lambda+\mu)^2} \tag{9.28a}$$

unavailability, $U = P_3$

$$= \frac{\lambda^2}{(\lambda+\mu)^2} \tag{9.28b}$$

It is interesting to note that, in this system, each component is independent, and the expressions for P_1, P_2 and P_3 together with the values of availability and unavailability could have been obtained directly from the results of the single component system, Equations 9.11, using the binomial expansion. This applies to any number of independent components and the reader should therefore be able to derive the equivalent equations for limiting state probabilities for a three component system from the binomial expansion and verify these using the technique described in this section.

9.6 Evaluating time dependent state probabilities

9.6.1 Differential equations method

The basic concepts of evaluating the time dependent state probabilities of Markov processes using differential equations was described in Section 9.2.2 and illustrated for a single repairable component. In more complicated systems it becomes increasingly difficult to obtain general time dependent expressions. In such cases it is better to use conventional numerical techniques for solving the associated differential equations of a particular system rather than deriving general expressions and substituting the numerical values into them. In mission orientated systems, the time dependent state probabilities are the primary reliability indices and it can prove to be quite difficult to obtain general expressions when component repair is permissible.

In order to illustrate the application of the differential equations method to more complicated systems and to verify the complexity that arises in attempting to derive general expressions, consider the two identical component system shown in Figure 9.4. Let

$P_1(t)$ = probability that both components are in an operative state at time t,

$P_2(t)$ = probability that one component is operative and one component is failed at time t, and

$P_3(t)$ = probability that both components are failed at time t.

Using the principle of Equation 9.4c, the differential equations for this system are

$$[P_1'(t) \quad P_2'(t) \quad P_3'(t)] = [P_1(t) \quad P_2(t) \quad P_3(t)] \begin{bmatrix} -2\lambda & 2\lambda & 0 \\ \mu & -(\lambda+\mu) & \lambda \\ 0 & 2\mu & -2\mu \end{bmatrix}$$

$$(9.29)$$

Assume that the system starts in state 1, then

$$P_1(0) = 1, \qquad P_2(0) = 0 \quad \text{and} \quad P_3(0) = 0$$

The solution of Equation 9.29 is derived in Appendix 4 using these initial conditions as an example of solving differential equations using Laplace transforms from which

$$P_1(t) = \frac{\mu^2}{(\lambda + \mu)^2} + \frac{2\lambda\mu}{(\lambda + \mu)^2} e^{-(\lambda + \mu)t} + \frac{\lambda^2}{(\lambda + \mu)^2} e^{-2(\lambda + \mu)t} \qquad (9.30a)$$

$$P_2(t) = \frac{2\lambda\mu}{(\lambda + \mu)^2} + \frac{2\lambda(\lambda - \mu)}{(\lambda + \mu)^2} e^{-(\lambda + \mu)t} - \frac{2\lambda^2}{(\lambda + \mu)^2} e^{-2(\lambda + \mu)t} \qquad (9.30b)$$

$$P_3(t) = \frac{\lambda^2}{(\lambda + \mu)^2} - \frac{2\lambda^2}{(\lambda + \mu)^2} e^{-(\lambda + \mu)t} + \frac{\lambda^2}{(\lambda + \mu)^2} e^{-2(\lambda + \mu)t} \qquad (9.30c)$$

It can be seen that the derivation (Appendix 4) and the resulting general expressions become rather complex even in the case of two identical and repairable components. In this case however, Equations 9.30 could have been derived in a similar manner to that described for the limiting state probabilities by applying the binomial expansion to the single component equations shown in Equations 9.10. Solving the system by numerical techniques using software normally found on most digital computers, however, permits the state probabilities to be evaluated with relative ease. When the individual state probabilities have been evaluated using either Equations 9.30 or numerical techniques, they can be combined together to give the time dependent probability of the system up state and system down state for either a series system or a parallel system using the principle of Equations 9.27 and 9.28, respectively.

It can be seen, as expected, that Equations 9.30 reduce to Equations 9.26 as time tends to infinity giving the limiting state probabilities.

9.6.2 Matrix multiplication method

An alternative method for evaluating time dependent probabilities is to use a matrix multiplication method based on that described for discrete Markov chains in Section 8.4.

In this method, the stochastic transitional probability matrix is constructed for a small interval of time Δt as illustrated in Equation 9.15 for the single repairable component. In this case however the value of Δt cannot be neglected as was possible when the limiting state probabilities were evaluated. The actual value of Δt must also be chosen so that the probability of two or more transitions occurring in this interval of time is negligible. This requires a thorough knowledge of the system being analysed, in some cases the increment must be much less than a minute if the transitions occur frequently whilst in others it can be an hour or more. No general conclusions can therefore be given that will apply to all systems. If there is doubt in any particular case, it is suggested that an estimate of Δt be made and the result calculated for this value. A re-calculation can then be made for a decreased value of Δt and this process continued until two sets of results are within an acceptable tolerance.

After having deduced the stochastic transitional probability matrix for the interval of time Δt, the matrix can be multiplied by itself continuously until the period of time required for study has been reached, for example, if the value of Δt is set to 10 minutes and a period of study of 8 hours is required, the matrix must be multiplied by itself $(8 \times 60)/10 = 48$ times. Although the number of multiplications in practice may seem large, the method is extremely fast on a digital computer, is much simpler than the differential equations method particularly for large systems and, for a reasonable choice of Δt, can give results with perfectly acceptable precision for all practical purposes.

9.7 Reliability evaluation in repairable systems

The state probability expressions given in Equations 9.30 were obtained for the system shown in Figure 9.4. These expressions give the probability of being found in each of the three states at a given time t in the future. These state probability values are sometimes called state availability values, which tends to cause some confusion if the word availability is associated strictly with a success state or situation. If this is the case then the system availability is the sum of the appropriate state probability values. This also applies to the system unavailability. Equations 9.30 cannot be used to obtain the system reliability if success in this case is defined as staying out of the failed state. This situation can be illustrated by considering the two identical component system illustrated in Figure 9.4. If the two components are connected to form a parallel redundant configuration then the failure state of the system is state 3. The limiting state probability associated with state 3 is the system unavailability (Equation 9.28b)

$$U = \frac{\lambda^2}{(\lambda + \mu)^2}$$

In order to calculate the system reliability, the process must come to a halt when state 3 is encountered. This can be achieved by modifying the state space diagram to make state 3 an absorbing state. When state 3 is encountered, the system effectively comes to a halt until the whole process is started again at state 1.

Equation 9.29 is modified as follows

$$[P_1'(t) \quad P_2'(t) \quad P_3'(t)] = [P_1(t) \quad P_2(t) \quad P_3(t)] \begin{bmatrix} -2\lambda & 2\lambda & 0 \\ \mu & -(\lambda + \mu) & \lambda \\ 0 & 0 & 0 \end{bmatrix}$$

$$(9.31)$$

This set of differential equations can be solved using Laplace transforms as described in Appendix 4. The reliability of the system is [29]

$$R(t) = P_1(t) + P_2(t)$$
$$= \frac{s_1 \exp(-s_2 t) - s_2 \exp(-s_1 t)}{s_1 - s_2}$$

(9.32)

where $s_1 = \frac{1}{2}(3\lambda + \mu + \sqrt{\lambda^2 + 6\lambda\mu + \mu^2})$

$s_2 = \frac{1}{2}(3\lambda + \mu - \sqrt{\lambda^2 + 6\lambda\mu + \mu^2})$

It is interesting to compare Equation 9.32 with the equation for the mission reliability of a two identical component redundant system without repair. In this case

$$R(t) = e^{-\lambda t} + e^{-\lambda t} - e^{-2\lambda t}$$
$$= 2e^{-\lambda t} - e^{-2\lambda t}$$

(9.33)

The fundamental difference between these two equations is that in the first case, the system will fail only if the remaining operating component fails before the failed component is repaired. In the second case, no repair is permitted and therefore system failure occurs when the last operating component fails. It can become quite difficult to obtain general reliability equations for more complex systems with repair. Numerical reliability solutions can be obtained by using either the differential equation approach or the matrix multiplication method described in Sections 9.6.1 and 9.6.2, respectively.

9.8 Mean time to failure

9.8.1 Evaluation concepts

As previously stated, it is virtually impossible to obtain a general expression that represents the time dependent state probabilities of complicated systems although numerical solutions using the differential equations method or the matrix multiplication method are usually possible. In some cases it is not necessary to evaluate the complete time dependent characteristic of the state probabilities as an evaluation of the MTTF is all that is required. This can be achieved using either differential equations or the stochastic transitional probability matrix. In both cases the concept of absorbing states is used. An absorbing state has been defined as a state which, once entered, cannot be left until the process starts again. Consequently, the MTTF can be equated to the average time before the system enters the absorbing state.

If the differential equations have been solved to obtain an expression for the system reliability $R(t)$, the MTTF can be evaluated from Equation 7.24 by integrating $R(t)$ over the range 0 to ∞.

$$MTTF = \int_0^\infty R(t)\, dt$$

In the case of the repairable redundant system for which $R(t)$ is given by Equation 9.32

$$MTTF = \frac{s_1 + s_2}{s_1 s_2}$$

$$= \frac{3\lambda + \mu}{2\lambda^2} \tag{9.34}$$

This can be compared with

$$MTTF = \frac{3}{2\lambda}$$

for the system of Equation 9.33.

9.8.2   Stochastic transitional probability matrix method

The differential equation method requires the differential equations to be solved. This can be very tedious if not impossible particularly if a generalized equation of the form of Equation 9.33 is required. An alternative method is to use the principle of the truncated probability matrix described in Section 8.6 in which the row and column associated with the absorbing state is deleted from the stochastic transitional probability matrix.

(a)   *Two component parallel redundant system*

The stochastic transitional probability matrix for the two identical component system was shown in Equation 9.22. If as in Section 9.7.2, state 3 is assumed to be the absorbing state, the truncated matrix Q is given by

$$Q = \begin{array}{cc} \hspace{0.5em} 1 & \hspace{1.5em} 2 \\ \begin{bmatrix} 1-2\lambda & 2\lambda \\ \mu & 1-\lambda-\mu \end{bmatrix} \end{array} \tag{9.35}$$

In Chapter 8, the matrix Q was used to deduce the average number of steps that would elapse before the system entered the absorbing state. In the case of a continuous Markov process, the same technique can be used to deduce the average time, i.e., MTTF, that would elapse before the system entered the absorbing state.

Therefore, using the principle of Section 8.6 and the matrix algebra techniques of Appendix 3

$$M = [I - Q]^{-1}$$

$$= \left[\begin{bmatrix} 1 & 0 \\ 0 & 1 \end{bmatrix} - \begin{bmatrix} 1-2\lambda & 2\lambda \\ \mu & 1-\lambda-\mu \end{bmatrix} \right]^{-1}$$

$$= \begin{bmatrix} 2\lambda & -2\lambda \\ -\mu & \lambda+\mu \end{bmatrix}^{-1}$$

$$= \frac{1}{2\lambda^2} \begin{bmatrix} \lambda+\mu & 2\lambda \\ \mu & 2\lambda \end{bmatrix} \qquad (9.36)$$

in which the element m_{ij} of M is the average time spent in state j given that the process starts in state i before being absorbed. The matrix M is generally defined as the fundamental matrix.

If the system starts in state 1, the MTTF of the system is

$$MTTF = m_{11} + m_{12}$$

$$= \frac{(\lambda+\mu)+(2\lambda)}{2\lambda^2}$$

$$= \frac{3\lambda+\mu}{2\lambda^2} \qquad (9.37)$$

which is identical to Equation 9.34 obtained using the differential equation method.

In the derivation of Equation 9.37, it was assumed that the system starts in state 1 and therefore this state is assumed to be the normal up state of the system. In some practical cases the system may be considered to be in the up state when only one component is operable i.e., state 2. In this case the MTTF of the system is

$$MTTF = m_{21} + m_{22}$$

$$= \frac{\mu+2\lambda}{2\lambda^2} \qquad (9.38)$$

In other more complicated systems, there may be several identifiable up states. In these cases the utilization of a recursive approach rather than the development of the fundamental matrix M for the system may be simpler and more convenient. This approach will be discussed in Chapter 10.

(b) *Two component series system*

In the case when the two components are connected in series, the same technique can be applied. In this case however, states 2 and 3 are failure states and therefore both can be declared absorbing states.

The truncated matrix Q now consists of a single element

$$Q = [1 - 2\lambda]$$

and $$M = [I - Q]^{-1}$$

$$= [2\lambda]^{-1}$$

and MTTF $= \dfrac{1}{2\lambda}$ (9.39)

(c) *Failure rate derivation*

As discussed in Section 9.2.1 and shown in Equations 9.12, the MTTF can be considered as the reciprocal of the failure rate of the system and vice versa. Therefore the MTTFs specified by Equations 9.37–9.39 and similar expressions for more complicated systems can be reciprocated to give the effective failure rate of the appropriate system, i.e.,

(a)   for a 2 component series system, from Equation 9.39

$$\text{effective failure rate} = 2\lambda \qquad (9.40)$$

(b)   for a 2 component parallel system in which both components being operable is considered the system up state, from Equation 9.37

$$\text{effective failure rate} = \frac{2\lambda^2}{3\lambda + \mu} \qquad (9.41)$$

It must be appreciated however that the MTTF or failure rate of a two component system cannot be associated with a single exponential function to give an expression for the reliability of the system. The MTTF and effective failure rate are simply average values of a non-exponential distribution although the individual components themselves may be represented by exponential distributions.

9.9   Application of techniques to complex systems

All the techniques described in this chapter have been illustrated in terms of simple systems. This is necessary in order to explain the logic of the techniques. It is however a relatively simple exercise in concept to extend these techniques to more complex problems. In all cases the principle to follow is:

(a)   Identify all states in which the system can reside.

(b)   Identify all possible transitions between these states and specify the numerical values of these transitions.

(c)   Construct the appropriate set of differential equations or the stochastic transitional probability matrix.

(d) Using the differential equation method or the multiplication method evaluate the time dependent state probabilities, if required.

(e) Using the principle of $\alpha P = \alpha$, evaluate the limiting state probabilities, if required.

(f) Identify the system up states, down states and derated states (if any).

(g) Combine the appropriate state probabilities evaluated in (d) and/or (e) to give the probability of the system being up, down or in derated state(s).

(h) Using the principle of absorbing states, solve the modified differential equations to obtain an equation for the system reliability and use this equation to obtain the MTTF. If the differential equations cannot be solved directly, the matrix multiplication approach can be used to obtain an estimate of $R(t)$ and the fundamental matrix developed to obtain the MTTF.

In order to illustrate some of these steps consider the three component series/parallel system shown in Figure 9.8.

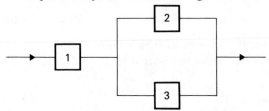

Fig. 9.8 A three component series/parallel system

(a) The states in which the system of Figure 9.8 can reside have already been shown in Figure 9.5.

(b) The transition rates assuming all components are repairable are also shown in Figure 9.5.

(c) The stochastic transitional probability matrix P is shown on the facing page.

(d) If each element of P is multiplied by a suitable time interval, the modified P can be multiplied by itself n times to give the probability of residing in each state of the system after $1, 2, 3, \ldots, n$ time intervals, i.e., the time dependent state probabilities.

(e) If a limiting state probability vector

$$[P_1 \quad P_2 \quad P_3 \quad P_4 \quad P_5 \quad P_6 \quad P_7 \quad P_8]$$

is defined, the equations $\alpha P = \alpha$ can be solved to deduce $P_1, P_2, \ldots, P_8$.

(f) If the system shown in Figure 9.8 can operate with either component 2 or 3 or both in an operable state, then for this system the

system up states are $1, 3, 4$

system down states are $2, 5, 6, 7, 8$

$$P =$$

	1	2	3	4	5	6	7	8
1	$(1-\lambda_1-\lambda_2-\lambda_3)$	λ_1	λ_2	λ_3	—	—	—	—
2	μ_1	$(1-\mu_1-\lambda_2-\lambda_3)$	—	—	λ_2	—	λ_3	—
3	μ_2	—	$(1-\mu_2-\lambda_1-\lambda_3)$	—	λ_1	λ_3	—	—
4	μ_3	—	—	$(1-\mu_3-\lambda_1-\lambda_2)$	—	λ_2	λ_1	—
5	—	μ_2	μ_1	—	$(1-\mu_2-\mu_1-\lambda_3)$	—	—	λ_3
6	—	—	μ_3	μ_2	—	$(1-\mu_2-\mu_3-\lambda_1)$	—	λ_1
7	—	μ_3	—	μ_1	—	—	$(1-\mu_1-\mu_3-\lambda_2)$	λ_2
8	—	—	—	—	μ_3	μ_1	μ_2	$(1-\mu_1-\mu_2-\mu_3)$

(g)   Therefore $P_{up} = P_1 + P_3 + P_4$

$$P_{down} = P_2 + P_5 + P_6 + P_7 + P_8$$

(h)   If the system shown in Figure 9.8 is in a fully up state only when both components 2 and 3 are operable and in a derated state when only 2 or 3 is operable, then the

   system up states are 1

   system derated states are 3, 4

   system down states are 2, 5, 6, 7, 8

(i)   Therefore $P_{up} = P_1$

$$P_{derated} = P_3 + P_4$$

$$P_{down} = P_2 + P_5 + P_6 + P_7 + P_8$$

(j)   If the system shown in Figure 9.8 can operate with either component 2 or 3 or both in an operable state, then, for this system, states 2, 5–8 are defined as absorbing states and deleted to give $\boldsymbol{Q}$ as

$$\boldsymbol{Q} = \begin{matrix} 1 \\ 3 \\ 4 \end{matrix} \begin{bmatrix} (1 - \lambda_1 - \lambda_2 - \lambda_3) & \lambda_2 & \lambda_3 \\ \mu_2 & (1 - \mu_2 - \lambda_1 - \lambda_3) & — \\ \mu_3 & — & (1 - \mu_3 - \lambda_1 - \lambda_2) \end{bmatrix}$$

from which the MTTF can be evaluated using $\boldsymbol{M} = [\boldsymbol{I} - \boldsymbol{Q}]^{-1}$. The system reliability can be obtained by solving the differential equations described by the $\boldsymbol{Q}$ matrix.

9.10   Conclusions

Markov models and evaluation techniques can play a vital role in the evaluation of system reliability. In the case of continuous processes the models are governed by sets of differential equations which can make them difficult to apply to complex systems. The solution techniques, however, can be considerably simplified by constructing and using the stochastic transitional probability matrix for evaluating not only the limiting state probabilities but also the time dependent values. The basic techniques described in this chapter can be enhanced considerably by introducing recursive techniques and frequency and duration concepts (*see* Chapter 10). Markov modelling techniques are essentially associated with constant hazard rates and are therefore strictly applicable only to exponential distributions. In the case of limiting state probabilities involving independent components the underlying distributional assumptions lose their significance. The distribution is, however, very important in the evaluation of time dependent probabilities. If exponential distributions are not valid for the components, these basic techniques cannot be used to evaluate time dependent probabilities. However, it is possible to extend the techniques to non-exponential distributions (*see* Chapter 12).

Problems

1 The state space diagram and transition rates in f/hr of a continuous Markov process is shown in Figure 9.9. Calculate:
   (a) The limiting probabilities of each state.
   (b) The availability of the system.
   (c) The MTTF for the following system operating conditions;
       (1) state 1 is the normally up state, state 2 is a standby state and state 3 is the failure state; and
       (2) state 1 is the operating state and states 2 and 3 are failure states.

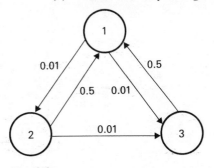

Fig. 9.9

2 The following stochastic transitional probability matrix P shows the transition rates in per hour of a continuous Markov process.
   (a) Construct the state space diagram and discuss particular features of it.
   (b) Evaluate the MTTF given that the system starts in state 1.
   (c) Derive the differential equations for the system.

$$P = \begin{array}{c} \\ 1 \\ 2 \\ 3 \end{array} \begin{array}{ccc} 1 & 2 & 3 \\ \left[\begin{array}{ccc} 0.90 & 0.05 & 0.05 \\ 0 & 0.95 & 0.05 \\ 0 & 0 & 1 \end{array}\right] \end{array}$$

3 A pumping station has two identical pumps connected in parallel, each capable of pumping 3000 gallons/hr. If the failure rate and repair rate of each is 0.5 f/hr and 4 r/hr respectively, construct the state space diagram and stochastic transitional probability matrix. Hence evaluate the average hourly throughput of the pumping station. What average throughputs would be obtained if the station had one pump having a capacity of 6000 gallons/hr or three pumps each having a capacity of 2000 gallons/hr?

4   A mission oriented system consists of 3 non-identical, non-repairable components, two of which must operate for system success. If the failure rates are
0.01, 0.05 and 0.1 f/10^6 hr, construct the stochastic transitional probability
matrix and hence evaluate the MTTF of the system.

5   A system has one normally operating component A, two standby components
B and C and a perfect and instantaneous changeover device. Construct the
state space diagram and stochastic transitional probability matrix of the system
if all components are repairable, component A is always used as the operating
component when available, component B is always used in preference to
component C and components do not fail when in the standby mode.

10 Frequency and duration techniques

10.1 Introduction

The Markov techniques described in the previous two chapters permit the probability of residing in each state of the system to be evaluated. The probability of being in the system up state, system down state and system derated state(s) can then be evaluated from these individual state probabilities knowing which of the individual system states contribute to the respective overall system states. These techniques can be used for either mission orientated or repairable systems, and can be extended to evaluate the MTTF of the system.

It is however extremely beneficial for a thorough understanding of system behaviour to evaluate additional reliability indices for systems that are continuously operated, repaired and maintained. Suggested additional indices are the frequency of encountering a system state and the average duration of residing in the state. The method of deriving these additional indices can be designated as the frequency and duration technique. The evaluation of the indices is based on state space diagrams and continuous Markov models as described in Chapter 9.

10.2 Frequency and duration concepts

The basic concepts associated with the frequency and duration technique are best described in terms of the single repairable component used to describe the continuous Markov process in Chapter 9. The state space diagram of this system is shown in Figure 10.1a and the probability of residing in the operable state (availability) and the probability of residing in the failed state (unavailability) were given in Equations 9.11 as

$$P_o = \frac{\mu}{\lambda + \mu} = \frac{m}{m + r} \tag{10.1a}$$

$$P_1 = \frac{\lambda}{\lambda + \mu} = \frac{r}{m + r} \tag{10.1b}$$

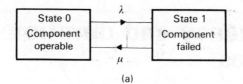

(a)

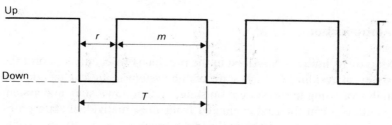

(b)

Fig. 10.1   Single component system. (a) State space diagram. (b) Mean time/state diagram

in which

λ = failure rate of the component

μ = repair rate of the component

m = mean operating time of the component

r = mean repair time of the component

The two system states and their associated transitions can be shown chronologically on a time graph. The mean values of up and down times can be used to give the average performance of this two state system. This is shown in Figure 10.1b.

In Figure 10.1b, the period T is the system cycle time and is equal to the sum of the mean time to failure (MTTF) and mean time to repair (MTTR). This cycle time is defined as the mean time between failures (MTBF). In some publications, MTBF is used in place of MTTF. It is evident however that there is a significant conceptual difference between MTTF and MTBF. The numerical difference between them will depend on the value of MTTR. In practice the repair time is usually very small compared with the operating time and therefore the numerical values of MTTF and MTBF are usually very similar. The following relationships can therefore be defined

$$m = \text{MTTF} = 1/\lambda \qquad (10.2a)$$

$$r = \text{MTTR} = 1/\mu \qquad (10.2b)$$

$$T = \text{MTBF} = m + r = 1/f \qquad (10.2c)$$

where $f =$ cycle frequency, i.e., the frequency of encountering a system state. In the case of the two state system representing the single component and shown in Figure 10.1a, the frequency of encountering the operating state is the same as that of encountering the failed state. The frequency of encountering each state of a more complex system will generally be different for each state of the system.

The problem of describing the behaviour of a system only by state probabilities can be illustrated by considering either Equation 10.1a or 10.1b. If we consider two single component systems, one having component reliability indices λ and μ and the other having indices 2λ and 2μ, the availability and unavailability are the same for both systems. The second system however fails twice as often but is repaired twice as fast. This situation can have a major effect on the operation of the system and its economics. Therefore, it can be vital to evaluate not only the availability (or unavailability) of the system but also the frequency and duration of encountering the various states of the system.

The method of evaluating the frequency and duration indices is based on the following concepts.

From Equation 10.1a and 10.1b, the probability of residing in any state of the system is equal to the mean residence time of that state divided by the mean cycle time for that state to occur. This concept, although self-evident for the two state system shown in Figure 10.1, applies to all repairable systems no matter how many system states exist. Therefore, if $P(S)$ is the probability of residing in state S, $m(S)$ is the mean time spent in state S and $T(S)$ is the mean time between encounters of state S

$$P(S) = \frac{m(S)}{T(S)} \tag{10.3}$$

Also from Equation 10.1a

$$P_o = \frac{m}{m+r} = \frac{m}{T} = \frac{1}{\lambda T} = \frac{f}{\lambda} \tag{10.4a}$$

and from Equation 10.1b

$$P_1 = \frac{r}{m+r} = \frac{r}{T} = \frac{1}{\mu T} = \frac{f}{\mu} \tag{10.4b}$$

From Equations 10.4, it is seen that

$$f = P_o\lambda = P_1\mu \tag{10.5}$$

which can be stated in words as: frequency of encountering the up state

$$= P_o\lambda = \text{(probability of being in the state)}$$

$$\times \text{(rate of departure from the state)}$$

or,

$= P_1 \mu = ($probability of NOT being in the state$)$

$\times ($rate of entry into the state$)$.

This concept only applies to the long term or average behaviour of the system and is not valid for time dependent probabilities or frequencies.

Therefore if $f(S)$ is the frequency of encountering a state, $P(S)$ is the probability of being in the state, $\bar{P}(\bar{S})$ is the probability of NOT being in the state, $\lambda_d(S)$ is the rate of departure from the state and $\lambda_e(S)$ is the rate of entry into the state.

$$f(S) = P(S)\lambda_d(S) = \bar{P}(\bar{S})\lambda_e(S) \tag{10.6}$$

Finally from Equations 10.3 and 10.6, since $T(S) = 1/f(S)$

$$m(S) = \frac{P(S)}{f(S)} = \frac{1}{\lambda_d(S)} \tag{10.7}$$

The concept of Equation 10.7, that is, the mean duration of a state, is the reciprocal of its rate of departure, has been established previously. Equation 10.7 also shows however that this mean duration is equal to the probability of residing in the state divided by the frequency of encountering the state. The concepts described by Equation 10.7 become important when individual states are combined or cumulated to give indices of system states.

10.3 Application to multi-state problems

10.3.1 Two component repairable system

The basic frequency and duration concepts described in Section 10.2 can be applied to any size of repairable system and have been applied in practice to power system generation problems containing several hundred individual units. The application of the techniques to multicomponent (or state) systems can be illustrated by considering a simple two component system, in which each component is considered to have an up state (operating) and a down state (failed) with failure and repair rates of λ_1, μ_1 and λ_2, μ_2 for components 1 and 2 respectively.

The state space diagram of this system, previously shown in Figure 9.3, is reproduced in Figure 10.2.

The stochastic transitional probability matrix for the system is

$$
\mathbf{P} = \begin{array}{c} \\ 1 \\ 2 \\ 3 \\ 4 \end{array}
\begin{array}{cccc}
\quad 1 \quad & \quad 2 \quad & \quad 3 \quad & \quad 4 \quad \\
\left[\begin{array}{cccc}
1-(\lambda_1+\lambda_2) & \lambda_1 & \lambda_2 & - \\
\mu_1 & 1-(\lambda_2+\mu_1) & - & \lambda_2 \\
\mu_2 & - & 1-(\lambda_1+\mu_2) & \lambda_1 \\
- & \mu_2 & \mu_1 & 1-(\mu_1+\mu_2)
\end{array}\right]
\end{array}
$$

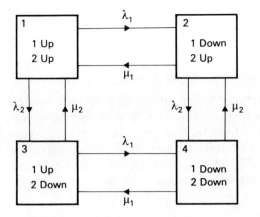

Fig. 10.2 State space diagram for two component system

10.3.2 State probabilities

The first step in the frequency and duration method is to evaluate the individual limiting state probabilities. The general method for evaluating these probabilities has been described in Chapter 9 and involves setting up the limiting state equations of the form $\alpha P = \alpha$ (see Equation 9.16 of Section 9.5.1). In this case the state probabilities can be obtained by simple independent combinations. The state probabilities are

$$P_1 = \frac{\mu_1 \mu_2}{(\lambda_1 + \mu_1)(\lambda_2 + \mu_2)} \tag{10.7a}$$

$$P_2 = \frac{\lambda_1 \mu_2}{(\lambda_1 + \mu_1)(\lambda_2 + \mu_2)} \tag{10.7b}$$

$$P_3 = \frac{\mu_1 \lambda_2}{(\lambda_1 + \mu_1)(\lambda_2 + \mu_2)} \tag{10.7c}$$

$$P_4 = \frac{\lambda_1 \lambda_2}{(\lambda_1 + \mu_1)(\lambda_2 + \mu_2)} \tag{10.7d}$$

If the two components are identical, i.e., $\lambda_1 = \lambda_2 = \lambda$ and $\mu_1 = \mu_2 = \mu$, Equations 10.7 would reduce to those given previously in Chapter 9, i.e., Equations 9.26.

Since the individual states of the system are mutually exclusive, the probabilities given by Equations 10.7 can be combined to give the probability of residing in any set of cumulated states. For example,

(a) for a series system, $P_{up} = P_1$

$$P_{down} = P_2 + P_3 + P_4$$

(b) for a parallel system, $P_{up} = P_1 + P_2 + P_3$

$$P_{down} = P_4$$

This principle of cumulating state probabilities was discussed in Section 9.3.3.

10.3.3 Frequency of encountering individual states

The second step in the evaluation of the frequency and duration indices of a system is to evaluate the frequency of encountering the individual states. This is obtained using Equation 10.6 and the individual state probabilities and the rates of departure or entry. The state probabilities were evaluated in Section 10.3.2. The rates of departure and entry to each state can be identified from both the state space diagram of Figure 10.2 and also from the stochastic transitional probability matrix P. These rates are tabulated in Table 10.1.

Table 10.1 Rates of departure and entry

State number	Component 1	Component 2	Rate of Departure	Entry
1	up	up	$\lambda_1 + \lambda_2$	$\mu_1 + \mu_2$
2	down	up	$\lambda_2 + \mu_1$	$\lambda_1 + \mu_2$
3	up	down	$\lambda_1 + \mu_2$	$\lambda_2 + \mu_1$
4	down	down	$\mu_1 + \mu_2$	$\lambda_1 + \lambda_2$

(a) *Frequency of encountering state 1*

From Equation 10.6, if $f_1 =$ frequency of encountering state 1

$$= P_1 \times (\text{rate of departure from state 1})$$

$$= \frac{\mu_1 \mu_2 (\lambda_1 + \lambda_2)}{(\lambda_1 + \mu_1)(\lambda_2 + \mu_2)} \tag{10.8}$$

also, from Equation 10.6,

$$f_1 = \bar{P}_1 \times (\text{rate of entry to state 1})$$

The application of this form of the concept must be treated with care since it applies only to the communicating states. Therefore, in the case of state 1, the only communicating states are 2 and 3, the rates of entry to state 1 from these being μ_1 and μ_2 respectively.

Thus

$$f_1 = P_2 \mu_1 + P_3 \mu_2$$

$$= \frac{\mu_1 \mu_2 (\lambda_1 + \lambda_2)}{(\lambda_1 + \mu_1)(\lambda_2 + \mu_2)} \quad (\text{as Equation 10.8})$$

(b) *Frequency of encountering state 4*

f_4 = frequency of encountering state 4

= $P_4 \times$ (rate of departure from state 4)

$$= \frac{\lambda_1\lambda_2(\mu_1+\mu_2)}{(\lambda_1+\mu_1)(\lambda_2+\mu_2)} \tag{10.9}$$

or,

$$f_4 = P_2\lambda_2 + P_3\lambda_1$$

$$= \frac{\lambda_1\lambda_2(\mu_1+\mu_2)}{(\lambda_1+\mu_1)(\lambda_\bullet+\mu_2)} \quad \text{(as Equation 10.9)}$$

Similar derivations may be made for f_2 and f_3, the frequencies of encountering states 2 and 3 respectively. The complete list of state probabilities and frequencies of encounter are shown in Table 10.2.

Table 10.2 State probabilities and frequencies

State number	Probability	Frequency of encounter
1	$\mu_1\mu_2/D$	$\mu_1\mu_2(\lambda_1+\lambda_2)/D$
2	$\lambda_1\mu_2/D$	$\lambda_1\mu_2(\mu_1+\lambda_2)/D$
3	$\mu_1\lambda_2/D$	$\mu_1\lambda_2(\lambda_1+\mu_2)/D$
4	$\lambda_1\lambda_2/D$	$\lambda_1\lambda_2(\mu_1+\mu_2)/D$

where $D = (\lambda_1+\mu_1)(\lambda_2+\mu_2)$

In the case when both components are identical, that is, $\lambda_1 = \lambda_2 = \lambda$ and $\mu_1 = \mu_2 = \mu$,

$$f_1 = \frac{2\lambda\mu^2}{(\lambda+\mu)^2} \tag{10.10}$$

$$f_4 = \frac{2\lambda^2\mu}{(\lambda+\mu)^2} \tag{10.11}$$

$$f_2 = f_3 = \frac{\lambda\mu}{\lambda+\mu} \tag{10.12}$$

10.3.4 Mean duration of individual states

Using the concept of Equation 10.7, the mean duration of each of the system states, i.e., the mean time of residing in each of the states, can be evaluated directly and simply from the rates of departure shown in Table 10.1. Therefore, if m_1, m_2, m_3 and m_4 are defined as the mean duration of states 1–4 respectively, then

$$m_1 = \frac{1}{\lambda_1 + \lambda_2} \qquad (10.13a)$$

$$m_2 = \frac{1}{\lambda_2 + \mu_1} \qquad (10.13b)$$

$$m_3 = \frac{1}{\lambda_1 + \mu_2} \qquad (10.13c)$$

$$m_4 = \frac{1}{\mu_1 + \mu_2} \qquad (10.13d)$$

which, for the case of identical components, become

$$m_1 = \frac{1}{2\lambda}, \qquad m_2 = m_3 = \frac{1}{\lambda + \mu}, \qquad m_4 = \frac{1}{2\mu} \qquad (10.14)$$

The value of m_1 has already been deduced as the MTTF or mean up time of a series system containing two identical components in Section 9.8.2.

Similarly the value m_4 is the mean down time or MTTR of a parallel system.

10.3.5 Cycle time between individual states

The cycle time T was defined in Equation 10.2c as the reciprocal of the frequency of encounter f. A cycle time for each individual state can therefore be deduced from the frequency of encountering this state. This value of cycle time represents the mean time between entering (or departing from) a given state to next entering (or next departing from) the same state. In the case of the two component system and considering the case of identical components

$$T_1 = \frac{(\lambda + \mu)^2}{2\lambda\mu^2} \qquad (10.15a)$$

$$T_2 = T_3 = \frac{\lambda + \mu}{\lambda\mu} = \frac{1}{\lambda} + \frac{1}{\mu} \qquad (10.15b)$$

$$T_4 = \frac{(\lambda + \mu)^2}{2\lambda^2\mu} \qquad (10.15c)$$

Consider the two cases of parallel redundant systems and series systems.

(a) *Parallel redundant systems*

The MTTF of a parallel redundant system is defined as the mean time between encounters of the state in which both components are down.

The MTTF is given in Equation 9.38 as

$$MTTF = \frac{2\lambda + \mu}{2\lambda^2}$$

and the MTTR is given by m_4 in Equation 10.14.

Since the MTBF of a parallel redundant system is given by the sum of the MTTF and MTTR, then

$$MTBF = \frac{2\lambda + \mu}{2\lambda^2} + \frac{1}{2\mu}$$

$$= \frac{\lambda^2 + 2\lambda\mu + \mu^2}{2\lambda^2\mu}$$

$$= \frac{(\lambda + \mu)^2}{2\lambda^2\mu} \tag{10.16}$$

which is identical to Equation 10.15c, obtained for the cycle time T_4 using the frequency and duration method. The latter technique does not require the concept of absorbing states and is generally a simpler method to use. The two results are expected to be identical because the MTBF of a parallel redundant system is equivalent to the system cycle time of encountering state 4, i.e., the state in which both components are failed.

(b) *Series system*

In the case of a series system the MTTF is $1/2\lambda$ (Equations 9.39 and 10.14) and the MTTR is $(\lambda + 2\mu)/2\mu^2$. The value of MTTR was not derived in Chapter 9 but can be verified by truncating state 1 from Equation 9.22 and solving for M as in Section 9.8.2.

Therefore

$$MTBF = \frac{1}{2\lambda} + \frac{\lambda + 2\mu}{2\mu^2}$$

$$= \frac{(\lambda + \mu)^2}{2\lambda\mu^2} \tag{10.17}$$

which is identical to the cycle time T_1 given by Equation 10.15a. Again, these two results are expected to be identical since the up state of the series system is state 1 when both components are up, and the MTBF of the system is given by the mean time of encountering this state.

10.3.6 Frequency of encountering cumulated states

In most system reliability evaluation problems, the frequency, duration and cycle time of individual states only provide a partial answer to the problem. As discussed in Chapter 9, there may be several states of the system which have a similar impact on the system behaviour. States leading to the same system outcome can be combined or cumulated to give, for example, the system up state, system down state and system derated states (if any).

The probability of residing in one of these cumulated states can be evaluated by simply summating the mutually exclusive probabilities of each appropriate state. A similar technique can be used to evaluate the frequency of encountering cumulated states. In order to illustrate this process consider the combination of states 3 and 4. Define the cumulative frequency of combining states 3 and 4 as f_{34}.

The transition frequencies to be included in f_{34} must include the frequencies of all transitions that leave and enter the combined state (3 and 4) but must ignore all transition frequencies that occur between states 3 and 4 since these do not represent transitions out of the combined state (3 and 4). Therefore

$$f_{34} = f_3 + f_4 - (\text{frequency of encounters between 3 and 4})$$

$$= f_3 + f_4 - (P_3\lambda_1 + P_4\mu_1)$$

$$= P_3(\lambda_1 + \mu_2) + P_4(\mu_1 + \mu_2) - P_3\lambda_1 - P_4\mu_1$$

$$= P_3\mu_2 + P_4\mu_2$$

$$= (P_3 + P_4)\mu_2 \tag{10.18}$$

Equation 10.18 illustrates an important underlying principle. The frequency of encountering the cumulated state (3 and 4) can be obtained by considering the expected number of transitions across the boundary wall surrounding the cumulated state. This has two components $P_3\mu_2$ and $P_4\mu_2$ arising from states 3 and 4, respectively. The frequency is therefore

$$f_{34} = P_3\mu_2 + P_4\mu_2$$

$$= (P_3 + P_4)\mu_2$$

Substituting for P_3 and P_4 in Equation 10.18 gives

$$f_{34} = \frac{\mu_2\lambda_2}{\mu_2 + \lambda_2} \tag{10.19}$$

Similarly

$$f_{12} = \text{frequency of encountering the combined state (1 and 2)}$$

$$= f_1 + f_2 - P_1\lambda_1 - P_2\mu_1$$

$$= (P_1 + P_2)\lambda_2$$

$$= \frac{\mu_2\lambda_2}{\mu_2 + \lambda_2} \tag{10.20}$$

It can be seen that Equations 10.19 and 10.20 are identical. This is to be expected since the system has been effectively reduced to two cumulated states (1 and 2) and (3 and 4), in which case the frequency of encountering each must be the same. The effective state space diagram of this system is shown in Figure 10.3.

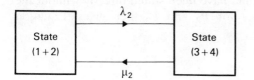

Fig. 10.3   Cumulated state space diagram

The states which have been combined in the above example do not give a cumulated set of states that represent a series or a parallel system. A series system would be represented by state 1 and the cumulated states (2, 3, 4) and a parallel redundant system by cumulated states (1, 2, 3) and state 4.

(a) *Series system*

$$f(\text{up}) = f_1$$

$$= \frac{\mu_1 \mu_2 (\lambda_1 + \lambda_2)}{(\lambda_1 + \mu_1)(\lambda_2 + \mu_2)} \qquad (10.21)$$

$f(\text{down}) = f_2 + f_3 + f_4 - (\text{frequency of encounters between 2 and 3,}$

between 3 and 4, between 2 and 4).

It should be appreciated that the solution to this equation should give the same result as Equation 10.21 because the system has been reduced to a two state system. The reduced equation can also be used to illustrate the boundary wall concept presented previously.

$$f(\text{down}) = P_2(\mu_1 + \lambda_2) + P_3(\lambda_1 + \mu_2) + P_4(\mu_1 + \mu_2)$$

$$- P_3\lambda_1 - P_4\mu_1 - P_2\lambda_2 - P_4\mu_2$$

$$= P_2\mu_1 + P_3\mu_2 \qquad (10.22)$$

This system has been effectively reduced to a two state system, i.e., state 1 and cumulated states (2, 3, 4). Equation 10.21 gives the expected transitions across the boundary wall when leaving the state. This must equal the expected number of transitions across the boundary wall when entering the state. Only those states which communicate directly across the boundary of the cumulated states contribute to the frequency of transitions across the boundary. Those states which do not have direct transitions across the boundary do not contribute. In this case only states 2 and 3 communicate across the boundary with transition rates of μ_1 and μ_2 respectively. The sum of their frequency contributions is given as Equation 10.22.

Therefore, Equation 10.22 could have been stated directly without the previous derivation. Substituting for P_2 and P_3 then gives Equation 10.21.

(b) *Parallel redundant system*

In this case

$$f(\text{down}) = f_4$$

$$= \frac{\lambda_1 \lambda_2 (\mu_1 + \mu_2)}{(\lambda_1 + \mu_1)(\lambda_2 + \mu_2)} \tag{10.23}$$

$f(\text{up}) = f_1 + f_2 + f_3 - (\text{frequency of encounters between 1 and 2}$

and 3) or, using the boundary wall concept

$f(\text{up}) = P_2 \lambda_2 + P_3 \lambda_1$

and subsequently to Equation 10.23.

10.3.7 Recursive evaluation of cumulative frequency

Ringlee et al. [30, 31] have formalized the procedure and concepts described in Section 10.3.6 into a recursive technique. The particular application was to electrical power generation systems. However, the technique has a much greater range of application. In essence, it has great scope for any system in which most of the individual states lead to different levels of system outcomes. In these cases the system cannot be described by simple up/down criteria but instead must be described by a series of possible output states. This is evident in a generating system in which an additional unit increases the output capacity of the system. It is also applicable to a range of process plant industries, chemical industries, pumping systems and other flow systems.

In the following discussion it is assumed that the limiting state probabilities of each system state have already been derived using the techniques of previous sections. The intention at this point is to evaluate the probability and frequency of the cumulated states.

The states of the system $(i = 1, 2, \ldots, n)$ must first be ordered so that the smallest output state (n) is considered first and the largest state (1) considered last. The reverse situation could be used if desired. Let

P_i be the limiting state probability of state i,
P'_i be the cumulative probability of residing in either state i or states below i; $i+1$, $i+2, \ldots, n$,
λ_{+i} be the rate of departure from state i to states of greater output; $i-1$, $i-2, \ldots, 1$,
λ_{-i} be the rate of departure from state i to states of smaller output; $i+1$, $i+2, \ldots, n$,
f_i be the frequency of encountering state i, and
f'_i be the cumulative frequency of encountering either state i or states below i; $i+1$, $i+2, \ldots, n$.

From Equation 10.6

$$f_i = P_i(\lambda_{+i} + \lambda_{-i}) \tag{10.24}$$

Since the states of the system are mutually exclusive

$$P'_i = P_i + \sum_{j=i+1}^{n} P_j$$
$$= P_i + P'_{i+1} \tag{10.25}$$

And from the principle discussed in Section 10.3.6:

$$f'_i = f_i + \left[\sum_{j=i+1}^{n} f_j - (\text{Frequency of encounters of states below } i+1) \right]$$
$$= P_i\lambda_{+i} + [f'_{i+1} - P_i\lambda_{-i}]$$
$$= f'_{i+1} + P_i(\lambda_{+i} - \lambda_{-i}) \tag{10.26}$$

Equations 10.25 and 10.26 are recursive such that the new values of P'_i and f'_i can be evaluated directly and simply from the old values. The process commences with $i = n$ and terminates with $i = 1$. Although these equations are ideally suited for use with numerical values, their application can be demonstrated in terms of the 2 component system used in the previous sections.

In this illustration, consider state 4 as the state with smallest system output ($=$ zero) followed in order by states 3, 2 and 1.

$$f'_4 = f_4 = \frac{\lambda_1\lambda_2(\mu_1 + \mu_2)}{(\lambda_1 + \mu_1)(\lambda_2 + \mu_2)}$$

$$f'_3 = f_{34} = f'_4 + P_3(\lambda_{+3} - \lambda_{-3})$$
$$= \frac{\lambda_1\lambda_2(\mu_1 + \mu_2)}{(\lambda_1 + \mu_1)(\lambda_2 + \mu_2)} + \frac{\mu_1\lambda_2}{(\lambda_1 + \mu_1)(\lambda_2 + \mu_2)} \cdot (\mu_2 - \lambda_1)$$

$$= \frac{\lambda_2\mu_2}{\lambda_2 + \mu_2} \quad \text{(as Equation 10.19)}$$

$$f_2' = f_{234} = f_3' + P_2(\lambda_{+2} - \lambda_{-2})$$

$$= \frac{\lambda_2\mu_2(\lambda_1 + \mu_1)}{(\lambda_1 + \mu_1)(\lambda_2 + \mu_2)} + \frac{\lambda_1\mu_2}{(\lambda_1 + \mu_1)(\lambda_2 + \mu_2)} \cdot (\mu_1 - \lambda_2)$$

$$= \frac{\mu_1\mu_2(\lambda_1 + \lambda_2)}{(\lambda_1 + \mu_1)(\lambda_2 + \mu_2)}$$

$$f_1' = f_{1234} = f_2' + P_1(0 - \lambda_{-1})$$

$$= \frac{\mu_1\mu_2(\lambda_1 + \lambda_2)}{(\lambda_1 + \mu_1)(\lambda_2 + \mu_2)} + \frac{\mu_1\mu_2}{(\lambda_1 + \mu_1)(\lambda_2 + \mu_2)} \cdot (0 - (\lambda_1 + \lambda_2))$$

$$= 0$$

This last value may seem strange but it has a definite physical significance. The cumulated states $(1, 2, 3, 4)$ represent the entire system. It is not possible to encounter the boundary wall which encompasses all the system states. Therefore, the expected frequency f_1' is zero. It is also evident from the above derivations that this recursive technique is quite straightforward and relatively simple if numerical values are used during the process rather than a derivation of equations as in this example.

10.3.8 Mean duration of cumulated states

The final step in the evaluation of the system frequency and duration indices is to evaluate the mean duration of residing in each of the cumulated system states.

These values can be evaluated using the principle of Equation 10.7 since the mean duration of any cumulated system state i, m_i', is

$$m_i' = \frac{\text{cumulative probability of being in state } i}{\text{cumulative frequency of encountering state } i}$$

$$= \frac{P_i'}{f_i'} \tag{10.27}$$

Reconsider the two component system used in the previous sections and define m_4', m_3', m_2' and m_1' as the mean duration of the cumulated states associated with the cumulative frequencies f_4', f_3', f_2' and f_1' deduced in Section 10.3.7. Then

$$m_4' = \frac{\lambda_1\lambda_2}{(\lambda_1 + \mu_1)(\lambda_2 + \mu_2)} \cdot \frac{(\lambda_1 + \mu_1)(\lambda_2 + \mu_2)}{\lambda_1\lambda_2(\mu_1 + \mu_2)}$$

$$= \frac{1}{\mu_1 + \mu_2}$$

$$m_3' = \frac{\lambda_1\lambda_2 + \mu_1\lambda_2}{(\lambda_1+\mu_1)(\lambda_2+\mu_2)} \cdot \frac{(\lambda_1+\mu_1)(\lambda_2+\mu_2)}{\lambda_2\mu_2(\lambda_1+\mu_1)}$$

$$= \frac{1}{\mu_2}$$

$$m_2' = \frac{\lambda_1\mu_2 + \mu_1\lambda_2 + \lambda_1\lambda_2}{(\lambda_1+\mu_1)(\lambda_2+\mu_2)} \cdot \frac{(\lambda_1+\mu_1)(\lambda_2+\mu_2)}{\mu_1\mu_2(\lambda_1+\lambda_2)}$$

$$= \frac{\lambda_1\mu_2 + \mu_1\lambda_2 + \lambda_1\lambda_2}{\mu_1\mu_2(\lambda_1+\lambda_2)}$$

$$m_1' = \frac{\mu_1\mu_2 + \lambda_1\mu_2 + \mu_1\lambda_2 + \lambda_1\lambda_2}{(\lambda_1+\mu_1)(\lambda_2+\mu_2)} \cdot \frac{1}{0}$$

$$= \infty$$

The last value simply indicates that the system is in one of the system states all of the time.

10.4 Frequency balance approach

An alternative approach to that discussed in the previous sections for determining the steady state or limiting state probability values is known as the frequency balance approach. This is a very useful technique for solving relatively small systems which do not require matrix formulation and subsequent solution using a digital computer. The basic concept in the frequency balance approach is that for any state in an ergodic system the expected frequency of leaving a state must equal the expected frequency of entering the state. The frequency equations can be written for each state. The unknown parameters in these equations are the state probabilities. These probabilities must also sum to unity. The approach can be most easily appreciated by using the two state model of Figure 10.1a.

The frequency balance equation in this case is

$$P_0\lambda = P_1\mu \tag{10.28}$$

Therefore,

$$P_1 = P_0\frac{\lambda}{\mu}$$

Using

$$P_0 + P_1 = 1$$

$$P_0\left(1+\frac{\lambda}{\mu}\right) = 1$$

From which

$$P_o = \frac{\mu}{\lambda + \mu} \quad \text{and} \quad P_1 = \frac{\lambda}{\lambda + \mu}$$

The application to slightly larger systems can be illustrated using the two identical component three state model of Figure 9.4.

The frequency balance equations written for each state are:

State 1 $\quad P_1 2\lambda = P_2 \mu$ (10.29a)

State 2 $\quad P_2(\mu + \lambda) = P_1 2\lambda + P_3 2\mu$ (10.29b)

State 3 $\quad P_3 2\mu = P_2 \lambda$ (10.29c)

There are only two independent equations in this set. Using Equations 10.29a and 10.29c

$$P_2 = P_1 \frac{2\lambda}{\mu}$$

$$P_3 = P_2 \frac{\lambda}{2\mu} = P_1 \frac{\lambda^2}{\mu^2}$$

Using $P_1 + P_2 + P_3 = 1$

$$P_1 \left(1 + \frac{2\lambda}{\mu} + \frac{\lambda^2}{\mu^2} \right) = 1$$

$$P_1 = \frac{\mu^2}{(\lambda + \mu)^2}$$

$$P_2 = \frac{2\lambda\mu}{(\lambda + \mu)^2}$$

$$P_3 = \frac{\lambda^2}{(\lambda + \mu)^2}$$

These expressions are identical to those in Equation 9.26. The application to a more general case can be seen by considering the four state system in Figure 10.4.

The frequency balance equations are as follows

State 1 $\quad P_1(\lambda_1 + \lambda_2) = P_2 \mu_1 + P_3 \mu_2$

State 2 $\quad P_2(\mu_1 + \lambda_2) = P_1 \lambda_1 + P_4 \mu_2$

State 3 $\quad P_3(\lambda_1 + \mu_2) = P_1 \lambda_2 + P_4 \mu_1$

State 4 $\quad P_4(\mu_1 + \mu_2) = P_2 \lambda_2 + P_3 \lambda_1$ (10.30)

There are three independent expressions in Equation 10.30. The state probabilities can be obtained by selecting three equations and the unity

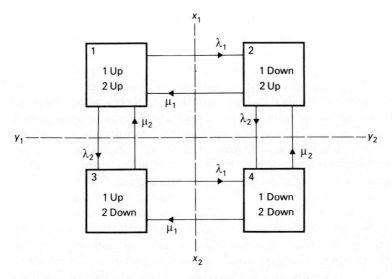

Fig. 10.4 State space diagram with designated boundaries

equation:

$$P_1 + P_2 + P_3 + P_4 = 1$$

The state probability expressions are given in Equations 10.7.

The frequency balance approach can become unwieldy when there is a high degree of communication between the system states. If it becomes necessary to use a matrix method for solution it is better to arrange the equations in this form using the stochastic transitional probability matrix. The frequency balance approach can prove useful when evaluating state probability expressions for relatively small systems with a relatively large number of one way state transitions. This type of system is illustrated in Figure 10.5.

The mean duration of each state can be deduced using the method of Section 10.3.4, after the limiting state probabilities and transition frequencies have been derived. The individual states can be cumulated to give the cumulative probability, cumulative frequency and cumulative mean duration using the techniques of Sections 10.3.6, 10.3.7 and 10.3.8.

10.5 Two stage repair and installation process

10.5.1 General concepts

In the previous sections of this chapter and in Chapter 9, it has been assumed that there are two transitions associated with each component;

the first represents its failure transition, and the second represents its repair transition. This model implies that the component becomes operative and in-service immediately following a repair action.

In many systems however, the restoration of a component to an in-service state may take place in two very distinct phases; the first is concerned with the removal and repair of the component, and the second is concerned with its re-installation in the system. Recognition of this two stage process is very important in systems that have one or more spare components which may be used to replace failed components. In these cases the failed components are removed, repaired and returned as spare components and not as in-service components.

This two stage repair and installation process can be modelled using a state space diagram (Section 9.3) and solved by Markov techniques. The effect of the number of spares on the unavailability of the system can be evaluated by repeating the analysis for a given system but with an increasing number of spares. An objective assessment of the required number of spares to achieve a required level of system reliability can then be made.

The application of these concepts can be illustrated by considering a set of examples in which the number of system components and number of available spares are varied.

10.5.2 One component system—no spare available

Consider a single component with no available spares. Let

λ = failure rate of the component,

μ = repair rate of the component, and

γ = installation rate of the component.

These transition rates are assumed to be constant and the associated times assumed to be exponentially distributed. The average operating,

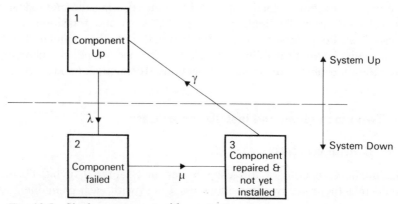

Fig. 10.5 Single component with no spare

repair and installation times are $1/\lambda$, $1/\mu$ and $1/\gamma$, respectively. The state space diagram for this system is shown in Figure 10.5.

In this diagram, state 1 represents the up state of the system and states 2 and 3 represent the down state of the system. State 3 represents the condition in which the component has been repaired and is therefore operable but has not yet been re-installed.

The reader using the techniques described previously should be able to verify that the limiting state probabilities for this system are

$$\text{availability, } A = P_1 = \frac{\mu\gamma}{\lambda\mu + \lambda\gamma + \mu\gamma} \tag{10.31}$$

$$\text{unavailability, } U = P_2 + P_3 = \frac{\lambda\gamma}{\lambda\mu + \lambda\gamma + \mu\gamma} + \frac{\lambda\mu}{\lambda\mu + \lambda\gamma + \mu\gamma}$$

$$= \frac{\lambda(\gamma + \mu)}{\lambda\mu + \lambda\gamma + \mu\gamma} \tag{10.32}$$

Also, the frequency of encountering the system states can be evaluated by using the concept of Equations 10.5 and 10.6, and the various frequencies are

$$f_1 = P_1\lambda = \frac{\lambda\mu\gamma}{\lambda\mu + \lambda\gamma + \mu\gamma}$$

$$f_2 = P_2\mu = \frac{\lambda\mu\gamma}{\lambda\mu + \lambda\gamma + \mu\gamma} = f_1$$

$$f_3 = P_3\gamma = \frac{\lambda\mu\gamma}{\lambda\mu + \lambda\gamma + \mu\gamma} = f_1$$

$$f(\text{up}) = f_1 = \frac{\lambda\mu\gamma}{\lambda\mu + \lambda\gamma + \mu\gamma}$$

$$f(\text{down}) = f_2 + f_3 - P_2 \cdot \mu = \frac{\lambda\mu\gamma}{\lambda\mu + \lambda\gamma + \mu\gamma} = f(\text{up}) \tag{10.33}$$

The mean duration, m, of residing in each state can be evaluated using the concept of Equations 10.7 and 10.27 and the various mean durations are

$$m_1 = \frac{P_1}{f_1} = \frac{1}{\lambda}$$

$$m_2 = \frac{P_2}{f_2} = \frac{1}{\mu}$$

$$m_3 = \frac{P_3}{f_3} = \frac{1}{\gamma}$$

$$m(\text{up}) = \frac{A}{f(\text{up})} = \frac{1}{\lambda} \tag{10.34}$$

$$m(\text{down}) = \frac{U}{f(\text{down})} = \frac{\gamma + \mu}{\mu\gamma} = \frac{1}{\mu} + \frac{1}{\gamma} \qquad (10.35)$$

Equation 10.35 shows that the mean down time is equal to the sum of the mean residence times of the two down states, states 2 and 3.

10.5.3 One component system—one spare available

Consider now the situation that would exist if one spare was normally available. In this case, when a component fails, it can be replaced by the spare component, provided that either the spare has not already been used or the component it has replaced has been repaired and is available as a spare. This produces the state space diagram shown in Figure 10.6.

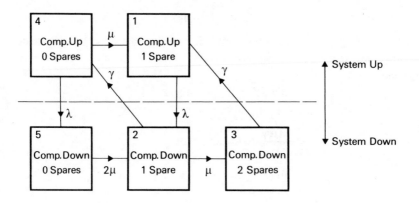

Fig. 10.6 Single component with one spare

States 1–3 in Figure 10.6 are similar to those of Figure 10.5. The system up state is given by states 1 and 4 and the system down state by states 2, 3 and 5. In state 5, both components (the original operating component and the original spare) are in a failed state and require repair. When one repair has been completed, the relevant transition takes the system into state 2. It has been assumed that sufficient manpower and facilities are available for both components to be undergoing repair at the same time and consequently the transition rate from this state is 2μ. If resources are limited and only one repair is possible at any particular time, this transition rate must be reduced to μ. The availability of repair resources can be imposed in the model and its effect on the system availability evaluated.

Assuming unrestricted repair resources and the model shown in Figure

10.6, the limiting state probabilities are

$$P_1 = \frac{2\gamma^2\mu^2 + 2\gamma\mu^2(\lambda + \mu)}{D}$$

$$P_2 = \frac{2\lambda\gamma\mu(\lambda + \mu)}{D}$$

$$P_3 = \frac{2\lambda\mu^2(\lambda + \mu)}{D} \quad\quad (10.36)$$

$$P_4 = \frac{2\lambda\gamma^2\mu}{D}$$

$$P_5 = \frac{\lambda^2\gamma^2}{D}$$

where $D = \lambda^2\gamma^2 + 2\mu[(\gamma + \mu)(\lambda + \gamma)(\lambda + \mu)]$

also, availability, $A = P_1 + P_4$

and unavailability, $U = P_2 + P_3 + P_5$

The cumulative frequencies of encountering the system up state $f(\text{up})$ and system down state $f(\text{down})$ are

$$f(\text{up}) = f_1 + f_4 - P_4\mu$$
$$= P_1\lambda + P_4(\lambda + \mu) - P_4\mu$$
$$= P_1\lambda + P_4\lambda$$
$$= (P_1 + P_4)\lambda$$

which is in agreement with the principle derived from Equation 10.22.

Therefore, $f(\text{up}) = \dfrac{2\lambda\mu\gamma(\lambda + \mu)(\gamma + \mu)}{D}$ \quad\quad (10.37)

This value must also be equal to $f(\text{down})$, a value which can be confirmed from

$$f(\text{down}) = f_2 + f_3 + f_5 - P_2\mu - P_52\mu$$
$$= P_2(\mu + \gamma) + P_3\gamma + P_52\mu - P_2\mu - P_52\mu$$
$$= P_2\gamma + P_3\gamma$$
$$= (P_2 + P_3)\gamma$$

which is in agreement with Equation 10.22 and therefore could have been written down directly. Thus

$$f(\text{down}) = \frac{2\lambda\mu\gamma(\lambda + \mu)(\gamma + \mu)}{D}$$

The average duration, m, of residing in each state can also be obtained. Consider only the case of residing in the system up state and system down state

$$m(\text{up}) = \frac{A}{f(\text{up})} = \frac{1}{\lambda} \tag{10.38}$$

$$m(\text{down}) = \frac{U}{f(\text{down})} = \frac{1}{\gamma} + \frac{\lambda\gamma}{2\mu(\lambda+\mu)(\gamma+\mu)} \tag{10.39}$$

It is evident from the form of the above equations, that it becomes rather impractical to derive general expressions for more complex systems. However, it is relatively simple to derive numerical results for any system configuration using a digital computer and the above derivations, i.e., to evaluate the individual state probabilities, the system up and down state probabilities, the individual state and cumulative state frequencies and finally the mean residence times for each individual and system state.

The modelling process is further illustrated by considering two more examples. The first is a single component system with two spares, and the second a two component system with one spare.

10.5.4 One component system—two spares available

If the system consists of a single component, but with two spares initially available, the logic used to construct the state space diagrams shown in Figures 10.5 and 10.6 can be extended to give the diagram shown in Figure 10.7.

In Figure 10.7, states 1 to 3 are similar to those for the one component system with no spares, and states 1 to 5 are similar to those for a one component system with one spare.

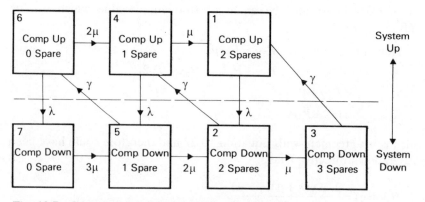

Fig. 10.7 One component system with two spares

As the number of spares is increased, the relevant state space diagram, constructed in the form shown in Figures 10.5 to 10.7, extends to the left. On this basis, it is relatively simple for the reader to extend the concept to any number of spares.

As discussed in Section 10.5.3, the values used for the repair transitions should be made appropriate to the availability of repair resources. In Figure 10.7 it has again been assumed that there are no limitations to the number of components that can be repaired at any one time. If, however, only two components can be in a repair process simultaneously, the transition from states 7 to 5 must be reduced to 2μ and if only one component can be in the repair process at any one time, the transitions from states 7 to 5, states 5 to 2 and states 6 to 4 must be reduced to μ.

10.5.5 Two component system—one spare available

This example assumes that both components and the spare are identical. A similar but extended model can be constructed if the operating components are not identical. It should be remembered however that in this case the available spares can only service those components for which the spares are being carried. Consequently, the status of each component in each state of the system must be clearly identified and only the appropriate transitions included. In practice, this complexity is not usually necessary since the requirement of this analysis is normally to evaluate the required number of spares needed to service a given type of component. In this case only the identical components need be considered. After obtaining the availability parameters for each set of identical components including their spares, the complete system indices can be evaluated by treating each subsystem as an equivalent component of the system and combining them using normal reliability evaluation techniques.

The state space diagram for two components with one spare is shown in Figure 10.8.

It is now evident that as the number of system components increases, the relevant state space diagram constructed in the form shown in Figure 10.8 extends downwards. The reader therefore should be able to construct a diagram for any number of spares, and any number of system operating components. In the case of spares, the diagram extends to the left, and in the case of system operating components, the diagram extends downwards.

The model shown in Figure 10.8 again assumes unrestricted repair resources and the values of repair transitions should be modified as discussed in Sections 10.5.3 and 10.5.4 if repair resources are restricted. The model also assumes unrestricted installation resources and the appropriate transition rate has been determined as the number of spares

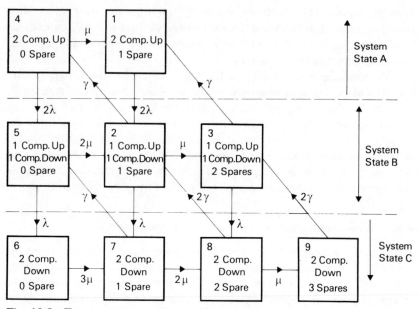

Fig. 10.8 Two component system with one spare

available or the number of failed components needing to be replaced, whichever is the smallest. If, however, there are manpower limitations to the number of installations that can be done at the same time, the value of installation transition rate must be modified in the same way as the repair rate.

Three system states, states A, B and C, have been inserted in Figure 10.8. Although state A is always a system up state and state C is always a system down state, state B depends upon the operating requirements of the system. If both components are required for system success, i.e., it is a series system, state B represents system failure but if only one component is required for system success, i.e., it is a parallel redundant system, state B represents system success. In either case, system state B can be combined with A or C as appropriate to given an equivalent two state representation of the system. In some cases, however, state B may be neither an up state nor a down state, but instead represents a derated, or partial output state. In this case the system can only be reduced to an equivalent three state system. In all cases however the relevant reliability indices of probability, frequency and duration can be evaluated using the techniques described in previous sections.

10.5.6 Limiting number of spares

It is evident that, as the number of spares being carried is increased, the availability of the system also increases and there is a limiting value of system availability as the number of spares tends to infinity. In order to establish the effect of increasing the number of spares, the appropriate state space diagram can be continuously extended and the system availability evaluated for each extension. It is not practical to continue this process indefinitely in order to establish the value of limiting availability. This limiting value is, however, of importance in order to determine how close the system availability, with a given number of spares, is to the theoretical limit.

This limiting availability can be evaluated easily if it is noted that, when there is an infinite number of spares, the repair process becomes irrelevant and can be ignored. The limiting state space diagram therefore reduces to one containing only two states, system up and system down, and only two transitions, system failure rate λ_e and installation rate γ. This diagram is shown in Figure 10.9.

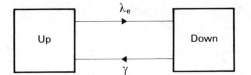

Fig. 10.9 Model for evaluating limiting availability

In Figure 10.9, the value of λ_e depends on the system. In the case of a single component having a failure rate λ, λ_e is equal to λ whereas in the case of a two component system each having a failure rate of λ, then λ_e is equal to 2λ.

Using the model shown in Figure 10.9, the system limiting availability A_1 is

$$A_1 = \frac{\gamma}{\lambda_e + \gamma} \qquad (10.40)$$

or the limiting unavailability U_1 is

$$U_1 = \frac{\lambda_e}{\lambda_e + \gamma} \qquad (10.41)$$

10.5.7 Application of the techniques

In order to illustrate the variation in the results that can be obtained by using the techniques presented in the previous sections, consider the case of a single component system with one spare. Using Equation 10.36 the variation of system unavailability with component failure rate is shown in Figure 10.10 for the values of repair and installation rates also shown in Figure 10.10. The variation of the system unavailability with increasing number of spares is shown in Figure 10.11 for the same system and for

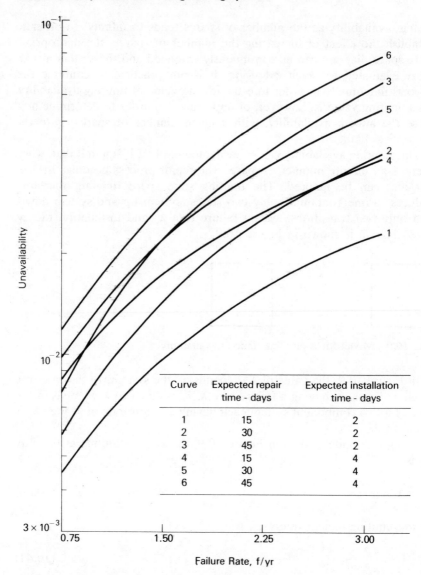

Curve	Expected repair time - days	Expected installation time - days
1	15	2
2	30	2
3	45	2
4	15	4
5	30	4
6	45	4

Failure Rate, f/yr

Fig. 10.10 Unavailability as a function of the failure, repair and installation rates for the system shown in Fig. 10.6

the same repair and installation rates. The limiting unavailability evaluated using Equation 10.41 is also shown in Figure 10.11.

As expected and discussed in Section 10.5.6, the system unavailability decreases as the number of spares is increased and tends to the limiting value of unavailability. As might be expected (see Section 7.6.4), the greatest gain is obtained by the provision of the first spare component and

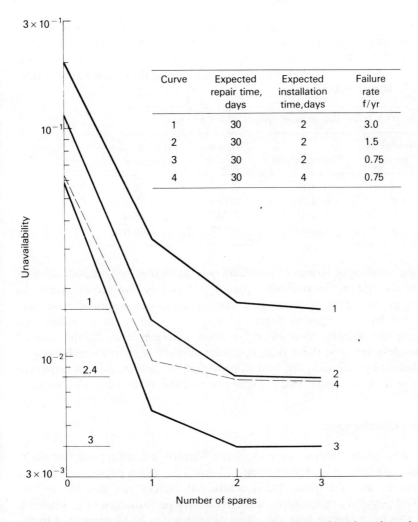

Fig. 10.11 Unavailability of single component system as a function of number of spares

the relative improvement decreases as the number of spare components is increased. The benefit gained by providing spare components is very dependent upon the parameters that influence the reliability, i.e., the failure, repair and installation rates. For instance, the results shown in Figure 10.11 indicate that the provision of a second spare component in the case of an installation time of 4 days gives a much smaller improvement than the case of an installation time of 2 days, all other parameters remaining constant.

Although Figures 10.10 and 10.11 only show the change in system unavailability, similar changes are evaluated for the values of frequency and duration. As an example, the results shown in Table 10.3 were obtained for the same single component system with one spare when the failure rate is 0.75 f/yr and the repair and installation times are 30 days and 2 days, respectively.

Table 10.3   One component system with one spare

Number of spares	Unavailability	Frequency per year	Average outage duration, hr
0	0.061697	0.704	768.0
1	0.005754	0.746	67.6
2	0.004123	0.747	48.4
3	0.004093	0.747	48.0

The number of spares required for any particular system is dependent upon the system, its reliability parameters and system requirements. In the case of safety systems, the number of spares required is usually dictated by the required degree of safety, i.e., sufficient to reduce the system unreliability to a value less than a target level. In the case of non-safety systems, there is an optimum number of spares which must be evaluated by including the cost of providing the spares, i.e., an economic appraisal of all capital and running costs of the system must be made.

10.6   Conclusions

This chapter has shown how the basic Markov modelling solution techniques can be extended to provide additional reliability parameters such as frequency and duration. These additional indices can provide an improved physical appreciation of the reliability performance of a system. It has also been shown how the effect of spares can be incorporated in the analysis of the system by subdividing the restoration process following a failure into two distinct phases, repair and installation. The approach described in this chapter can be extended to a wide range of practical configurations for which the criteria for system success and failure can be defined. Although it is impractical to derive general expressions for complex systems, the logic described for the simple systems is readily extendable to more complex systems using the numerical capabilities of digital computers. When the system becomes very complex and the techniques discussed in this chapter become less amenable, approximate evaluation techniques based on the models described in this chapter can be used as alternative methods. These methods will be discussed in the next chapter.

Problems

1 Reconsider Problem 1 of Chapter 9. Evaluate the frequency of encountering and duration of residing in each of the three states.

2 Reconsider Problem 3 of Chapter 9. Evaluate the frequency of encountering and duration of residing in each possible throughput state for the single and two pump cases.

3 Evaluate the frequency and duration of each possible throughput state for the single pump case of Problem 3 of Chapter 9, if an identical pump is carried as a spare which has an installation rate of 10 repl/hr. Assume there are no restrictions on installation or repair.

4 A repairable system contains three different units, and all must operate for system success. If one unit fails, no further failures can occur until the failed unit is repaired and the system placed back into service. Develop an expression for the probability of the system being in the operable state and calculate the frequency of encountering the failed state. What is the average duration of a failed state? Use the expressions to calculate the probability, frequency and duration of failure if all units are identical and have a failure rate of 1 f/yr and a repair rate of 100 repairs/yr.

5 A system contains two components. Both components are required for system success. If one component fails, the other cannot fail while the failed component is being repaired. If the component failure and repair rates are λ_1, λ_2, μ_1 and μ_2 respectively, determine the probability of failure, the frequency of failure and the average downtime of the system. Evaluate these indices if $\lambda_1 = \lambda_2 = 0.1$ f/yr and $\mu_1 = \mu_2 = 365$ repairs/yr.

6 Evaluate the same indices for the system described in Problem 5 if both components are identical and a similar component is carried as a spare having an average installation time of 1 hr.

7 Use the frequency balance approach to evaluate the frequency of encountering and duration of residing in each of the states shown in Figure 10.12 where rates are expressed in occurrences/yr.

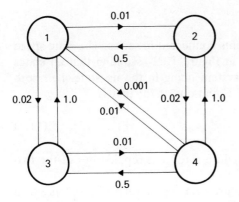

Fig. 10.12

11 Approximate system reliability evaluation

11.1 Introduction

As discussed in Chapters 8 to 10, the Markov technique and the frequency and duration approach form sound and precise modelling and evaluation methods for reliability applications. They become less amenable, however, for hand calculations and even for digital computer solutions as the system becomes larger and more complex. In such cases, alternative methods are available which are based on the Markov approach and which use a set of appropriate but approximate equations. The essence of these approximate techniques is to derive a set of equations suitable for a series system in which all components must operate for system success and for a parallel system in which only one component need work for system success. These equations can then be used in conjunction with the network modelling techniques described in Chapters 4 and 5 to give rapid and sufficiently accurate results for a wide range of practical systems. In addition they are ideally suited for both hand calculations and digital computer implementation.

In this chapter the basic sets of equations are initially derived and used. These are then extended to more complex systems and applications.

11.2 Series systems

Consider the case of two components connected in series. The state space diagram for this system is shown in Figure 10.2 assuming that all states can exist. The probability of the system being in the up state, i.e., both components operating is given by Equation 10.7a; that is

$$P_{up} = \frac{\mu_1 \mu_2}{(\lambda_1 + \mu_1)(\lambda_2 + \mu_2)} \tag{11.1}$$

where λ_1, λ_2 and μ_1, μ_2 are the failure rates and repair rates of the two components, respectively.

It is necessary to find the failure and repair rates, λ_s and μ_s, of a single component that is equivalent to the two components in series. This

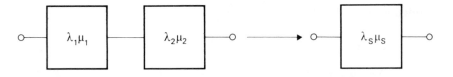

Fig. 11.1 Representation of a two component series system

is shown in Figure 11.1. The probability of the single component being in the up state is

$$P_{up} = \frac{\mu_s}{\lambda_s + \mu_s} \tag{11.2}$$

For the single component to be equivalent to the two series components, Equations 11.1 and 11.2 must be identical, i.e.,

$$\frac{\mu_1 \mu_2}{(\lambda_1 + \mu_1)(\lambda_2 + \mu_2)} = \frac{\mu_s}{\lambda_s + \mu_s} \tag{11.3}$$

Also, since the transition rate from the system up state, for the single equivalent component, is λ_s, and for the two component series system, is $(\lambda_1 + \lambda_2)$, then

$$\lambda_s = \lambda_1 + \lambda_2 \tag{11.4}$$

Substituting Equation 11.4 into 11.3 and replacing the repair rates, μ_i, by the reciprocal of the average repair times, r_i, gives

$$r_s = \frac{1}{\mu_s} = \frac{\lambda_1 r_1 + \lambda_2 r_2 + \lambda_1 \lambda_2 r_1 r_2}{\lambda_s} \tag{11.5}$$

In many systems the product $(\lambda_i r_i)$ is very small and therefore $\lambda_1 \lambda_2 r_1 r_2 \ll \lambda_1 r_1$ and $\lambda_2 r_2$. In such cases Equation 11.5 reduces to

$$r_s = \frac{\lambda_1 r_1 + \lambda_2 r_2}{\lambda_s} \tag{11.6}$$

It should be noted that, although Equation 11.6 is an approximation for a two component series system in which all four states of Figure 10.2 exist, it is an exact expression for the situation in which state 4 of Figure 10.2 does not exist, i.e., when one component has failed, the second component cannot fail. This occurs in practice when, after failure of the first component, the failure rates for the remaining operative but not-working components either decrease to zero or become negligible.

Using the logic expressed in Equations 11.4 and 11.5, the failure rate and average outage duration of a general n-component series system may be deduced as

$$\lambda_s = \sum_{i=1}^{n} \lambda_i \tag{11.7}$$

$$r_s = \frac{\sum_{i=1}^{n} \lambda_i r_i}{\lambda_s} \tag{11.8}$$

The probability of the system being in the down state, i.e., the unavailability U_s can be related to r_s and the frequency of encountering the down state f_s using the concepts of frequency and duration established in Chapter 10, i.e., from Equation 10.3

$$U_s = f_s r_s \tag{11.9}$$

As discussed in Chapters 9 and 10, MTTF $(= 1/\lambda)$ and MTBF $(= 1/f)$ are conceptually different although for many practical systems they are numerically almost identical. In such cases, Equation 11.9 may be approximated to

$$U_s \approx \lambda_s r_s = \sum_{i=1}^{n} \lambda_i r_1 \tag{11.10}$$

If the units of time for λ_s and r_s are the same, the value of U_s is strictly a probability. If the units are different, e.g., λ_s is expressed in failures per year and r_s is expressed in hours, the value of U_s has dimensional units associated with it, e.g. hours per year. (This dimensional form is a useful descriptive form as it represents the expected annual outage time.)

In summary, the set of equations frequently used for a series system is

$$\lambda_s = \sum_{i=1}^{n} \lambda_i, \qquad r_s = \frac{\sum_{i=1}^{n} \lambda_i r_i}{\lambda_s} \qquad U_s = \lambda_s r_s$$

$$= U_s / \lambda_s, \qquad = \sum_{i=1}^{n} \lambda_i r_i \tag{11.11}$$

The following three important points should be noted:
(a) Before using this set of equations, it is necessary to establish whether they are valid for the system being analysed, i.e., to check whether the model on which they are based is appropriate.
(b) The equations only give the mean or expected values of the parameter being evaluated. In addition there is a distribution associated with these values which is not exponential even if the component indices were exponentially distributed.
(c) Although the equations were derived from a knowledge of Markov processes and the underlying assumption of exponential distributions, they are equally suitable for evaluating the long-term mean values of other distributions. This point is discussed and substantiated in Chapter 12.

Example 11.1

The failure rates of three components are 0.05 f/yr, 0.01 f/yr and 0.02 f/yr respectively and their average repair times are 20 hr, 15 hr and 25 hr respectively. Evaluate the system failure rate, average repair time and unavailability if all three components must operate for system success.

From Equations 11.11

$$\lambda_s = 0.05 + 0.01 + 0.02 = 0.08 \text{ f/yr}$$

$$U_s = 0.05 \times 20 + 0.01 \times 15 + 0.02 \times 25 = 1.65 \text{ hr/yr}$$

$$r_s = \frac{1.65}{0.08} = 20.6 \text{ hr}$$

11.3 Parallel systems

11.3.1 Two component system

Consider initially the case of a two component system for which the relevant state space diagram is shown in Figure 10.2. The probability of the system being in the down state is given by Equation 10.7d, i.e.,

$$P_{\text{down}} = \frac{\lambda_1 \lambda_2}{(\lambda_1 + \mu_1)(\lambda_2 + \mu_2)} \qquad (11.12)$$

In this case the failure rate λ_p and repair rate μ_p of a single component that is equivalent to the two components in parallel is required. This is illustrated in Figure 11.2.

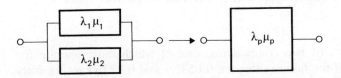

Fig. 11.2 Representation of a two component parallel system

The probability of the single component being in the down state is

$$P_{\text{down}} = \frac{\lambda_p}{\lambda_p + \mu_p} \qquad (11.13)$$

Since Equations 11.12 and 11.13 must be identical

$$\frac{\lambda_p}{\lambda_p + \mu_p} = \frac{\lambda_1 \lambda_2}{(\lambda_1 + \mu_1)(\lambda_2 + \mu_2)} \qquad (11.14)$$

The rate of transition from the down state of the two component system is $\mu_1 + \mu_2$ and this must be equivalent to μ_p, i.e.

$$\mu_p = \mu_1 + \mu_2 \tag{11.15a}$$

or $\quad \dfrac{1}{r_p} = \dfrac{1}{r_1} + \dfrac{1}{r_2} \tag{11.15b}$

giving $r_p = \dfrac{r_1 r_2}{r_1 + r_2} \tag{11.15c}$

This value of r_p represents the average period of time during which both components are concurrently out of service, i.e., it represents the period during which the two failures overlap. For this reason r_p is generally known as the overlapping repair or outage time of components 1 and 2. The failure event caused by the failure of components 1 and 2 is generally known as an overlapping failure event.

Substituting Equation 11.15 into 11.14 gives

$$\lambda_p = \frac{\lambda_1 \lambda_2 (r_1 + r_2)}{1 + \lambda_1 r_1 + \lambda_2 r_2} \tag{11.16}$$

If, as is frequently the case in practice, $(\lambda_1 r_1)$ and $(\lambda_2 r_2)$ are much less than unity, then

$$\lambda_p \simeq \lambda_1 \lambda_2 (r_1 + r_2) \tag{11.17}$$

Finally, as in Section 11.2

$$U_p = \lambda_p r_p = \lambda_1 \lambda_2 r_1 r_2 \tag{11.18}$$

It should be noted that the three important points made at the end of Section 11.2 are equally applicable in the case of parallel systems.

Example 11.2

A system consists of two components, one of which must operate for system success. If the failure rates are 0.05 f/yr and 0.02 f/yr respectively and the average repair times are 20 hr and 25 hr respectively, evaluate the system failure rate, average repair time and unavailability.

From Equations 11.15, 11.17 and 11.18

$$\lambda_p = 0.05 \times 0.02 \, (20 + 25)/8760$$
$$= 5.14 \times 10^{-6} \text{ f/yr}$$

(where 8760 is the number of hours in a year)

$$r_p = \frac{20 \times 25}{20 + 25} = 11.1 \text{ hr}$$

$$U_p = \lambda_p r_p = 5.71 \times 10^{-5} \text{ hr/yr}$$

11.3.2   Systems with more than two components

Unlike the case of series systems, it is not possible to extend easily the equations for a 2-component parallel system to a general n-component system.

It is possible in certain systems to combine two components at a time using Equations 11.15 to 11.18. This method must be treated with the utmost care because it becomes invalid if the concepts of a single failure rate per component, or a single environmental state, are extended to more complex situations. It is better to use an appropriate set of equations for the number of components that require combining.

It is evident that such equations can be deduced from first principles using the concepts of Section 11.3.1. It is simpler to deduce the equations from the logic of Equations 11.15 to 11.18. In order to understand this logic, rewrite Equation 11.17 in the form

$$\lambda_p = \lambda_1(\lambda_2 r_1) + \lambda_2(\lambda_1 r_2) \tag{11.19}$$

This equation may be expressed in words as:

'failure of the system occurs if (component 1 fails followed by failure of component 2 during the repair time of component 1) or (component 2 fails followed by failure of component 1 during the repair time of component 2)'.

The product terms contained by the parentheses in Equation 11.19 represent the probability that one component fails during the outage time of the other; this condition being the only way in which a parallel system can fail. The 'time' parameter within the parentheses is generally known as the 'exposure time' during which the associated component must fail for the system to fail.

Using this logic the expression for the failure rate of a system containing three or more components can be deduced. Consider for example, the case of a three component (A, B and C) parallel system. In this case the failure expression is:

'failure of the system occurs if
(A fails followed by failure of B during repair of A followed by failure of C during the overlapping repair of A and B) OR
(A fails followed by failure of C during repair of A followed by failure of B during the overlapping repair of A and C) OR
(Plus 4 more similar statements for the failure sequences BAC, BCA, CAB, CBA)'

which, expressed in mathematical form and using Equation 11.15c, gives

$$\lambda_p = \lambda_A(\lambda_B r_A)\left(\lambda_C \frac{r_A r_B}{r_A + r_B}\right) + \lambda_A(\lambda_C r_A)\left(\lambda_B \frac{r_A r_C}{r_A + r_C}\right)$$

$$+ \lambda_B(\lambda_A r_B)\left(\lambda_C \frac{r_A r_B}{r_A + r_B}\right) + \lambda_B(\lambda_C r_B)\left(\lambda_A \frac{r_B r_C}{r_B + r_C}\right)$$

$$+ \lambda_C(\lambda_A r_C)\left(\lambda_B \frac{r_A r_C}{r_A + r_C}\right) + \lambda_C(\lambda_B r_C)\left(\lambda_A \frac{r_B r_C}{r_B + r_C}\right)$$

$$= \lambda_A \lambda_B \lambda_C (r_A r_B + r_B r_C + r_C r_A) \tag{11.20}$$

Also, from the logic of Equation 11.15a,

$$\mu_p = \mu_A + \mu_B + \mu_C$$

$$\frac{1}{r_p} = \frac{1}{r_A} + \frac{1}{r_B} + \frac{1}{r_C}$$

$$r_p = \frac{r_A r_B r_C}{r_A r_B + r_B r_C + r_C r_A} \tag{11.21}$$

and $U_p = \lambda_p r_p = \lambda_A \lambda_B \lambda_C r_A r_B r_C$ (11.22)

11.4 Network reduction techniques

Most systems do not consist of only series chain or parallel configurations but more often a combination of both. The general principles and concepts of such networks were discussed in Chapters 4 and 5 and it is therefore not intended to repeat these details at this point. Briefly, however, one method for solving these networks is sequentially to reduce the network using appropriate equations for series and parallel combinations until the network is reduced to a single equivalent component. This method, known as network reduction, was described in Chapter 4 and the reliability parameters of the equivalent component are the parameters of the complete system.

Consider the following numerical example to illustrate the application of the series and parallel equations derived in Sections 11.2 and 11.3 to the network reduction technique.

Example 11.3

Reconsider Example 4.8 and evaluate the system failure rate, average repair time and unavailability if all components are identical and have a failure rate of 0.05 f/yr and an average repair time of 20 hours.

The system in this example is shown in Figure 4.7. The first reduction requires combining components 3 and 4 in parallel to give equivalent component 6. Using Equations 11.15 to 11.18 gives

$$\lambda_6 = 0.05 \times 0.05(20 + 20)/8760 = 1.14 \times 10^{-5} \text{ f/yr}$$

$$r_6 = \frac{20 \times 20}{20 + 20} = 10 \text{ hr}$$

The second reduction requires combining components 1, 2 and 6 in series to give equivalent component 7. Using Equations 11.11 gives

$$\lambda_7 = 0.05 + 0.05 + 1.14 \times 10^{-5} = 0.10 \text{ f/yr}$$

$$r_7 = \frac{0.05 \times 20 + 0.05 \times 20 + 1.14 \times 10^{-5} \times 10}{0.10} = 20 \text{ hr}$$

The final reduction requires combining components 5 and 7 in parallel to give equivalent component 8 which then represents the system indices. Using Equations 11.15 to 11.18 gives

$$\lambda_8 = 0.05 \times 0.10(20 + 20)/8760 = 2.28 \times 10^{-5} \text{ f/yr}$$

$$r_8 = \frac{20 \times 20}{20 + 20} = 10 \text{ hr}$$

$$U_8 = 2.28 \times 10^{-4} \text{ hr/yr}$$

This example shows that a series/parallel system can be evaluated by sequential application of the series and parallel equations. This method however cannot be used directly if the system is more complex, i.e. a non-series/parallel configuration such as the bridge network shown in Figure 5.1. Some authors [32, 33] have suggested that such a network can be transformed into one containing only series/parallel branches using a method known as the star–delta transformation. This method can become quite tedious and the minimal cut set technique is usually preferable. The advantages of the minimal cut set approach are that it eliminates the need for complicated transformation, and it directly indicates the predominant failure modes of the system. The importance of retaining a physical appreciation of the system and its failure modes is a fundamental requirement in overall system reliability evaluation.

11.5 Minimal cut set/failure modes approach

The minimal cut set method was described in detail in Chapter 5 and will not be discussed at length here. However, it should be recalled that it enables a reliability network, expressed in terms of minimal cut sets, to be deduced from the system operational logic and/or system network diagram. This reliability network consists of a number of minimal cut sets connected in series and each cut set consists of a number of components connected in parallel. It follows that the series/parallel equations derived in Sections 11.2 and 11.3 can be applied directly to a minimal cut set diagram. The procedure is to apply the equations for parallel systems to each cut set in order to evaluate the equivalent indices for each cut set and then to combine these equivalent indices using the equations for series systems to give the overall system reliability indices.

In order to illustrate the application of the equations to the minimal cut set method, reconsider Example 11.3.

A visual inspection of Figure 4.7 identifies two second-order and one third-order cut sets. These are (1 and 5), (2 and 5), (3 and 4 and 5). Equations 11.15 to 11.18 can be applied to the first two cut sets and Equations 11.20 to 11.22 can be applied to the third one. This gives the results shown in Table 11.1.

After evaluating the reliability indices for each cut set, Equations 11.11 can be used to evaluate the system indices. This is most conveniently accomplished by summating the values of λ to give λ_s, by summating the values of U to give U_s and then evaluating r_s by dividing the value of U_s by λ_s. These system indices are also shown in Table 11.1 and can be compared with those obtained previously in Section 11.4 using network reduction.

Table 11.1   Minimal cut set analysis of Example 11.3

Cut set	$\lambda\, f/yr$	$r\, hr$	$U\, hr/yr$
1 and 5	1.14×10^{-5}	10	1.14×10^{-4}
2 and 5	1.14×10^{-5}	10	1.14×10^{-4}
3 and 4 and 5	1.95×10^{-9}	6.67	1.30×10^{-8}
Total	2.28×10^{-5}	10	2.28×10^{-4}
	$= \lambda_s$	$= r_s$	$= U_s$
	$= \sum \lambda$	$= U_s/\lambda_s$	$= \sum U$

The following comments can be made in the light of these results and the analysis used to achieve them:

(a)   The system indices are generally dominated by the low order cut sets which, in the case of the above example, are the two second order cuts. Sufficient precision is therefore generally achieved by ignoring cut sets that are more than one or two orders greater than the lowest order cut sets that exist. It must be stressed that this assumption may not be as valid if the components forming the lower order cuts are very reliable and the components forming the higher order cuts are very unreliable.

(b)   The minimal cut sets of the system define directly the failure modes of the system. The system will fail in the above example if components 1 and 5 are failed or if 2 and 5 are failed or if 3 and 4 and 5 are failed. In addition the method quantifies the impact of each failure event on the system in terms of λ, r and U. Therefore, it is possible to determine from this analysis not only the system reliability indices but also the contributions made to the system indices by the various failure modes. This information is very important in any properly structured reliability assessment since it identifies critical areas of system weakness and suggests where reinforcement and investment should be made. None of this information is readily obtained from the network reduction method.

(c)   From an assessment of this type, it may be decided that reinforcement and investment should be made to improve the system reliability. This investment could be in the quality of the components or redundancy of the system thus decreasing the failure rate or in the availability of spares and repair facilities thus decreasing the average repair time. There are many possible alternatives and each can be studied in turn to identify its effect on the system performance. The evaluation of λ, r and U in a failure modes and effect analysis however is of enormous benefit in deciding which components and area needs due consideration, and which of the alternatives may give the most desirable result.

11.6   Inclusion of scheduled maintenance

The previous sections of this chapter have assumed that the system is operated with all components in service until a forced outage or failure occurs. In practice, systems frequently change their state because various system components are removed at intervals in order to perform preventive maintenance.

This effect can be included in the assessment by dividing the total period of interest into intervals for which each interval represents one particular operating state of the system. The reliability indices of the system can then be evaluated for each time interval. Finally the system indices for the whole period of interest can be evaluated by weighting the indices for each interval by the probability of that interval and summating the weighted results together.

This method is both tedious and frequently unnecessarily complicated.

An alternative and practical method is to consider the maintenance outages in a similar manner to the forced outages but with a particular constraint attached, this being: *a component will not be taken out for maintenance if this will cause failure of the system.*

With this constraint imposed, the principles used to deduce the equations for parallel systems can be extended and the probability of a component in the system being already out for maintenance when a forced outage or failure of another component occurs can be included. The equation for the failure rate of a two component parallel system or second order minimal cut set (Equation 11.19) was

$$\lambda_p = \lambda_1(\lambda_2 r_1) + \lambda_2(\lambda_1 r_2)$$

In terms of maintenance, this equation can be expressed in words as: *failure of the system occurs if (component 1 is out for maintenance followed by failure of component 2 during the maintenance time of component 1) or (component 2 is out for maintenance followed by failure of component 1 during the maintenance time of component 2).*

Because of the above constraint, the condition: *component 1 fails followed by a maintenance outage of component 2 during the repair time of component 1* and vice versa is not included because this would fail the system by the simple action of commencing maintenance.

Defining

λ_1'', λ_2'' as maintenance outage rate/year
r_1'', r_2'' as average maintenance time/outage

Equation 11.19, for the case of a failure event overlapping a maintenance outage, becomes

$$\lambda_p'' = \lambda_1''(\lambda_2 r_1'') + \lambda_2''(\lambda_1 r_2'') \tag{11.23}$$

The evaluation of overlapping repair time is more complicated in this case unless components 1 and 2 are identical. In the general case when components 1 and 2 are different, the overlapping repair time r_a'' of the first term of Equation 11.23 is different from that, r_b'', of the second term. Using the same concept as Equation 11.15c

$$r_a'' = \frac{r_1'' r_2}{r_1'' + r_2} \quad \text{and} \quad r_b'' = \frac{r_1 r_2''}{r_1 + r_2''} \tag{11.24}$$

Therefore, since either term 1 or term 2 of Equation 11.23 will cause system failure, the principle of series systems (Equation 11.8) can be used to give

$$r_p'' = \frac{\sum \lambda r}{\sum \lambda}$$

$$= \frac{\lambda_1''(\lambda_2 r_1'')}{\lambda_p''}\left[\frac{r_1'' r_2}{r_1'' + r_2}\right] + \frac{\lambda_2''(\lambda_1 r_2'')}{\lambda_p''}\left[\frac{r_1 r_2''}{r_1 + r_2''}\right] \tag{11.25}$$

$$U_p'' = \lambda_p'' r_p'' \tag{11.26}$$

There are now two contributions to system failure, the first being component failure overlapping component failure and the second being component failure overlapping component maintenance. There is a set of indices associated with each contribution. Since either contribution will cause system failure, they can be combined by using the principle associated with series systems, i.e., $\lambda_s = \sum \lambda_i$ and $r_s = \dfrac{\sum \lambda_i r_i}{\lambda_s}$. Consequently, the combined effect of both contributions gives

$$\lambda_{pT} = \lambda_p + \lambda_p'' \tag{11.27}$$

$$r_{pT} = \frac{\lambda_p r_p + \lambda_p'' r_p''}{\lambda_{pT}} \tag{11.28}$$

$$U_{pT} = \lambda_{pT} r_{pT} \tag{11.29}$$

The principles and concepts used to derive the expressions which include maintenance for two parallel components or second order minimal cut sets can be further extended to three or more parallel components. This derivation is left to the reader although one point which must be considered in such a derivation will be discussed here. In the previous derivation it was assumed that maintenance would not be done if, by this action alone, it caused system failure. This constraint is also applicable to the third and higher order cases. In addition it must be decided if a maintenance outage will take place if another outage already exists. For instance, consider the failure sequence A followed by B followed by C.

Maintenance of C would never be done in this chronological sequence although maintenance of A would be considered. The main question is whether maintenance of B should or should not be considered, and if it is, whether it should only be considered if A is forced out of service or whether it should also be considered if A is on maintenance. All possibilities can be considered and the equations structured accordingly. It is not possible to generalize on this point: it depends greatly on operating policy. However, it is reasonable to consider maintenance only on the first component of a chronological sequence because, if considered on a subsequent component, the system, already weakened by one outage, is further weakened by the deliberate action of a maintenance outage. In order to illustrate the inclusion of maintenance outages, consider the following numerical example.

Example 11.4

Evaluate the reliability indices of the system shown in Figure 11.3 for the component reliability data shown in Table 11.2.

Using Equations 11.5 to 11.18 for the case of failures overlapping failures and Equations 11.23 to 11.26 for the case of failures overlapping maintenance, gives the system reliability results shown in Table 11.3.

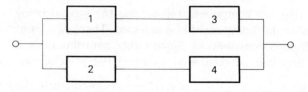

Fig. 11.3 System used in Example 11.4

Table 11.2 Component data for Example 11.4

Component	Failures $\lambda f/yr$	$r\,hr$	Maintenance $\lambda''\,o/yr$	$r''\,hr$
1	0.5	10	1	8
2	0.5	10	1	8
3	0.01	100	1	8
4	0.01	100	1	8

Table 11.3 Systems results for Example 11.4

Failure event	Failures overlapping failures λ f/yr	r hr	U hr/yr	Failures overlapping maintenance λ'' f/yr	r'' hr	U'' hr/yr
1 and 2	5.71×10^{-4}	5	2.85×10^{-3}	9.13×10^{-4}	4.4	4.06×10^{-3}
1 and 4	6.28×10^{-5}	9.1	5.71×10^{-4}	4.66×10^{-4}	4.5	2.10×10^{-3}
2 and 3	6.28×10^{-5}	9.1	5.71×10^{-4}	4.66×10^{-4}	4.5	2.10×10^{-3}
3 and 4	2.28×10^{-6}	50	1.14×10^{-4}	1.83×10^{-5}	7.4	1.35×10^{-4}
Sub totals	6.99×10^{-4}	5.9	4.11×10^{-3}	1.86×10^{-3}	4.5	8.39×10^{-3}
Total	2.56×10^{-3}	4.9	1.25×10^{-2}			

11.7 Common mode failures

11.7.1 General concepts

The preceding sections and chapters of this book have generally assumed that the failure of any one component is independent of the failure of any other. This assumption is usually made in the reliability analysis of most systems. In practice, however, it is sometimes found that a system fails more frequently than the value predicted using this assumption of independence. In some cases it has been found that the probability of failure is one, two or more orders of magnitude greater than predicted. This does not automatically mean that probability theory is invalid in this case. It simply means that the analyst has failed to recognize one, or more, dominant causes of system failure and, therefore, has evaluated a more optimistic prediction than found in practice.

One of the most important modes of failure and one which can severely degrade the actual operating reliability is a *common mode failure* sometimes referred to as *common cause failure*. This type of failure involves the simultaneous outage of two or more components owing to a common cause. Several practical examples can be given to illustrate this type of failure.

(a) A single fire in a nuclear reactor plant causes the failure of both the normal cooling water system and the emergency cooling water system because the pumps for both systems are housed in the same pumping room.

(b) The crash of a light aircraft causes the failure of a two-circuit transmission line because both lines are on the same towers.

In the first example, the system should be designed so that this type of common mode failure does not occur. A main function of a reliability assessment is to highlight this type of event and its probability of occurrence. If the probability of the event is unacceptable, the system should be redesigned.

In the second example, the common mode failure event may have to be accepted because environmental constraints force designers to use common towers and common rights-of-way. The function of the reliability assessment is to establish the significance of the event in order to determine what other actions need to be taken to minimize its effect.

These two examples are good illustrations of the practical problems encountered with common mode failures because they indicate the two classes into which most failures can be grouped. The first group (a) are those common mode failures which must be identified and eliminated if at all possible. The second group (b) are those common mode failures which must be accepted, but their effect must be minimized.

Considerable attention [20, 34–41] has been given to this type of failure in recent years both in terms of their definition and in the methods for evaluating their effect.

Many definitions have been proposed although no general acceptance has yet been approved particularly across the boundaries of the engineering disciplines. In principle however all definitions are of the form [41]: *a common mode failure is an event having a single external cause with multiple failure effects which are not consequences of each other.*

The most important features of such a definition are:

(1) The cause must be a single external event and therefore an internal system event causing the failure of one or more other components

should not be included. The latter type of event is a dependent failure and is best considered using standard conditional probability theory, i.e., given one internal event has occurred, what is the probability of failure of another component?

(2) The single cause produces multiple effects. Essentially this means that more than one component fails. It ignores however one vital aspect. Consider, for example, the fire in a nuclear reactor plant ((a) above). This may burn for several hours and the time interval between both the normal and emergency cooling systems failing may be very long. The question is, 'is this still a common mode failure?'. It has been suggested that a time interval should be included in the definition during which all the multiple events must occur for it to be a common mode failure. If such a time interval is included, then the length of time is likely to be a function of the system since it should be at least equal to the time required to take remedial action for averting subsequent failure events. In the case of power systems, the time may be seconds, whereas for an aircraft in flight it may be hours.

It is clear therefore that many questions still need to be answered concerning common mode failures. However, it is a fundamentally important aspect and one that all engineers responsible for reliability assessments should consider.

The second major consideration is in the methods for evaluating their effect. Some basic models and evaluation techniques which are essentially based on the Markov approach are considered in the next section.

11.7.2 Modelling and evaluation techniques

In order to evaluate the effect of common mode failures on the reliability of a system, a reliability model and component reliability data are required.

Reliability data is outside the scope of this book but can be achieved in practice with the implementation of a suitable data collection scheme. Consequently, this section is restricted to the consideration of some basic models, the reliability evaluation of these models and an illustration of the type of results that can be achieved.

Several models have been proposed [40], two of which are represented by the state space diagrams shown in Figure 11.4. These models represent the inclusion of a common mode failure rate, λ_{12}, of a two component parallel system or of a second order minimal cut set. The models can therefore be included as part of a network reduction evaluation or as part of a minimal cut set/failure modes and effect analysis. They can also be extended to third or higher order events provided the appropriate transitions between the states can be identified.

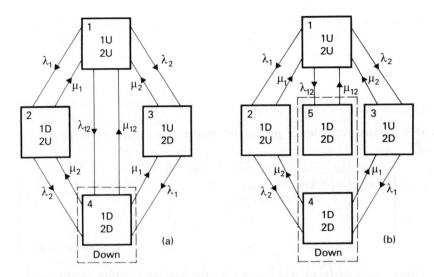

Fig. 11.4 State space diagrams including common mode failures

The state space diagrams shown in Figure 11.4 can represent three different failure/repair processes. These are:

(a) The repair process on all failed (independent and common mode) components are conducted simultaneously and each is returned to service as soon as it is repaired—Figure 11.4a with $\mu_{12} = 0$.

(b) As in (a) but the components may be returned to service either simultaneously or separately—Figure 11.4a with $\mu_{12} > 0$.

(c) The components outaged by common mode failures are returned to service simultaneously but those outaged by independent failures are replaced as in (a)—Figure 11.4b.

This is not an exhaustive list of the various failure/repair processes that can occur. For instance, it is possible that realistic transitions could occur between states 5 and 2 and states 5 and 3 of Figure 11.4b. It is also possible that the transitions of λ_2 between states 2 and 4 and λ_1 between states 3 and 4 of Figure 11.4a do not exist, or that state 4 of Figure 11.4b does not exist. Therefore, it is important that the analyst should establish the correct model for the system being considered and modify the subsequent derivations and solution techniques accordingly.

Two alternative solution techniques are possible after choosing the appropriate model to represent the system behaviour. The first is to construct the stochastic transitional probability matrix and solve this using the Markov approach previously described in Chapter 9. This gives [38] the probability of residing in each of the system states and, by combining the appropriate state probabilities, the probability of being in the down state or up state of the system can be deduced.

As discussed in Section 11.1 this method is less amenable for large systems and an alternative method [39] is to derive a set of appropriate equations for each model in a similar way to that done in Sections 11.2 and 11.3 for series and parallel systems.

(a)   *Evaluation of Figure 11.4a*

The stochastic transitional probability matrix for Figure 11.4a is:

$$
\begin{array}{cccc}
 & 1 & 2 & 3 & 4 \\
\begin{array}{c} 1 \\ 2 \\ 3 \\ 4 \end{array} &
\left[\begin{array}{cccc}
1-(\lambda_1+\lambda_2+\lambda_{12}) & \lambda_1 & \lambda_2 & \lambda_{12} \\
\mu_1 & 1-(\lambda_2+\mu_1) & 0 & \lambda_2 \\
\mu_2 & 0 & 1-(\lambda_1+\mu_2) & \lambda_1 \\
\mu_{12} & \mu_2 & \mu_1 & 1-(\mu_1+\mu_2+\mu_{12})
\end{array}\right]
\end{array}
$$

Using this matrix to deduce the probability of residing in the down state (state 4) together with the concepts of the technique described in

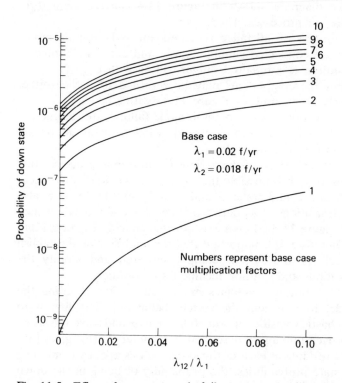

Fig. 11.5   Effect of common mode failures on probability of down state

Section 11.3 and the following assumptions

$$\lambda_1 + \mu_1 \approx \mu_1, \qquad \lambda_2 + \mu_2 \approx \mu_2, \qquad \lambda_2 + \mu_1 \approx \mu_1, \qquad \lambda_1 + \mu_2 \approx \mu_2,$$

$$\lambda_{12} + \mu_1 + \mu_2 \approx \mu_1 + \mu_2, \qquad \mu_{12}(\lambda_1 \mu_1 + \lambda_2 \mu_2) \ll \mu_{12}\mu_1\mu_2,$$

$$\mu_1^2\lambda_{12} + \mu_2^2\lambda_{12} \ll \mu_1^2\mu_2 + \mu_2^2\mu_1$$

it can be shown that

$$\lambda = \lambda_1\lambda_2(r_1 + r_2) + \lambda_{12} \tag{11.30}$$

$$r = \frac{r_1 r_2 r_{12}}{r_1 r_2 + r_2 r_{12} + r_{12} r_1} \tag{11.31}$$

$$U = \lambda r \tag{11.32}$$

The probability of being in the down state using Equation 11.32 and $\mu_1 = 693.5$ repairs/yr, $\mu_2 = 839.5$ repairs/yr and $\mu_{12} = 36.5$ repairs/year for different values of λ_1, λ_2 and λ_{12} is shown in Figure 11.5. These results show that even small percentages of common mode failures increase very significantly the probability of the system being in the down state and substantiates the need to include such failures in a reliability assessment.

(b)   *Evaluation of Figure 11.4b*

The stochastic transitional probability matrix for the case of Figure 11.4b is

$$
\begin{array}{c}
\begin{array}{ccccc}
1 & \quad\quad 2 & \quad\quad 3 & \quad\quad 4 & \quad\quad 5
\end{array} \\
\begin{array}{c} 1 \\ 2 \\ 3 \\ 4 \\ 5 \end{array}
\begin{bmatrix}
1-(\lambda_1+\lambda_2+\lambda_{12}) & \lambda_1 & \lambda_2 & 0 & \lambda_{12} \\
\mu_1 & 1-(\lambda_2+\mu_1) & 0 & \lambda_2 & 0 \\
\mu_2 & 0 & 1-(\lambda_1+\mu_2) & \lambda_1 & 0 \\
0 & \mu_2 & \mu_1 & 1-(\mu_1+\mu_2) & 0 \\
\mu_{12} & 0 & 0 & 0 & (1-\mu_{12})
\end{bmatrix}
\end{array}
$$

Using this matrix to deduce the probability of being in the down state (states 4 and 5) together with the concepts of Section 11.3 and the following assumptions

$$\lambda_1\lambda_2\mu_{12} \ll \mu_1\mu_2\mu_{12}, \qquad \lambda_1 + \mu_2 \approx \mu_2, \qquad \lambda_2 + \mu_1 \approx \mu_1,$$

$$\lambda_1 + \mu_1 \approx \mu_1, \qquad \lambda_2 + \mu_2 \approx \mu_2, \qquad \mu_1\mu_2 + \lambda_1\mu_2 + \lambda_2\mu_1 \approx \mu_1\mu_2,$$

$$\lambda_{12} + \mu_{12} \approx \mu_{12}$$

it can be shown that

$$\lambda = \lambda_1\lambda_2(r_1 + r_2) + \lambda_{12} \tag{11.33}$$

$$U = \lambda_1\lambda_2 r_1 r_2 + \lambda_{12} r_{12} \tag{11.34}$$

$$r = U/\lambda \tag{11.35}$$

Example 11.5

A second order minimal cut set of a system contains components 1 and 2. Evaluate the values of λ, r and U if
(a)   only independent failures are considered,
(b)   common mode failures are considered using Figure 11.4a, and
(c)   common mode failures are considered using Figure 11.4b.
   Let $\lambda_1 = \lambda_2 = 0.2$ f/yr, $r_1 = r_2 = 12$ hr, $\lambda_{12} = 0.02$ f/yr, $\mu_{12} = 36.5$ repairs/yr ($\equiv 240$ hr) for case (b) and $r_{12} = 18$ hr for case (c).
(a)   from Equations 11.15 to 11.18

$$\lambda = 0.2 \times 0.2(12 + 12)/8760 = 1.096 \times 10^{-4} \text{ f/yr}$$

$$r = \frac{12 \times 12}{12 + 12} = 6 \text{ hr}$$

$$U = \lambda r = 6.575 \times 10^{-4} \text{ hr/yr}$$

(b)   from Equations 11.30 to 11.32

$$\lambda = 1.096 \times 10^{-4} + 0.02 = 0.020 \text{ f/yr}$$

$$r = \frac{12 \times 12 \times 240}{12 \times 12 + 12 \times 240 + 240 \times 12} = 5.85 \text{ hr}$$

$$U = \lambda r = 0.118 \text{ hr/yr}$$

(c)   from Equations 11.33 to 11.35

$$\lambda = 0.020 \text{ f/yr}$$

$$U = \frac{0.2 \times 0.2 \times 12 \times 12}{8760} + 0.02 \times 18 = 0.361 \text{ hr/yr}$$

$$r = \frac{U}{\lambda} = 17.94 \text{ hr.}$$

These results show that:
—although the common mode failure rate is only 10% of the independent failure rate, the system failure rate is dominated by the common mode failures.
—if the common mode failures are assumed to be governed by the model of Figure 11.4a, the system average outage time is approximately equal to the overlapping time associated with the independent failures
—if the common mode failures are assumed to be governed by the model of Figure 11.4b, the system average outage time is approximately equal to the repair time associated with the common mode failures.
   These results indicate the need to include common mode failures in the assessment if they are known to exist. The results also indicate the importance of using the most appropriate model to represent system behaviour.

11.8   Conclusions

This chapter has shown that it is possible to evaluate the three basic reliability indices of a system, namely, failure rate, average duration and unavailability, by the use of relatively simple sets of equations. These equations when used in conjunction with a network reduction method, minimal cut set method or failure modes analysis can give rapid and sufficiently accurate results for a wide range of practical systems. It was also shown how the basic sets of equations derived for simple series and parallel configurations can be extended to account for both scheduled maintenance outages and common mode failures. All possibilities have not been considered in the case of these two extensions because the number of variations is too great. However, the models, examples and equations included in the chapter should provide a guide for the analyst to tackle other relevant problems.

Problems

1   A system consists of five identical components, all of which must operate for system success. If the failure rate and average repair time of each component is 0.01 f/yr and 48 hr respectively, calculate the system failure rate, average down time and unavailability.

2   The system described in Problem 1 is reinforced by connecting a second identical system in parallel with the first. Evaluate the new system failure rate, average down time and unavailability.

3   If each of the series chains in Problem 2 is maintained once a year for an average time of 8 hr, evaluate the new system reliability indices.

4   Derive an expression for the contribution of component failures overlapping a maintenance outage for a parallel system consisting of three components. Assume that maintenance of a component will not be started if another component is already failed or is already out on maintenance.

5   Evaluate the three system reliability indices for the bridge network shown in Figure 5.1 if all components are identical having $\lambda = 0.1$ f/yr, $\lambda'' = 1$ outage/yr $r = 48$ hr and $r'' = 8$ hr. In the case of the maintenance contribution assume the same constraints as in Section 11.6 and Problem 4.

6   A system consists of two components 1 and 2 of which at least one must operate for system success. Evaluate the system failure rate, average repair time and unavailability if the common-mode state space diagram shown in Figure 11.4a is applicable and $\lambda_1 = 0.01$ f/yr, $\lambda_2 = 0.02$ f/yr, $\lambda_{12} = 0.001$ f/yr, $\mu_1 = 0.5$ r/yr, $\mu_2 = 1.0$ r/yr and $\mu_{12} = 0.01$ r/yr. Compare your results with those of Problem 7 in Chapter 10.

12 Systems with non-exponential distributions

12.1 Introduction

The derivations in many of the preceding chapters have been made assuming that the underlying distributions for the component state resident times are exponential. This is particularly the case in Chapter 8 onwards. It has been stressed in these preceding chapters that, although the assumption of exponential distributions may have been made, the results and equations are equally applicable to all distributions if only the limiting state or long term average values are being evaluated for systems containing statistically independent components. This is not true if the time dependent values are being evaluated. The effect of typical distributions on limiting state values is demonstrated in Section 12.6. If the underlying distribution is non-exponential, then the process becomes non-Markovian. The techniques proposed in Chapter 8 onwards are no longer applicable and the problem has to be treated differently. Before discussing these additional techniques, it is worth examining the assumption of exponential distributions a little more deeply.

With systems that are governed by the exponential distribution, the transition rate from one state to another state of a system is constant and does not depend on how long the system spends in a given state nor does it depend on how it arrived at a particular state. This assumption is valid for the failure events of many engineering problems, especially those in which all components are properly burnt in and do not enter the wearout region. In these cases the failure rates are constant and the exponential distribution is valid. It is debatable whether the exponential distribution is as valid for the repair process and in many practical cases the assumption is not realistic. It should be noted however that many systems are designed so that those components which fail most frequently require less time to repair and vice versa. This is illustrated in Figure 12.1, from which it is seen that, if the shortest repair times are the most frequent, then the distribution approaches that of the exponential. In addition, there are practical cases in which the repair times are truly exponentially distributed. If the repair times are or can be approximated to exponential distributions, then the techniques described in preceding chapters for both time dependent and limiting state values are applicable. If they are

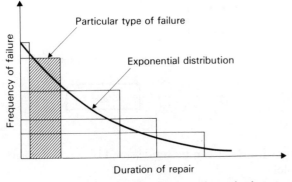

Fig. 12.1   Exponential distribution of repair time

not exponentially distributed then additional techniques are required to evaluate the time dependent values.

There are several techniques [42, 43] available for solving this problem, one of which is known as the method or device of stages. The concept and essential steps of this technique are discussed in subsequent sections of this chapter. A more detailed description of the relevant mathematics and applications is given in other texts [43].

12.2   Method of stages

It was found in previous chapters that, when the reliability indices of two or more components were combined either in series or parallel, the resulting expression was not exponentially distributed even if those of the individual components were exponential. In general terms, therefore, it can be concluded that if two or more exponentially distributed states are combined, the resulting state will not be exponentially distributed. The actual shape of the resultant distribution depends upon the number of states being combined and whether they are in series, in parallel or in series/parallel. It follows that the reverse process is also true, i.e., if a state is not exponentially distributed, then it can be divided into a number of sub-states each of which is exponentially distributed. The essence of the problem is to deduce the number of sub-states, the way they are connected and their numerical parameters in order to represent the state being considered.

This process of dividing a system state into sub-states, each sub-state being defined as a stage, is known as the *method of stages*. This method has been described in detail by Singh and Billinton [43], who have shown that three important distributions can be represented as follows:

(a)   Weibull distribution with $\beta \geqslant 1$ can be represented by a set of stages connected in series.

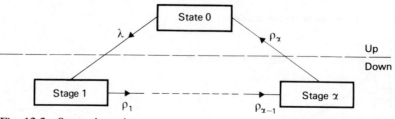

Fig. 12.2 Stages in series

(b) Weibull distribution with $\beta < 1$ can be represented by a set of stages connected in parallel.

(c) Lognormal distribution can be represented by a set of series stages connected in series with two parallel stages.

These stage combinations are shown for a single component system in Figures 12.2, 12.3 and 12.4 respectively, assuming the up or operating state to be exponentially distributed and the down or failed state to be non-exponentially distributed. Other distributions can be represented but these three are particularly useful. The lognormal distribution is widely accepted as a frequently occurring repair-time distribution and the

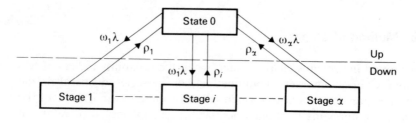

Fig. 12.3 Stages in parallel

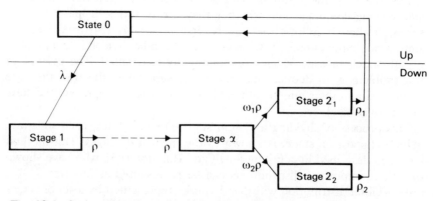

Fig. 12.4 Series stages in series with two parallel stages

Weibull distribution is very useful as a means of producing a wide variety of shapes for the probability density function.

12.3 Stages in series

In this case (Figure 12.2) the stages are traversed in a sequential order and the continuous random variable representing the state duration is the sum of α independent exponentially distributed random variables. It can be shown that the probability density function for this device is

$$f(x) = \sum_{i=1}^{\alpha} A_i \rho_i \exp\left(-\rho_i x\right) \tag{12.1}$$

If all the stages are identical with parameter ρ, the corresponding probability density function is the Special Erlangian distribution having

$$f(x) = \frac{\rho(\rho x)^{\alpha-1} e^{-\rho x}}{(\alpha-1)!} \tag{12.2}$$

for which the rth moment is given by

$$m_r = \frac{1}{\rho^r} \prod_{k=1}^{r} (\alpha + k - 1) \tag{12.3}$$

This stage device has two parameters, α and ρ. In order to establish these values for the particular distribution being modelled, the first two moments of the stage device can be matched with the corresponding moments of the distribution.

Letting $r = 1$ and $r = 2$ in Equation 12.3 gives, for the stage device

$$m_1 = \alpha/\rho \tag{12.4}$$

and

$$m_2 = \frac{\alpha(\alpha+1)}{\rho^2} \tag{12.5}$$

Let M_1 and M_2 be the first two moments of the Weibull distribution being modelled, then

$$m_1 - M_1 = 0 \quad \text{and} \quad m_2 - M_2 = 0 \tag{12.6}$$

Substituting Equations 12.4 and 12.5 into 12.6 gives

$$\alpha = \frac{M_1^2}{M_2 - M_1^2} \tag{12.7a}$$

$$\rho = \frac{M_1}{M_2 - M_1^2} \tag{12.7b}$$

In the evaluation of Equation 12.7, the value of α must be an integer and the calculated value of α should be rounded up or down as appropriate.

Example 12.1

A component has a constant failure rate of 0.1 f/yr and a repair time that follows a Special Erlangian distribution. Construct the state space diagram for this component if the repair times have a mean value of 20 hr and a standard deviation of 10 hr (Figure 12.5).

$$M_1 = \mu = 20$$

$$M_2 = \sigma^2 + \mu^2 = 10^2 + 20^2 = 500$$

therefore,

$$\alpha = \frac{20^2}{500 - 20^2} = 4$$

$$\rho = \frac{20}{500 - 20^2} = 0.2 \text{ repairs/hr} = 1752 \text{ repairs/yr}$$

The system can now be solved using the conventional Markov approach described in Chapter 9.

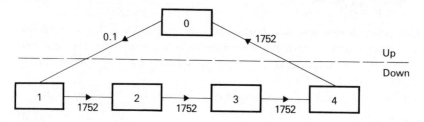

Fig. 12.5 State space diagram of Example 12.1

12.4 Stages in parallel

When the stages are in parallel, there is a probability ω_i of beginning the ith stage, the life thereafter consisting only of a single stage. The probability density function of this model is

$$f(x) = \sum_{i=1}^{\alpha} \omega_i \rho_i \exp(-\rho_i x) \tag{12.8}$$

which, in the case of two parallel stages, becomes

$$f(x) = \omega_1 \rho_1 \exp(-\rho_1 x) + \omega_2 \rho_2 \exp(-\rho_2 x) \tag{12.9}$$

in which $\omega_2 = 1 - \omega_1$.

Equation 12.9 has an rth moment given by

$$m_r = \frac{\omega_1}{\rho_1^r} \prod_{k=1}^{r} k + \frac{\omega_2}{\rho_2^r} \prod_{k=1}^{r} k \tag{12.10}$$

There are three independent parameters, ρ_1, ρ_2 and ω_1, and therefore the first three moments must be matched in order to evaluate these parameters. Unfortunately, explicit functions in terms of the three distribution moments cannot be deduced. Instead an iterative technique such as the Newton–Raphson method must be used. Once the three parameters have been obtained, however, the solution then continues as for the conventional Markov process.

12.5 Series stages in series with two parallel stages

In the lognormal case, there are five independent parameters, ρ, α, ρ_1, ρ_2 and ω_1 since $\omega_2 = 1 - \omega_1$ and the probability density function is

$$f(x) = \omega_1 \rho_1 \left(\frac{\rho}{\rho - \rho_1} \right)^\alpha \left[\exp\left(-\rho_1 x\right) - \exp\left(-\rho x\right) \sum_{i=1}^{\alpha} \frac{\{(\rho - \rho_1)x\}^{i-1}}{(i-1)!} \right]$$
$$+ \omega_2 \rho_2 \left(\frac{\rho}{\rho - \rho_2} \right)^\alpha \left[\exp\left(-\rho_2 x\right) - \exp\left(-\rho x\right) \sum_{i=1}^{\alpha} \frac{\{(\rho - \rho_2)x\}^{i-1}}{(i-1)!} \right] \tag{12.11}$$

This is a much more difficult example to solve and it is suggested that the problem should be divided into the two separate routes which can be traversed since either route can be followed, but not both. Having considered the two routes separately they can then be combined as if they were completely in parallel. Consider therefore the route, stage 1—stage α—stage 2_1. The moments of this route are

$$\rho\rho_1 m_1' = \alpha\rho_1 + \rho \quad \text{for} \quad r = 1 \tag{12.12}$$

$$\rho\rho_1 m_2' - \{2\rho + (\alpha + 1)\rho_1\}m_1' = -(\alpha + 1) \quad \text{for} \quad r = 2 \tag{12.13}$$

$$\rho\rho_1 m_r' - \{r\rho + (\alpha + r - 1)\rho_1\}m_{r-1}' + (r-1)(\alpha + r - 1)m_{r-2}' = 0 \quad \text{for} \quad r > 2 \tag{12.14}$$

The second route, state 1—stage α—state 2_2, will lead to similar expressions for m_1'', m_2'' and m_r''.

The two sets of expressions can then be combined to give

$$m_r = \omega_1 m_r' + \omega_2 m_r'' \tag{12.15}$$

In order to determine the five independent parameters, the first five moments must be matched. As in the case of parallel stages, explicit functions of the parameters in terms of the moments of the distribution cannot be derived, and therefore an iterative procedure must again be used. Once the parameters have been obtained, however, the solution continues as for the conventional Markov process.

12.6 Time dependent and limiting state probabilities

It is possible to choose an appropriate combination of stages and the values of the stage parameters to represent the state being considered using the techniques described in the previous sections. A complete state space diagram consisting of a series of stages, each exponentially distributed, is therefore obtained.

At this point, there are alternative methods for evaluating the time dependent probabilities of each stage of the system; the differential equation method and the matrix multiplication method. Both of these have been described in detail in Chapter 9 and will not be discussed further because they can be applied directly with no modifications. Having evaluated the stage probabilities as a function of time, it is then a simple task to summate the values for each stage to give the time dependent probabilities of each system state.

Using the techniques described in Chapter 9, it is possible to evaluate the limiting state probabilities by considering the state space diagram that includes all the individual stages. However, it is not necessary to make the problem so complex because this gives the same results as would be obtained if it were assumed that all system states were exponentially distributed. In order to illustrate this aspect, consider systems represented by stages in series and stages in parallel.

(a) *Exponentially distributed states*

Consider a single component system having a constant failure rate of λ and a constant repair rate of μ. This system is shown in Figure 12.6.

Using Equations 10.1 and 10.5

$$P_{up} = P_0 = \frac{\mu}{\lambda + \mu} \tag{12.16}$$

$$P_{down} = P_1 = \frac{\lambda}{\lambda + \mu} \tag{12.17}$$

$$f_{up} = f_{down} = \frac{\lambda\mu}{\lambda + \mu} \tag{12.18}$$

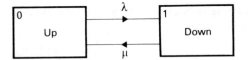

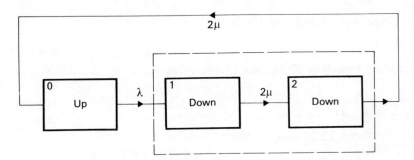

Fig. 12.6 Exponentially distributed down state

(b) *Stages in series*

Now, consider the same system but with the down state represented by two stages in series as shown in Figure 12.7.

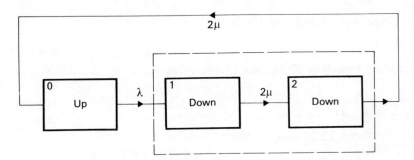

Fig. 12.7 Two stages in series

In this case the transition rates between, and from, the two down state stages are made twice the value of the exponential case in order to keep the mean residence time in the down state equal in both cases. This requirement can easily be verified from Equations 12.7 in which $\alpha = 2$.

From Equation 12.7a

$$M_2 = \tfrac{3}{2}M_1^2$$

Substituting into Equation 12.7b gives

$$\rho = \frac{2}{M_1}$$

and since $M_1 = 1/\mu$

$$\rho = 2\mu \quad \text{as required.}$$

The stochastic transitional probability matrix for this system is:

$$
\begin{array}{c}
 \\
0 \\
1 \\
2
\end{array}
\begin{array}{ccc}
0 & 1 & 2
\end{array}
\left[
\begin{array}{ccc}
1-\lambda & \lambda & 0 \\
0 & 1-2\mu & 2\mu \\
2\mu & 0 & 1-2\mu
\end{array}
\right]
$$

which, using the technique of $\alpha P = \alpha$ in Section 9.5, gives the following limiting state probability equations

$$-P_0\lambda + P_2 2\mu = 0 \tag{12.19a}$$

$$P_0\lambda - P_1 2\mu = 0 \tag{12.19b}$$

$$P_1 2\mu - P_2 2\mu = 0 \tag{12.19c}$$

$$P_0 + P_1 + P_2 = 1 \tag{12.19d}$$

From Equation 12.19c

$$P_1 = P_2 \tag{12.20}$$

From Equations 12.19d and 12.20

$$P_0 = 1 - 2P_1 \tag{12.21}$$

Substituting Equation 12.21 into 12.19b gives

$$P_1 = \frac{\lambda}{2(\lambda + \mu)} \tag{12.22}$$

From Equations 12.20 and 12.22

$$P_2 = \frac{\lambda}{2(\lambda + \mu)} \tag{12.23}$$

From Equations 12.21 and 12.22

$$P_0 = \frac{\mu}{\lambda + \mu} \tag{12.24}$$

Therefore

$$P_{up} = P_0 = \frac{\mu}{\lambda + \mu} \tag{12.25}$$

and

$$P_{down} = P_1 + P_2 = \frac{\lambda}{\lambda + \mu} \tag{12.26}$$

which are identical to those for the exponentially distributed system (Equations 12.16 and 12.17). Also, from Equation 10.5

$$f_{up} = P_0 \lambda$$

$$= \frac{\lambda\mu}{\lambda + \mu} \tag{12.27}$$

which is identical to Equation 12.18 for the exponential case, and

$$f_{down} = P_1 \cdot 2\mu + P_2 \cdot 2\mu - P_1 \cdot 2\mu = \frac{\lambda\mu}{\lambda + \mu} \tag{12.28}$$

which is also identical to Equation 12.18.

(c)   *Stages in parallel*

Now, consider the same system as in (b) but with the down state represented by two parallel stages as shown in Figure 12.8.

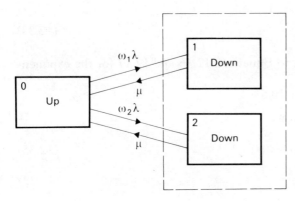

Fig. 12.8   Two stages in parallel

The stochastic transitional probability matrix for this system is

$$
\begin{array}{c c c c}
 & 0 & 1 & 2 \\
\begin{array}{c} 0 \\ 1 \\ 2 \end{array} &
\left[\begin{array}{ccc}
1-(\omega_1\lambda + \omega_2\lambda) & \omega_1\lambda & \omega_2\lambda \\
\mu & 1-\mu & 0 \\
\mu & 0 & 1-\mu
\end{array} \right]
\end{array}
$$

which gives the following limiting state probability equations

$$-(\omega_1\lambda + \omega_2\lambda)P_0 + \mu P_1 + \mu P_2 = 0 \qquad (12.29\text{a})$$
$$\omega_1\lambda P_0 - \mu P_1 = 0 \qquad (12.29\text{b})$$
$$\omega_2\lambda P_0 - \mu P_2 = 0 \qquad (12.29\text{c})$$
$$P_0 + P_1 + P_2 = 1 \qquad (12.29\text{d})$$

Since $\omega_1 + \omega_2 = 1$, Equation 12.29a becomes

$$-\lambda P_0 + \mu(P_1 + P_2) = 0 \qquad (12.30)$$

Also, since $P_0 = P_{\text{up}}$ and $P_1 + P_2 = P_{\text{down}}$, Equation 12.30 gives

$$P_{\text{up}} = \frac{\mu}{\lambda} \cdot P_{\text{down}} \qquad (12.31)$$

Similarly, from Equation 12.29d

$$P_{\text{up}} = 1 - P_{\text{down}} \qquad (12.32)$$

Therefore, from Equations 12.31 and 12.32

$$P_{down} = \frac{\lambda}{\lambda + \mu}$$ (12.33)

and

$$P_{up} = \frac{\mu}{\lambda + \mu}$$ (12.34)

which are again identical to Equations 12.16 and 12.17 for the exponential case.

Finally, from Equation 10.5

$$f_{up} = P_0 \cdot \omega_1 \lambda + P_0 \cdot \omega_2 \lambda$$

$$= \frac{\lambda \mu}{\lambda + \mu} \quad \text{since } \omega_1 + \omega_2 = 1$$ (12.35)

and

$$f_{down} = P_1 \mu + P_2 \mu$$

$$= P_{down} \cdot \mu$$

$$= \frac{\lambda \mu}{\lambda + \mu}$$ (12.36)

Once again Equations 12.35 and 12.36 are identical to Equation 12.18.

This consideration of two simple systems indicates that the limiting state probabilities and frequencies of a system having non-exponential distributions are identical to those evaluated under the assumption that the states are exponentially distributed. The concepts and conclusions derived in this section are equally applicable to more complex systems and arrangements provided that the components are statistically independent. Therefore, if limiting state values only are required, it is not necessary to be overly concerned about the underlying distribution. This becomes important only if time dependent values are required, or if it is necessary to know the shape of the resultant distribution.

12.7   Conclusions

This chapter has considered some of the problems that can be encountered when the components do not comply with the exponential distribution and one approach, known as the method of stages, which can be used to overcome the problem. An important feature of the chapter is the illustration of the concept that exponentially distributed state residence times can be tacitly assumed in the evaluation of limiting state probabilities and frequencies. The techniques described in Chapters 8–11 for determining these values are applicable for all distributions provided the components are statistically independent. However, this is not true when time dependent probabilities are required, for in this case a technique such as the method of stages must be used. There are also other methods available. One is to divide the total time period into intervals during which it can be assumed that the transition rates remain constant. The established techniques can then be used for each interval. This becomes a piece-wise solution and the amount of effort required to solve it can be substantial, depending upon the number of time intervals required to give a good approximation to the physical change in the parameters or transition rates of the components.

Problem

1   A component has a constant failure rate of 10^{-6} f/hr and a down time distribution that obeys the Special Erlangian distribution. From historical data the down times have a mean value of 48 hr and a standard deviation of 24 hr. Construct the state space diagram for this component using the method of stages. Hence, determine the limiting state values of the probability of residing in and the frequency of encountering the down state. Compare these results with those that would be given if the component down state were assumed to follow an exponential distribution.

13 Epilogue

This book has been written primarily for the practising engineer, technical manager and engineering student who has little or no formal background in the area of statistics, probability theory and reliability evaluation techniques. It attempts to illustrate the theoretical concepts and practical formulae required to evaluate quantitatively the reliability of systems. It must be stressed that there is no single all-purpose technique that can be used to solve all reliability problems and great care must be given in selecting the most appropriate model and evaluation technique.

Throughout the book the aim has been to indicate the weaknesses and strengths of each technique and also to identify the relationship between one method and another. It should be evident to the reader that, although many techniques may appear to exist, several of them are extremely similar and the differences between them are mainly due to their formalized presentation.

One very important aspect in reliability evaluation is associated with the component data used in the reliability evaluation of a system. Although this topic is outside the scope of this book, it is a vital aspect and has been mentioned briefly at various places in the text. In practice the mechanics of data collection are seldom very exciting but without consistent and comprehensive data, any subsequent reliability analysis could be quite incorrect and perhaps quite misleading. Many organizations have created data collection schemes which are appropriate for their present needs but which must be continuously updated and enhanced as future needs increase and reliability modelling and evaluation techniques are extended.

We believe that the techniques described in this book will be sufficient for most analysts to perform routine day-to-day reliability evaluation studies. In addition, we feel that the analyst will be in a position to extend himself by reading appropriate literature in his own engineering discipline and area of work. There are some excellent textbooks available for those inclined to more advanced reading of the subject and to more detailed and rigorous mathematical treatment. References 1, 25, 26, 43, 45, 46 provide a rather arbitrary suggested list.

Appendix 1—**Rules of Boolean algebra**

Basic rules

$$AA = A$$
$$A + A = A$$
$$A(A + B) = A$$
$$A + AB = A$$
$$A\bar{A} = 0$$
$$A + \bar{A} = 1$$

Commutative rules

$$AB = BA$$
$$A + B = B + A$$

Associative rules

$$A(BC) = (AB)C$$
$$A + (B + C) = (A + B) + C$$

Distributive rules

$$A(B + C) = AB + AC$$
$$A + BC = (A + B)(A + C)$$

Rules involving 1 and 0

$$0A = 0$$
$$1A = A$$
$$0 + A = A$$
$$1 + A = 1$$

Rules of De Morgan

$$\overline{AB} = \bar{A} + \bar{B}$$
$$\overline{A + B} = \bar{A}\bar{B}$$

Appendix 2—The normal distribution function

The following table gives the area under the normal probability density function between the limits of $Z = 0$ and $Z = (x - \mu)/\sigma$, i.e.,

$$F(z) = \frac{1}{\sqrt{2\pi}} \int_0^Z \exp\left(\frac{-z^2}{2}\right) dz$$

Z	0.00	0.01	0.02	0.03	0.04	0.05	0.06	0.07	0.08	0.09
0.0	0.0000	0.0040	0.0080	0.0120	0.0159	0.0199	0.0239	0.0279	0.0319	0.0359
0.1	0.0398	0.0438	0.0478	0.0517	0.0557	0.0596	0.0636	0.0675	0.0714	0.0753
0.2	0.0793	0.0832	0.0871	0.0909	0.0948	0.0987	0.1026	0.1064	0.1103	0.1141
0.3	0.1179	0.1217	0.1255	0.1293	0.1331	0.1368	0.1406	0.1443	0.1480	0.1517
0.4	0.1555	0.1591	0.1628	0.1664	0.1700	0.1736	0.1772	0.1808	0.1844	0.1879
0.5	0.1915	0.1950	0.1985	0.2019	0.2054	0.2088	0.2123	0.2157	0.2190	0.2224
0.6	0.2257	0.2291	0.2324	0.2356	0.2389	0.2421	0.2454	0.2486	0.2517	0.2549
0.7	0.2580	0.2611	0.2642	0.2673	0.2703	0.2734	0.2764	0.2793	0.2823	0.2852
0.8	0.2881	0.2910	0.2939	0.2967	0.2995	0.3023	0.3051	0.3078	0.3108	0.3133
0.9	0.3159	0.3186	0.3212	0.3238	0.3264	0.3289	0.3315	0.3340	0.3365	0.3389
1.0	0.3413	0.3437	0.3461	0.3485	0.3508	0.3531	0.3554	0.3577	0.3599	0.3621
1.1	0.3643	0.3665	0.3686	0.3708	0.3729	0.3749	0.3770	0.3790	0.3810	0.3830
1.2	0.3849	0.3869	0.3888	0.3906	0.3925	0.3943	0.3962	0.3980	0.3997	0.4015
1.3	0.4032	0.4049	0.4066	0.4082	0.4099	0.4115	0.4131	0.4147	0.4162	0.4177
1.4	0.4192	0.4207	0.4222	0.4236	0.4251	0.4265	0.4279	0.4292	0.4306	0.4319
1.5	0.4332	0.4345	0.4357	0.4370	0.4382	0.4394	0.4406	0.4418	0.4429	0.4441
1.6	0.4452	0.4463	0.4474	0.4484	0.4495	0.4505	0.4515	0.4525	0.4535	0.4545
1.7	0.4554	0.4564	0.4573	0.4582	0.4591	0.4599	0.4608	0.4616	0.4625	0.4633
1.8	0.4641	0.4648	0.4656	0.4664	0.4671	0.4678	0.4686	0.4693	0.4699	0.4706
1.9	0.4713	0.4719	0.4726	0.4732	0.4738	0.4744	0.4750	0.4756	0.4761	0.4767
2.0	0.4772	0.4778	0.4783	0.4788	0.4793	0.4798	0.4803	0.4808	0.4812	0.4817
2.1	0.4821	0.4826	0.4830	0.4834	0.4838	0.4842	0.4846	0.4850	0.4854	0.4857
2.2	0.4861	0.4864	0.4868	0.4871	0.4874	0.4878	0.4881	0.4884	0.4887	0.4890
2.3	0.4893	0.4896	0.4898	0.4901	0.4904	0.4906	0.4909	0.4911	0.4913	0.4916
2.4	0.4918	0.4920	0.4922	0.4924	0.4927	0.4929	0.4930	0.4932	0.4934	0.4936
2.5	0.4938	0.4940	0.4941	0.4943	0.4945	0.4946	0.4948	0.4949	0.4951	0.4952
2.6	0.4953	0.4955	0.4956	0.4957	0.4958	0.4960	0.4961	0.4962	0.4963	0.4964
2.7	0.4965	0.4966	0.4967	0.4968	0.4969	0.4970	0.4971	0.4972	0.4973	0.4974
2.8	0.4974	0.4975	0.4976	0.4977	0.4977	0.4978	0.4979	0.4979	0.4980	0.4981
2.9	0.4981	0.4982	0.4982	0.4983	0.4984	0.4984	0.4985	0.4985	0.4986	0.4986
3.0	0.4986	0.4987	0.4987	0.4988	0.4988	0.4989	0.4989	0.4989	0.4990	0.4990
3.1	0.4990	0.4991	0.4991	0.4991	0.4991	0.4992	0.4992	0.4992	0.4993	0.4993
3.2	0.4993	0.4993	0.4994	0.4994	0.4994	0.4994	0.4994	0.4995	0.4995	0.4995
3.3	0.4995	0.4995	0.4995	0.4996	0.4996	0.4996	0.4996	0.4996	0.4996	0.4996
3.4	0.4997	0.4997	0.4997	0.4997	0.4997	0.4997	0.4997	0.4997	0.4997	0.4998

Appendix 3—Elementary matrix algebra

A3.1 Concepts of matrices

A matrix is an array of numbers or algebraic quantities. It has no single numerical value although the determinant of a matrix does have a single numerical value. A matrix is dimensioned $m \times n$ where m = number of rows and n = number of columns. The general form of a matrix is shown in Expression A3.1.

$$\mathbf{A} = \begin{bmatrix} a_{11} & a_{12} & a_{13} & \cdots a_{1j} & \cdots a_{1n} \\ a_{21} & a_{22} & a_{23} & \cdots a_{2j} & \cdots a_{2n} \\ \vdots & \vdots & \vdots & \vdots & \vdots \\ a_{i1} & a_{i2} & a_{i3} & \cdots a_{ij} & \cdots a_{in} \\ \vdots & \vdots & \vdots & \vdots & \vdots \\ a_{m1} & a_{m2} & a_{m3} & \cdots a_{mj} & \cdots a_{mn} \end{bmatrix} \qquad \text{(A3.1)}$$

A3.2 Square matrix

A matrix is said to be square if the number of rows equals the number of columns, i.e., $m = n$. An example is shown in Expression A3.2.

$$\mathbf{A} = \begin{bmatrix} 1 & -3 & 0 \\ 2 & 0 & 1 \\ 4 & 1 & 3 \end{bmatrix} \qquad \text{(A3.2)}$$

A3.3 Column matrix (or vector)

If a matrix has only one column, i.e., $n = 1$, it is defined as a column vector. An example is shown in Expression A3.3.

$$\mathbf{A} = \begin{bmatrix} 1 \\ 2 \\ 4 \end{bmatrix} \qquad \text{(A3.3)}$$

A3.4 Row matrix (or vector)

If a matrix has only one row, i.e., $m = 1$, it is defined as a row vector. An example is shown in Expression A3.4.

$$\mathbf{A} = [1 \quad -3 \quad 0] \tag{A3.4}$$

A3.5 Transposed matrix

If the elements of a matrix $\mathbf{A}$, a_{ij} and a_{ji}, for all i and j, are interchanged, then the resulting matrix is defined as the transpose of matrix $\mathbf{A}$ and designated as $\mathbf{A}^T$. An example is shown in Expression A3.5. If

$$\mathbf{A} = \begin{bmatrix} 1 & 3 & 2 \\ 0 & 4 & -1 \end{bmatrix} \tag{A3.5a}$$

$$\mathbf{A}^T = \begin{bmatrix} 1 & 0 \\ 3 & 4 \\ 2 & -1 \end{bmatrix} \tag{A3.5b}$$

A3.6 Diagonal matrix

If all elements of a square matrix are zero, except those on the main diagonal (this being the diagonal that runs from top left to bottom right), it is defined as a diagonal matrix. An example is shown in Expression A3.6.

$$\mathbf{A} = \begin{bmatrix} 3 & 0 & 0 \\ 0 & 4 & 0 \\ 0 & 0 & 2 \end{bmatrix} \tag{A3.6}$$

A3.7 Identity (or unit) matrix

A diagonal matrix in which all the main diagonal elements are unity is defined as an identity or unit matrix and designated as $\mathbf{I}$. The third order identity matrix is shown in Expression A3.7.

$$\mathbf{I} = \begin{bmatrix} 1 & 0 & 0 \\ 0 & 1 & 0 \\ 0 & 0 & 1 \end{bmatrix} \tag{A3.7}$$

A3.8 Symmetric matrix

If a square matrix A and its transpose A^T are identical, the matrix is said to be symmetrical. An example is shown in Expression A3.8.

$$A = A^T = \begin{bmatrix} 4 & 2 & 0 \\ 2 & 3 & -1 \\ 0 & -1 & 2 \end{bmatrix} \qquad \text{(A3.8)}$$

A3.9 Determinant of a matrix

A square matrix of any order has an associated determinant which has a single value that may be negative, zero or positive. If the determinant is negative or positive, the matrix is said to be non-singular but if it is zero, it is said to be singular. The evaluation of determinants is shown in Section A3.11. The general form of the determinant associated with the matrix shown in Expression A3.1 is given in Expression A3.9.

$$|A| = \begin{vmatrix} a_{11} & a_{12} & \cdots & a_{1j} & \cdots & a_{1n} \\ a_{21} & a_{22} & \cdots & a_{2j} & \cdots & a_{2n} \\ \vdots & & & & & \\ a_{i1} & a_{i2} & \cdots & a_{ij} & \cdots & a_{in} \\ \vdots & & & & & \\ a_{m1} & a_{m2} & \cdots & a_{mj} & \cdots & a_{mn} \end{vmatrix} \qquad \text{(A3.9)}$$

A3.10 Co-factors

The co-factor F_{ij} of a matrix is defined as $(-1)^{i+j}$ times the determinant that remains when the ith row and jth column of the matrix are deleted.

Considering the matrix given by Expression A3.2, then

$$F_{11} = (-1)^2 \begin{vmatrix} 0 & 1 \\ 1 & 3 \end{vmatrix} = \begin{vmatrix} 0 & 1 \\ 1 & 3 \end{vmatrix} \qquad \text{(A3.10a)}$$

$$F_{12} = (-1)^3 \begin{vmatrix} 2 & 1 \\ 4 & 3 \end{vmatrix} = - \begin{vmatrix} 2 & 1 \\ 4 & 3 \end{vmatrix} \qquad \text{(A3.10b)}$$

A3.11 Evaluation of determinants

The numerical value of a determinant is evaluated by considering all the elements of any *one* row or column, multiplying each of these elements by its associated co-factor and summating these products, i.e.,

$$|A| = \sum_{i=1}^{m} a_{ij}F_{ij} \qquad\qquad \text{(A3.11a)}$$

or

$$|A| = \sum_{j=1}^{n} a_{ij}F_{ij} \qquad\qquad \text{(A3.11b)}$$

The following algebraic and numerical examples illustrate the application of this method.

$$\begin{vmatrix} a_{11} & a_{12} \\ a_{21} & a_{22} \end{vmatrix} = a_{11}a_{22} - a_{12}a_{21} \qquad\qquad \text{(A3.12)}$$

since the co-factors of a_{11} and a_{12} are the single elements a_{22} and $-a_{21}$, respectively.

$$\begin{vmatrix} a_{11} & a_{12} & a_{13} \\ a_{21} & a_{22} & a_{23} \\ a_{31} & a_{32} & a_{33} \end{vmatrix} = a_{11}\begin{vmatrix} a_{22} & a_{23} \\ a_{32} & a_{33} \end{vmatrix} - a_{12}\begin{vmatrix} a_{21} & a_{23} \\ a_{31} & a_{33} \end{vmatrix} + a_{13}\begin{vmatrix} a_{21} & a_{22} \\ a_{31} & a_{32} \end{vmatrix}$$

$$\text{(A3.13)}$$

In this case, the 2×2 co-factors are determinants and must themselves be evaluated before the final value of the determinant can be deduced.

$$\begin{vmatrix} 1 & -3 & 0 \\ 2 & 0 & 1 \\ 4 & 1 & 3 \end{vmatrix} = 1\begin{vmatrix} 0 & 1 \\ 1 & 3 \end{vmatrix} + 3\begin{vmatrix} 2 & 1 \\ 4 & 3 \end{vmatrix} + 0\begin{vmatrix} 2 & 0 \\ 4 & 1 \end{vmatrix}$$

$$= 1(0-1) + 3(6-4) + 0(2-0)$$

$$= 5$$

A3.12 Addition of matrices

Two or more matrices having the same dimension $m \times n$, can be added by summating the elements in corresponding matrix positions to give a new matrix of the same dimension. For example

$$\begin{bmatrix} 1 & 3 & 4 \\ 2 & 1 & 5 \end{bmatrix} + \begin{bmatrix} 2 & 0 & -3 \\ -1 & 3 & 2 \end{bmatrix} = \begin{bmatrix} 1+2 & 3+0 & 4+(-3) \\ 2+(-1) & 1+3 & 5+2 \end{bmatrix}$$

$$= \begin{bmatrix} 3 & 3 & 1 \\ 1 & 4 & 7 \end{bmatrix} \qquad\qquad \text{(A3.14)}$$

It should be noted that $A + B = B + A$.

A3.13   Subtraction of matrices

Two matrices both having the same dimension $m \times n$, can be subtracted by taking the difference between elements in corresponding matrix positions to give a third matrix of the same dimension. For example

$$\begin{bmatrix} 1 & 3 & 4 \\ 2 & 1 & 5 \end{bmatrix} - \begin{bmatrix} 2 & 0 & -3 \\ -1 & 3 & 2 \end{bmatrix} = \begin{bmatrix} 1-2 & 3-0 & 4-(-3) \\ 2-(-1) & 1-3 & 5-2 \end{bmatrix}$$

$$= \begin{bmatrix} -1 & 3 & 7 \\ 3 & -2 & 3 \end{bmatrix} \tag{A3.15}$$

It should be noted in the case of subtraction that $\boldsymbol{A} - \boldsymbol{B} \neq \boldsymbol{B} - \boldsymbol{A}$.

A3.14   Multiplication of matrices

Two matrices may be multiplied if the number of columns of the first matrix is equal to the number of rows of the second matrix to give a third matrix having a number of rows equal to that of the first matrix and a number of columns equal to the second. That is,

if $\boldsymbol{A}$ has dimensions $l \times m$
and $\boldsymbol{B}$ has dimensions $m \times n$
Then $\boldsymbol{C} = \boldsymbol{A} \times \boldsymbol{B}$ exists having dimensions $l \times n$.

In this case of $\boldsymbol{A}$ and $\boldsymbol{B}$, the product $\boldsymbol{B} \times \boldsymbol{A}$ does not exist and in general $\boldsymbol{A} \times \boldsymbol{B} \neq \boldsymbol{B} \times \boldsymbol{A}$.

To indicate precisely the order in which two matrices are multiplied, the terms premultiplication and postmultiplication are used. In the product $\boldsymbol{A} \times \boldsymbol{B}$, the matrix $\boldsymbol{B}$ is said to be premultiplied by $\boldsymbol{A}$, or the matrix $\boldsymbol{A}$ is said to be postmultiplied by $\boldsymbol{B}$.

The multiplication method is best illustrated by the following algebraic and numerical examples.

$$\begin{bmatrix} a_{11} & a_{12} & a_{13} \\ a_{21} & a_{22} & a_{23} \end{bmatrix} \begin{bmatrix} b_{11} & b_{12} \\ b_{21} & b_{22} \\ b_{31} & b_{32} \end{bmatrix}$$

$$= \begin{bmatrix} a_{11}b_{11} + a_{12}b_{21} + a_{13}b_{31} & a_{11}b_{12} + a_{12}b_{22} + a_{13}b_{32} \\ a_{21}b_{11} + a_{22}b_{21} + a_{23}b_{31} & a_{21}b_{12} + a_{22}b_{22} + a_{23}b_{32} \end{bmatrix} \tag{A3.16a}$$

$$\begin{bmatrix} 1 & 3 \\ 2 & 0 \\ -3 & 1 \end{bmatrix} \begin{bmatrix} 2 & 1 & 0 \\ 3 & 4 & -1 \end{bmatrix}$$

$$= \begin{bmatrix} 1\times2+3\times3 & 1\times1+3\times4 & 1\times0+3\times(-1) \\ 2\times2+0\times3 & 2\times1+0\times4 & 2\times0+0\times(-1) \\ -3\times2+1\times3 & -3\times1+1\times4 & -3\times0+1\times(-1) \end{bmatrix}$$

$$= \begin{bmatrix} 11 & 13 & -3 \\ 4 & 2 & 0 \\ -3 & 1 & -1 \end{bmatrix} \tag{A3.16b}$$

A3.15 Multiplication by a constant

If a matrix is multiplied by a single number, all elements of the matrix are multiplied by that number, for example

$$c \times \begin{bmatrix} a_{11} & a_{12} & a_{13} \\ a_{21} & a_{22} & a_{23} \end{bmatrix} = \begin{bmatrix} ca_{11} & ca_{12} & ca_{13} \\ ca_{21} & ca_{22} & ca_{23} \end{bmatrix} \tag{A3.17}$$

A3.16 Inverse of a matrix

Unlike normal algebra, a matrix cannot be divided by another matrix. On the other hand a matrix A which is square and non-singular has an inverse matrix designated as A^{-1} and defined by

$$A^{-1}A = AA^{-1} = I \tag{A3.18}$$

The elements $\hat{a}_{ij}$ of the inverse matrix A^{-1} can be evaluated from the elements a_{ij} of the matrix A using

$$\hat{a}_{ij} = \frac{F_{ji}}{|A|} \tag{A3.19}$$

in which it should be noted that the subscripts of F are an interchange of the subscripts of $\hat{a}$.

The following numerical example illustrates this inversion process.

$$A = \begin{bmatrix} 1 & -3 & 0 \\ 2 & 0 & 1 \\ 4 & 1 & 3 \end{bmatrix}$$

From Section A3.11

$$|A| = 5$$

From Expression A3.19

$$\hat{a}_{11} = \begin{vmatrix} 0 & 1 \\ 1 & 3 \end{vmatrix} \qquad \hat{a}_{12} = \begin{vmatrix} -3 & 0 \\ 1 & 3 \end{vmatrix} \qquad \hat{a}_{13} = \begin{vmatrix} -3 & 0 \\ 0 & 1 \end{vmatrix}$$

$$= -1 \qquad\qquad = 9 \qquad\qquad = -3$$

Similarly

$$\hat{a}_{21} = -2 \qquad \hat{a}_{22} = 3, \qquad \hat{a}_{23} = -1$$
$$\hat{a}_{31} = 2, \qquad \hat{a}_{32} = -13, \qquad \hat{a}_{33} = 6$$

$$\mathbf{A}^{-1} = 1/5 \begin{bmatrix} -1 & 9 & -3 \\ -2 & 3 & -1 \\ 2 & -13 & 6 \end{bmatrix} \tag{A3.20}$$

A3.17 Solution of simultaneous equations

Consider the equations

$$x_1 - 3x_2 \qquad = 1$$
$$2x_1 \qquad + x_3 = 1$$
$$4x_1 + x_2 + 3x_3 = 1$$

These can be written in matrix form as

$$\begin{bmatrix} 1 & -3 & 0 \\ 2 & 0 & 1 \\ 4 & 1 & 3 \end{bmatrix} \begin{bmatrix} x_1 \\ x_2 \\ x_3 \end{bmatrix} = \begin{bmatrix} 1 \\ 1 \\ 1 \end{bmatrix} \tag{A3.21}$$

The reader can verify that the matrix form is the same as the original equations by using the multiplication techniques of Section A3.14.

Equation A3.21 can be expressed as

$$\mathbf{AX} = \mathbf{b} \tag{A3.22}$$

where $\mathbf{A}$ is the coefficient matrix, $\mathbf{X}$ is the column vector of unknown quantities, and $\mathbf{b}$ is the column vector of known quantities.

The problem is to solve for $\mathbf{X}$.

If $\mathbf{A}$ is square and non-singular then Equation A3.22 becomes

$$\mathbf{A}^{-1}\mathbf{AX} = \mathbf{A}^{-1}\mathbf{b}$$
$$\mathbf{IX} = \mathbf{A}^{-1}\mathbf{b} \tag{A3.23}$$
$$\mathbf{X} = \mathbf{A}^{-1}\mathbf{b}$$

Therefore the values of $\mathbf{X}$ can be found by premultiplying the vector of known quantities by the inverse of the coefficient matrix $\mathbf{A}$.

The inverse of A can be deduced using the techniques described in Section A3.16.

In the case of A in Equation A3.21, A^{-1} was found in Section A3.16 and shown in Equation A3.20.

Therefore

$$\begin{bmatrix} x_1 \\ x_2 \\ x_3 \end{bmatrix} = 1/5 \begin{bmatrix} -1 & 9 & -3 \\ -2 & 3 & -1 \\ 2 & -13 & 6 \end{bmatrix} \begin{bmatrix} 1 \\ 1 \\ 1 \end{bmatrix} = \begin{bmatrix} 1 \\ 0 \\ 1 \end{bmatrix}$$

giving $x_1 = 1$ $x_2 = 0$ and $x_3 = 1$.

This is a fairly straightforward method for solving simultaneous equations. A similar, but alternative method is known as Cramer's rule which is described in the next section.

A3.18 Cramer's rule for solving simultaneous equations

To explain Cramer's rule, consider the following third order set of equations

$$\begin{bmatrix} a_{11} & a_{12} & a_{13} \\ a_{21} & a_{22} & a_{23} \\ a_{31} & a_{32} & a_{33} \end{bmatrix} \begin{bmatrix} x \\ y \\ z \end{bmatrix} = \begin{bmatrix} d_1 \\ d_2 \\ d_3 \end{bmatrix} \tag{A3.24}$$

Using the determinant method of Section A3.17, we have

$$\begin{bmatrix} x \\ y \\ z \end{bmatrix} = \frac{1}{|A|} \begin{bmatrix} b_{11} & b_{12} & b_{13} \\ b_{21} & b_{22} & b_{23} \\ b_{31} & b_{32} & b_{33} \end{bmatrix} \begin{bmatrix} d_1 \\ d_2 \\ d_3 \end{bmatrix} \tag{A3.25}$$

Therefore,

$$x = \frac{1}{|A|} (b_{11}d_1 + b_{12}d_2 + b_{13}d_3) \tag{A3.26}$$

where

$$b_{11} = \begin{vmatrix} a_{22} & a_{23} \\ a_{32} & a_{33} \end{vmatrix}, \qquad b_{12} = -\begin{vmatrix} a_{12} & a_{13} \\ a_{32} & a_{33} \end{vmatrix}, \qquad b_{13} = \begin{vmatrix} a_{12} & a_{13} \\ a_{22} & a_{23} \end{vmatrix}$$

From this knowledge, Equation A3.26 can also be expressed as

$$x = \frac{1}{|A|} \begin{vmatrix} d_1 & a_{12} & a_{13} \\ d_2 & a_{22} & a_{23} \\ d_3 & a_{32} & a_{33} \end{vmatrix} \tag{A3.27}$$

By evaluating the determinant in Equation A3.27, the reader can easily verify that Equations A3.26 and A3.27 are identical.

The logic behind Cramer's rule can now be deduced. The first unknown quantity (x) can be evaluated by replacing the first column of A by the vector of known quantities, evaluating the resulting associated determinant and dividing by the determinant of the original coefficient matrix. The second unknown quantity can be evaluated by replacing the second column of A by the vector of known quantities, and so on. Therefore for Equation A3.24

$$y = \frac{1}{|A|} \begin{vmatrix} a_{11} & d_1 & a_{13} \\ a_{21} & d_2 & a_{23} \\ a_{31} & d_3 & a_{33} \end{vmatrix} \qquad z = \frac{1}{|A|} \begin{vmatrix} a_{11} & a_{12} & d_1 \\ a_{21} & a_{22} & d_2 \\ a_{31} & a_{32} & d_3 \end{vmatrix}$$

Reconsider now the set of equations given by Equation A3.21. From Cramer's rule

$$x_1 = \frac{1}{|A|} \begin{vmatrix} 1 & -3 & 0 \\ 1 & 0 & 1 \\ 1 & 1 & 3 \end{vmatrix}$$

$$= 1/5 \left[1 \begin{vmatrix} 0 & 1 \\ 1 & 3 \end{vmatrix} + 3 \begin{vmatrix} 1 & 1 \\ 1 & 3 \end{vmatrix} + 0 \begin{vmatrix} 1 & 0 \\ 1 & 1 \end{vmatrix} \right]$$

$$= 1/5[1(0-1)+3(3-1)+0(1-0)]$$

$$= 1$$

Similarly

$$x_2 = 1/5 \begin{vmatrix} 1 & 1 & 0 \\ 2 & 1 & 1 \\ 4 & 1 & 3 \end{vmatrix} = 0$$

$$x_3 = 1/5 \begin{vmatrix} 1 & -3 & 1 \\ 2 & 0 & 1 \\ 4 & 1 & 1 \end{vmatrix} = 1$$

It should be noted that the co-factor method and Cramer's rule are very convenient methods for solving a small set of simultaneous equations by hand, but are not particularly suitable for use in digital computer solutions of large sets of equations. In the latter case more suitable techniques are Gaussian elimination or sparsity techniques [28].

Appendix 4—Differential equations and Laplace transforms

A4.1 Differential equations

There is a wide range of differential equations. Most occur in one form or another in a variety of engineering applications. This Appendix concerns itself with only one type of differential equation—relevant to Markov models. This type of differential equation is known as a first-order linear differential equation with constant coefficients. It is the simplest type of differential equation and can be expressed in the form

$$a\frac{dy}{dt} + by = f(t) \qquad (A4.1)$$

There are a number of ways in which such equations can be solved but one of the most convenient is to use Laplace transforms.

A4.2 Laplace transforms

If $f(t)$ is a function of t and s is a parameter, the Laplace transform $F(s)$ is defined as

$$F(s) = \int_0^\infty e^{-st} f(t)\, dt \qquad (A4.2)$$

Consider the application of Equation A4.2 to a few functions.
(a) $f(t) = 1$

$$F(s) = \int_0^\infty e^{-st} \cdot 1 \, dt$$

$$= \left[-\frac{1}{s} e^{-st} \right]_0^\infty$$

$$= \frac{1}{s}$$

(b) $f(t) = t$

$$F(s) = \int_0^\infty e^{-st} \cdot t \, dt$$

$$= \left[-\frac{1}{s} t e^{-st} \right]_0^\infty + \frac{1}{s} \int_0^\infty e^{-st} \, dt$$

$$= 0 + \frac{1}{s} \left[-\frac{1}{s} e^{-st} \right]_0^\infty$$

$$= \frac{1}{s^2}$$

(c) $f(t) = e^{kt}$

$$F(s) = \int_0^\infty e^{-st} e^{kt} \, dt$$

$$= \int_0^\infty e^{-(s-k)t} \, dt$$

$$= \left[\frac{-1}{s-k} e^{-(s-k)t} \right]_0^\infty$$

$$= \frac{1}{s-k}$$

The examples shown above are known as Laplace transforms. An inverse Laplace transform also exists which is the reverse of those shown above. That is, if

$$F(s) = \frac{1}{s} \quad \text{then} \quad f(t) = 1$$

$$F(s) = \frac{1}{s^2} \quad \text{then} \quad f(t) = t$$

$$F(s) = \frac{1}{s+k} \quad \text{then} \quad f(t) = e^{-kt}$$

(d)   if $y(t)$ has a transform $F(s)$ then the Laplace transform of dy/dt, defined as $\mathscr{L}\{dy/dt\}$ is:

$$\mathscr{L}\left\{ \frac{dy}{dt} \right\} = \int_0^\infty e^{-st} \frac{dy}{dt} \, dt$$

$$= [e^{-st} y]_0^\infty + s \int_0^\infty e^{-st} y \, dt$$

$$= -y(0) + sF(s)$$

since $\int_0^\infty e^{-st}y \, dt$ is the Laplace transform of $y(t)$. Therefore,

$$\mathcal{L}\left\{\frac{dy}{dt}\right\} = sF(s) - y(0)$$

where $y(0)$ is the value of $y(t)$ at $t = 0$.

The above transforms together with a few of the more important ones that the reader may encounter are shown in Table A4.1.

Table A4.1   Selected Laplace Transforms

$f(t)$	$F(s)$
1	$\dfrac{1}{s}$
t	$\dfrac{1}{s^2}$
e^{-kt}	$\dfrac{1}{s+k}$
$\sin kt$	$\dfrac{k}{s^2 + k^2}$
$\cos kt$	$\dfrac{s}{s^2 + k^2}$
$\dfrac{1}{(n-1)!} t^{n-1} e^{-kt}$	$\dfrac{1}{(s+k)^n}$
$\dfrac{dy}{dt}$	$sF(s) - y(0)$

A4.3   Solving differential equations using Laplace transforms

The advantage of using Laplace transforms in the solution of differential equations is that, by transforming from the time-domain to the s-domain, the problem is reduced from a set of differential equations to a set of simultaneous linear equations which are consequently much easier to solve.

One application of using Laplace transforms to solve differential equations was described in Section 9.2.2. In order to illustrate the application to a more complicated problem, consider the solution of Equation 9.29.

Equation 9.29 expressed in explicit form gives

$$P_1'(t) = -P_1(t)2\lambda + P_2(t)\mu \tag{A4.3a}$$

$$P_2'(t) = P_1(t)2\lambda - P_2(t)(\lambda + \mu) + P_3(t)2\mu \tag{A4.3b}$$

$$P_3'(t) = P_2(t)\lambda - P_3(t)2\mu \tag{A4.3c}$$

These equations can be transformed into the s-domain by using the transforms shown in Table A4.1 to give

$$sP_1(s) - P_1(0) = -2\lambda P_1(s) + \mu P_2(s) \tag{A4.4a}$$

$$sP_2(s) - P_2(0) = 2\lambda P_1(s) - (\lambda + \mu)P_2(s) + 2\mu P_3(s) \tag{A4.4b}$$

$$sP_3(s) - P_3(0) = \lambda P_2(s) - 2\mu P_3(s) \tag{A4.4c}$$

where $P_1(0)$, $P_2(0)$, $P_3(0)$ are the probabilities of being in states 1, 2, 3 respectively at time $t = 0$.

Letting $P_1(0) = 1$ and $P_2(0) = P_3(0) = 0$ and rearranging Equations A4.4 gives

$$(s + 2\lambda)P_1(s) = 1 + \mu P_2(s) \tag{A4.5a}$$

$$(s + \lambda + \mu)P_2(s) = 2\lambda P_1(s) + 2\mu P_3(s) \tag{A4.5b}$$

$$(s + 2\mu)P_3(s) = \lambda P_2(s) \tag{A4.5c}$$

Solving these equations as simultaneous linear equations with variables $P_1(s)$, $P_2(s)$ and $P_3(s)$ gives

$$P_2(s) = \frac{2\lambda s + 4\mu\lambda}{s(s + \lambda + \mu)(s + 2\lambda + 2\mu)} \tag{A4.6}$$

similar expressions can be derived for $P_1(s)$ and $P_3(s)$.

Equation A4.6 cannot be transformed directly back into the time-domain, but first must be subdivided into individual terms using partial fractions. Thus

$$\frac{2\lambda s + 4\lambda\mu}{s(s + \lambda + \mu)(s + 2\lambda + 2\mu)} \equiv \frac{A}{s} + \frac{B}{s + \lambda + \mu} + \frac{C}{s + 2\lambda + 2\mu}$$

from which

$$2\lambda s + 4\lambda\mu \equiv A(s + \lambda + \mu)(s + 2\lambda + 2\mu) + Bs(s + 2\lambda + 2\mu) + Cs(s + \lambda + \mu) \tag{A4.7}$$

Since the identity A4.7 must be true for all values of s, let

(a) $s = 0$ from which $A = \dfrac{2\lambda\mu}{(\lambda + \mu)^2}$

(b) $s = -(\lambda + \mu)$ from which $B = \dfrac{2\lambda(\lambda - \mu)}{(\lambda + \mu)^2}$

(c) $s = -(2\lambda + 2\mu)$ from which $C = \dfrac{-2\lambda^2}{(\lambda + \mu)^2}$

therefore,

$$P_2(s) = \frac{2\lambda\mu}{s(\lambda + \mu)^2} + \frac{2\lambda(\lambda - \mu)}{(s + \lambda + \mu)(\lambda + \mu)^2} - \frac{2\lambda^2}{(s + 2\lambda + 2\mu)(\lambda + \mu)^2} \tag{A4.8}$$

Similar expressions can be derived in terms of partial fractions for $P_1(s)$ and $P_3(s)$.

Equation A4.8 can now be transformed back into the time-domain using the transformations in Table A4.1 to give

$$P_2(t) = \frac{2\lambda\mu}{(\lambda+\mu)^2} + \frac{2\lambda(\lambda-\mu)}{(\lambda+\mu)^2} e^{-(\lambda+\mu)t} - \frac{2\lambda^2}{(\lambda+\mu)^2} e^{-2(\lambda+\mu)t} \qquad (A4.9)$$

which is the equation previously quoted in Chapter 9, Equation 9.30b.

The similar equations for $P_1(s)$ and $P_3(s)$ can also be transformed back into the time-domain to give Equations 9.30a and 9.30c.

Appendix 5—Confidence levels and limits

A5.1 Introduction

An important factor in quantitative reliability evaluation and particularly in the model development and analysis presented in this book is the appreciation of the accuracy inherent in the calculation process. This involves two basic elements. The first of these relates to the physical validity of the model used. This aspect has been emphasized throughout the book. The second is the validity of the data used in the model. The results obtained using a valid model can be quite precise but highly inaccurate if the data is incorrect or invalid for the purposes of the study.

Most organizations operate some form of reliability data collection scheme, the purpose of which is to establish the relevant component data needed for predicting the reliability of systems in the planning, design and operation phases. One of the greatest problems associated with such a data collection scheme is the limited amount of data that is available, particularly if the sample size and the failure rate of components is small. It is relatively simple to establish the average value or single point estimate for a particular type of component but this single point estimate gives no indication of the confidence that can be placed in its value. It is possible however to apply confidence bounds to both the failure probability and failure rate. Using these techniques, the range in which the failure rate or probability falls within a fixed degree of confidence can be established.

This appendix describes the theoretical development of confidence limits for both failure probability, i.e., unavailability, and failure rate. It is important to appreciate that these two parameters are entirely different and therefore the confidence limit analysis is also different for each one.

A5.2 Unavailability at selected confidence levels

The approach used for developing the confidence limits of unavailability was introduced [44] in 1959 for power generating equipment. It is equally applicable to all components that can exist in one of two states, up and down, and for which the up-times and down-times are exponentially distributed.

If λ and μ are the failure and repair rates respectively and U is the component unavailability, then from Equation 9.11

$$U = \frac{\lambda}{\lambda + \mu} \tag{A5.1}$$

The essence of the practical problem is the estimation of U from historical and, often, limited data.

The average up-time duration m and average down-time duration r can be evaluated from the recorded data of up-times and down-times. Using these two values, a single point estimate of the unavailability can be evaluated from Equation 9.13

$$\hat{U} = \frac{r}{r + m} \tag{A5.2}$$

In addition, an estimate of U at a given confidence level can also be made from the same set of recorded data.

It was shown [44] that

$$\text{Prob}\,[\beta''_{a,b} \leqslant F_{2a,2b} \leqslant \beta'_{a,b}] = \text{Prob}\left[\frac{r}{r + \beta'm} \leqslant \frac{\lambda}{\lambda + \mu} \leqslant \frac{r}{r + \beta''m}\right] \tag{A5.3}$$

where $\beta'_{a,b}$ and $\beta''_{a,b}$ are constants depending upon the chosen confidence level

$F_{2a,2b}$ = Snedecor's F-statistic with $2a$ degrees of freedom in the numerator and $2b$ in the denominator.

a = number of consecutive or randomly chosen down-time durations.

b = number of consecutive or randomly chosen up-time durations.

The values of $\beta'_{a,b}$ and $\beta''_{a,b}$ should be determined for a specific probability γ of the above limits of $\lambda/(\lambda + \mu)$.

$\beta'_{a,b}$ is obtained from

$$\text{Prob}\,[F_{2a,2b} \geqslant \beta'] = \frac{1 - \gamma}{2} \tag{A5.4}$$

and $\beta''_{a,b}$ from

$$\text{Prob}\,[F_{2a,2b} \leqslant \beta''] = \frac{1 - \gamma}{2} \tag{A5.5}$$

Since the upper tails of the F-distribution are usually tabulated [9], it is more convenient to express Equation A5.5 as

$$\text{Prob}\left[\frac{1}{F_{2a,2b}} \geqslant \frac{1}{\beta''}\right] = \frac{1-\gamma}{2} \tag{A5.6}$$

or $$\text{Prob}\left[F_{2b,2a} \geqslant \frac{1}{\beta''}\right] = \frac{1-\gamma}{2} \tag{A5.7}$$

The values of $\beta'_{a,b}$ and $\beta''_{a,b}$ evaluated as described in Equations A5.4 to A5.7 ensures that, with probability γ, the following limits enclose the true values of U.

$$\text{upper limit, } U_u = \frac{r}{r+\beta''m} \tag{A5.8}$$

$$\text{lower limit, } U_l = \frac{r}{r+\beta'm} \tag{A5.9}$$

Example A5.1

Consider a component for which:

$a = b = 10$

$r = 5$ days

$m = 195$ days

Evaluate (a) the single point estimate of U, (b) the limits of U to give 90% confidence of enclosing the true value.

(a)   From Equation A5.2,

$$\hat{U} = \frac{5}{195+5} = 0.025$$

(b)   From information given:

$$\gamma = 0.90 \quad \text{and} \quad \frac{1-\gamma}{2} = 0.05$$

From Equation A5.4

$$\text{Prob}\,[F_{20,20} \geqslant \beta'] = 0.05$$

which, using F-distribution tables [9] gives

$$\beta' = 2.12$$

Also, from Equation A5.7

$$\text{Prob}\left[F_{20,20} \geqslant \frac{1}{\beta''}\right] = 0.05$$

giving

$$\beta'' = \frac{1}{\beta'} = 0.471$$

Therefore from Equations A5.8 and A5.9

$$U_u = \frac{5}{5 + 0.471 \times 195} = 0.052$$

and

$$U_l = \frac{5}{5 + 2.12 \times 195} = 0.012$$

From this example the following statements can be made:
(i)   the single point estimate of unavailability is 0.025,
(ii) there is a 90% probability that the true unavailability lies between 0.012 and 0.052,
(iii) there is a 95% probability that the true unavailability is less than 0.052, and
(iv) there is a 95% probability that the true unavailability is greater than 0.012.

Example A5.2

Consider the same component as in Example A5.1 but now let $a = b = 20$ and the values of m and r remain unchanged.

(a) $\hat{U} = \dfrac{5}{5 + 195} = 0.025$ (unchanged)

(b) $\beta' = 1.69$ and $\beta'' = 0.591$

giving

$$U_u = 0.042 \quad \text{and} \quad U_l = 0.015$$

It is evident that these limits are closer than in Example A5.1. This confirms that, as more information becomes available (the sample size is increased or more failures occur), the range is reduced while the designated degree of confidence is maintained.

A5.3   Failure rate at selected confidence levels

Failures are considered to occur purely by chance for a component which is operating within its useful life period. Under these conditions the failure frequency is the reciprocal of the mean time between failures

MTBF and failure rate is the reciprocal of the mean time to failure MTTF. If instant repair is assumed, the frequency and failure rate become identical both conceptually and numerically.

The Poisson distribution previously discussed in Section 6.6 can be used in this case. From Equation 6.19, the probability of x failures or less in a total time t is

$$P_x = \sum_{k=0}^{x} \frac{(t/m)^k e^{-t/m}}{k!} \tag{A5.10}$$

where m = mean time to failure = reciprocal of failure rate, λ.

An upper bound on the failure rate can be obtained directly from the application of Equation A5.10. This is best illustrated by considering numerical examples.

Example A5.3

Consider a component which has experienced zero failures in time t.
From Equation A5.10

$$\text{Probability of zero failure} = e^{-t/m}$$
$$= e^{-\lambda t}$$

A value of λ exists, λ' say, such that $\lambda' > \lambda$ and the probability of actually getting zero failures is $1 - P_c$ where P_c is the confidence level. Consider a confidence level of 95%, then

$$1 - 0.95 = e^{-\lambda' t}$$
$$\lambda' t = 3.0$$
$$\lambda' = \frac{3.0}{t}$$

or $\qquad m' = 0.33t$

This implies that if zero failures have occurred in time t, then there is a 95% confidence that the failure rate is less than $3/t$ and that the MTTF is greater than $0.33t$.

Example A5.4

Consider now that 1 failure has occurred in time t. Assuming the same confidence level of 95%, Equation A5.10 gives

$$\sum_{k=0}^{1} \frac{(\lambda t)^k e^{-\lambda t}}{k!} = 0.05$$

i.e.,

$$e^{-\lambda t}(1 + \lambda t) = 0.05$$

from which

$$\lambda' = \frac{4.74}{t} \quad \text{or} \quad m' = 0.211t$$

This result implies that if one failure has occurred in time t, then there is a 95% confidence that the failure rate is less than $4.74/t$ and that the MTTF is greater than $0.211t$, i.e., as expected, the failure rate has increased and the MTTF decreased.

As the number of failures increase, it becomes rather unwieldy to attempt to obtain the confidence limits from the summation of a Poisson distribution. It is possible to replace the cumulative density function of the Poisson distribution by that of the gamma distribution. However, this does not help significantly because tabulated values are not normally available. However, the chi-squared distribution for which tabulated values are available [9] is a special case of the gamma distribution (see Section 6.10) and can be used for the purpose of evaluating confidence limits.

From this it is possible to say that, for a time truncated test, the true mean time to failure is equal to or greater than the value m' where

$$m' = \frac{2 \times (\text{total test time})}{\chi^2_{\alpha, 2x+2}} \tag{A5.11}$$

where $\alpha = 1 - \text{confidence level}$

$x = \text{number of failures}$

Example A5.5

Reconsider Example A5.4. In this example

$P_c = 0.95$ and therefore $\alpha = 0.05$

$x = 1$

$$m' = \frac{2t}{\chi^2_{0.05,4}}$$

$$= \frac{2t}{9.488}$$

$$= 0.211t \quad \text{as obtained in Example A5.4.}$$

If the total test time is 100 days during which one failure occurred then
(a) the single point estimate of failure rate is $1/100 = 0.01$ f/day,
(b) one can be 95% confident that the failure rate is less than or equal to 0.0474 f/day, and
(c) one can be 95% confident that the MTTF is greater than or equal to 211 days.

Example A5.6

In this example consider the test time increased to 200 days during which 2 failures occurred.

In this case, the single point estimate remains unchanged at 0.01 f/day. The 95% mean failure time is now

$$m \geqslant \frac{2 \times 200}{\chi^2_{0.05,6}}$$

$$\geqslant \frac{2 \times 200}{12.592}$$

$$\geqslant 31.8 \text{ days.}$$

In this case one can now be 95% confident that the MTTF is greater than or equal to 31.8 days and that the failure rate is less than or equal to 0.0314 f/day.

This result shows that, as further information becomes available, the upper bound tends to decrease for any given value of confidence level.

The simplicity of Equation A5.11 permits a normalized set of graphs to be constructed which eliminates the need to constantly refer to chi-squared distribution tables. This set of graphs is shown in Figure A5.1. After monitoring the number of failures and deciding on the most appropriate confidence level, the value of the multiplication factor K can be obtained

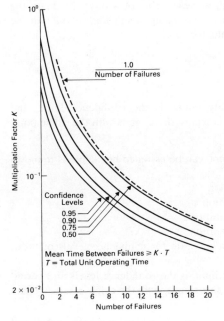

Fig. A5.1   Multiplication factor K

from Figure A5.1. The mean time to failure can then be evaluated from:

$$m \geqslant Kt \qquad\qquad (A5.12)$$

where t is the total operating time.

Although not particularly evident from Figure A5.1, the value of K tends to the same value for all confidence levels as the number of failures tends to infinity.

A5.4 Conclusions

In many reliability assessments, the evaluation is performed by using the single point estimates of component indices. This appendix has briefly illustrated how the component history can be used to obtain statistics at selected levels of confidence. The concepts associated with placing confidence limits on the basic component parameters of unavailability and failure rate illustrate the uncertainty associated with estimating these parameters, from a given amount of operating data.

Problems

1   A particular component has a constant failure rate of 3 f/yr and a repair time that is exponentially distributed with a mean value of 4 days. Evaluate the 80%, 90% and 98% confidence limits of the component's unavailability if the component failure/repair data is evaluated after
   (a)   1 failure/repair cycle
   (b)   6 failure/repair cycles
   (c)   15 failure/repair cycles
   (d)   60 failure/repair cycles.
   Observe the change in unavailability limits as the confidence limits and number of cycles are changed. Also, compare these limits with the single point estimate of unavailability.

2   A component for which the repair time can be assumed negligible is found to have the following historical data
   (a)   1 failure in 150 days of operation
   (b)   5 failures in 750 days of operation
   (c)   10 failures in 1500 days of operation
   (d)   24 failures in 3600 days of operation.
   Evaluate the upper limit of the failure rate for confidence levels of 90%, 95% and 99%.
   Observe the change in failure rate limit as the confidence levels and period of operation changes. Also, compare these limits with the single point estimate of failure rate.

References

1. Bagowsky, I., *Reliability Theory and Practise*, Prentice-Hall (1961).
2. Briepohl, A. M., *Probabilistic Systems Analysis*, John Wiley (1970).
3. Papoulis, A., *Probability, Random Variables and Stochastic Processes*, McGraw-Hill (1965).
4. Feller, W., *An Introduction to Probability Theory and Its Applications*, Vol. 1, John Wiley (1968).
5. Meyer, P. L., *Introductory Probability and Statistical Applications*, Addison-Wesley (1965).
6. Drake, A. W., *Fundamentals of Applied Probability Theory*, McGraw-Hill (1967).
7. Neville, A. M., Kennedy, J. B., *Basic Statistical Methods for Engineers and Scientists*, International Textbook Co. (1964).
8. Mosteller, F., Rourke, R. E. K., Thomas, G. B., *Probability with Statistical Applications*, Addison-Wesley (1961).
9. Odeh, R. E., Owen, D. B., Birnbaum, Z. W., Fisher, L., *Pocket Book of Statistical Tables*, Marcel Dekker (1977).
10. *Tables of Binomial Probability Distribution*, National Bureau of Standards (USA), Applied Mathematics Series 6 (1950).
11. AIEE Committee Report, *Tables of Binomial Probability Distribution to Six Decimal Places*, AIEE Transactions (August 1952), pp. 597–620.
12. Singh, C., Billinton, R., 'A new method to determine the failure frequency of a complex system', *Microelectronics and Reliability*, **12** (1973), pp. 459–465.
13. Allan, R. N., Billinton, R., De Oliveira, M. F., 'An efficient algorithm for deducing the minimal cuts and reliability indices of a general network configuration', *IEEE Trans. on Reliability*, **R-25** (1976), pp. 226–233.
14. Jensen, P. A., Bellmore, M., 'An algorithm to determine the reliability of a complex network', *IEEE Trans. on Reliability*, **R-18** (1969), pp. 169–174.
15. Nelson, A. C., Batts, J. R., Beadles, R. L., 'A computer program for approximating system reliability', *IEEE Trans. on Reliability*, **R-19** (1970), pp. 61–65.
16. Hansler, E., 'A fast recursive algorithm to calculate the reliability of

communication network', *IEEE Trans. Communications,* **COM-20** (1972), pp. 637–640.

17. Fussell, J. B., Vesely, W. E., 'A new methodology for obtaining cut sets for fault trees', *Trans. Amer. Nucl. Soc.,* **15** (1972).

18. Garriba, S., Mussio, P., Naldi, F., Reina, G., Volta, G., 'Efficient construction of minimal cut sets from fault trees', *IEEE Trans. on Reliability,* **R-26** (1977), pp. 88–93.

19. Rasmuson, D. M., Marshall, N. H., FATRAM: A core efficient cut set algorithm. *IEEE Trans. on Reliability,* **R-27** (1978), pp. 250–253.

20. US Atomic Energy Commission, *Reactor Safety Study: An Assessment of Accident Risks in US Commercial Nuclear Plants,* Report WASH-1400, USAEC., Washington D.C.

21. Kapur, K. C., Lamberson, L. R., *Reliability in Engineering Design,* John Wiley (1977).

22. Dodge, H. F., Romig, H. G., *Sampling Inspection Tables,* John Wiley (1966).

23. Pearson, K., *Tables of Incomplete Gamma Function,* Cambridge University Press (1922).

24. Hahn, G. J., Shapiro, S. S., *Statistical Models in Engineering,* John Wiley (1967).

25. Shooman, M. L., *Probabilistic Reliability, An Engineering Approach.* McGraw-Hill (1968).

26. Sandler, G. H., *System Reliability Engineering,* Prentice-Hall (1963).

27. Kemeny, J. G., Snell, J. L., *Finite Markov Chains,* Van Nostrand (1960).

28. Brameller, A., Allan, R. N., Hamam, Y. M., *Sparsity, Its Practical Application to Systems Analysis,* Pitman (1976).

29. Epstein, B., Hosford, J., 'Reliability of some two unit redundant systems', Sixth National Symposium on Reliability and Quality Control in Electronics, Washington, D.C. (January 1960).

30. Hall, J. D., Ringlee, R. J., Wood, A. J., 'Frequency and duration methods for power system reliability calculations, Part I, Generation system model', *IEEE Trans.,* **PAS-87** (1968), pp. 1787–1796.

31. Billinton, R., Ringlee, R. J., Wood, A. J., *Power System Reliability Calculations,* MIT Press (1973).

32. Banerjee, S. K., Rajamani, K., 'Closed form solutions for delta-star and star-delta conversions of reliability networks', *IEEE Trans. on Reliability,* **R-25** (1976), pp. 118–119.

33. Rosenthal, A., Frisque, D., 'Transformation methods for computing network reliabilities', *Networks,* **7** (1977), pp. 97–111.

34. Fussell, J. B., Burdick, G. R. (eds), *Nuclear Systems Reliability Engineering and Risk Assessment,* SIAM (1977).
    (a) Epler, E. P., 'Diversity and periodic testing in defense against common mode failure', pp. 269–288.

(b) Wagner, D. P., Cate, C. L., Fussell, J. B., 'Common cause failure analysis methodology for complex systems', pp. 289–313.

(c) Vesely, W. E., 'Estimating common cause failure probabilities in reliability and risk analyses', pp. 314–341.

35. Epler, E. P., 'Common mode failure considerations in the design of systems for protection and control', *Nuclear Safety*, **10** (1969), pp. 38–45.

36. Edwards, G. T., Watson, I. A., *A Study of Common Mode Failures*, National Centre of Systems Reliability, Report SRD R 146 (1979).

37. Gangloff, W. C., 'Common mode failure analysis', *IEEE Trans. on Power Apparatus and Systems*, **PAS-94** (1970), pp. 27–30.

38. Billinton, R., Medicherla, T. K. P., Sachdev, M. S., 'Common cause outages in multiple circuit power lines', *IEEE Trans. on Reliability*, **R-27** (1978), pp. 128–131.

39. Allan, R. N., Dialynas, E. N., Homer, I. R., *Modelling Common Mode Failures in the Reliability Evaluation of Power System Networks*, IEEE PES Winter Power Meeting, New York (1979), paper A79 040-7.

40. Billinton, R., *Transmission Systems Reliability Models*, EPRI Publication, WS-77-60, pp. 2.10–2.16.

41. 'Task force of the IEEE APM subcommittee—Common mode forced outages of overhead transmission lines', *IEEE Trans. on Power Apparatus and Systems*, **PAS-95** (1976), pp. 859–864.

42. Cox, D. R., 'The analysis of non-Markovian stochastic processes by the inclusion of supplementary variables', *Proc. Camb. Phil. Soc.*, **61** (1955), pp. 433–441.

43. Singh, C., Billinton, R., *System Reliability Modelling and Evaluation*, Hutchinson (1977).

44. Baldwin, C. J., Billings, J. E., Gaver, D. P., Hoffman, C. H., 'Mathematical models for use in the simulation of power generation outage, II, Power system forced outage distributions', *AIEE Trans.*, **78** (1954), TP 59–849.

45. Green, A. E., Bourne, A. J., *Reliability Technology*, John Wiley (1972).

46. Barlow, R. E., Proschan, F., *Mathematical Theory of Reliability*, John Wiley (1965).

47. Abramovitz, M., Stegun, I. A., *Handbook of Mathematical Functins*, National Bureau of Standards (1968).

48. Allan, R. N., Rondiris, I. L., Fryer, D. M., 'An efficient computational technique for evaluating the cut/tie sets and common-cause failures of complex systems', *IEEE Trans. on Reliability*, **R-30** (1981), pp. 101–109.

Solutions

Chapter 2

1. 0.72, 0.08, 0.18, 0.98
2. 0.06
3. 31/60
4. 0.6120, 0.003, 0.997
5. 6/36, 23/36, 12/36, 5/36
6. 5/8, 4/5
7. 0.3409, 0.4091, 0.1136
8. 1/10, 6/20, 1/2

Chapter 3

1. 0.0092283, 0.095424
2. 0.293601
3. 0.004975 MW, 2.168 h/yr, 0.0782273 MW, 66.16 hr/yr
4. 0 MW (0.576), 20 MW (0.288), 40 MW (0.100), 60 MW (0.032), 80 MW (0.004)
5. 0.3222, 2.0
6. 0.0001% MW, 0.00876 hr/yr, 0.00307% MW, 2.61 hr/yr, 0.01495% MW, 2.61 hr/yr, 0.019867% MW, 5.19 hr/yr
7. $219.02

Chapter 4

1. 0.66354
2. 0.9477, 0.99144
3. 100% (0.56), 75% (0.07), 50% (0.09), 25% (0.04), 0% (0.24)
4. 0.9990
5. 52
6. 0.3690
7. 7

Chapter 5

1   0.98739, 0.98901
2   25.09
3   0.968266
5   7.13×10^{-4}, 7.5×10^{-4}

Chapter 6

1    $45.74
2   0.367879, 0.367879, 0.183939, 0.061313, 0.015328
3   0.143, 1, 2, 1 or 2, 1.782, 0.218
    0.3235, 2, 2, 1 or 2, 1.458, 0.542
    0.0535, 0, 2, 1 or 2, 1.9291, 0.0709
4   2, 1
5   0.1645
6   89.04, 11.51, 0.82
7   82.6
8   0.9505, 0.9010, 0.5906, 0.0067
9   0.2042
10   0.81
11   0.32, 0.28, 0.045
12   0.729, 0.493, 0.368, 20 yr
13   a, $b/\sqrt{6}$, 0.75

Chapter 7

2   0.979, 0.965
3   0.951229, 0.997621
5   0.999922
6   0.976959, 10313 hr, 0.779027

Chapter 8

1   36.4%
2   0.4, 0.45, 0.15
3   0.5000, 0.3125, 0.1875, 0.5000, 0.3125, 0.1875, 5.33
4   0.421874
5   0.55, 0.575, 0.60
6   1/2, 0, 1/4, 2/5
7   0.7, 0.74, 0.75 (going right)
8   5/18, 0.30
9   1/3, 1/3, 1/6, 1/6
10   0.6

Chapter 9

1 0.9615, 0.0189, 0.0196; 0.9804, 0.9615; 100 hr, 50 hr
2 20 hr
3 5333, 5333, 5333 gal/hr
4 19.9×10^6 hr

Chapter 10

1 1.92×10^{-2}, 9.64×10^{-3}, 9.80×10^{-3} occ/hr; 50, 1.96, 2 hr
2 0.4445 occ/hr; 2, 0.25 hr; 0.7901, 0.8888, 0.0984 occ/hr; 1, 0.222, 0.125 hr
3 0.473 occ/hr, 2 hr; 0.473 occ/hr, 0.11 hr
4 0.0291, 2.91 f/yr, 3.65 days
5 5.48×10^{-4}, 2.0×10^{-1} f/yr, 1 day
6 2.30×10^{-5}, 2.0×10^{-1} f/yr, 1.01 hr
7 0.9591, 0.0204, 0.0195, 0.001; 2.97×10^{-2}, 1.06×10^{-2}, 1.97×10^{-2}, 1.51×10^{-3} occ/yr, 32.3, 1.92, 0.99, 0.66 yr

Chapter 11

1 0.05 f/yr, 48 hr, 2.4 hr/yr
2 2.74×10^{-5} f/yr, 24 hr, 6.58×10^{-4} hr/yr
3 4.84×10^{-4} f/yr, 7.83 hr, 3.79×10^{-3} hr/yr
5 5.85×10^{-4} f/yr, 13.3 hr, 7.77×10^{-3} hr/yr
6 1.6×10^{-3} f/yr, 242 days, 0.387 days/yr

Chapter 12

1 4.802×10^{-5}, 1×10^{-6} occ/yr

Appendix A5

1 $3.64 \times 10^{-3}/0.228$, $1.73 \times 10^{-3}/0.383$, $3.32 \times 10^{-4}/0.767$
   0.015/0.066, 0.012/0.081, 0.008/0.120
   0.020/0.050, 0.018/0.057, 0.014/0.073
   0.025/0.040, 0.024/0.042, 0.021/0.048
2 0.026, 0.032, 0.044; 0.012, 0.014, 0.017; 0.010, 0.011, 0.013; 0.009, 0.009, 0.011 f/day

Index